A D O N   O L A M

A D O N
O L A M

A Search for Meaning

ZALMAN WEISS

HONG KONG · JERUSALEM · USA

ISBN NO. 978-1-940516-12-7

FOR ORDERS:
INTERNET: www.menorah-books.com
EMAIL: orders@menorah-books.com

COVER DESIGN: Yochanan Jones
LAYOUT AND TYPOGRAPHY: Gal Narunsky

Printed in Jerusalem

This book is dedicated with love and appreciation
to my father,

Leonard Weiss (Laibel ben Noach) z"l

Table of Contents

Section One
ADON OLAM, The Personal Master   1

Section Two
V'Acharei, When All is Over and Done With   149

Section Three
V'Hu Echad, Monotheism   227

Section Four
V'Hu Eli, Taking Global Theory and Making It Personal 277

Section Five
B'Yado, Into His Hand 317

Rabbi Yisroel Dov Wiesel   הרב ישראל דוב הלוי ויזל

9 Nechemia St.   רחוב נחמיה 9

טלפון 03/5708514

פקס 03/5796314

בס"ד

כד חשון תשע"ד

APPROBATION

(Translation of the Hebrew)

It is a moment of joy to see the great work of my dear friend, Rabbi Zalman Weiss, reaching the point of conclusion.

I have been in close contact with Rabbi Weiss for many years, seeing him grow in his devotion to learning Torah, adherence to keeping the Mitzvoth to the finest details and his great love of fellow Jews, ready to help materially and spiritually.

The present work is a result of extensive self study and consultation in search of the exact truth and meaning of the fundamentals of the Emunah, passing it on to his pupils in the lively manner found in the pages of the book.

The interesting form of the presentation causes the beginner to become involved and be drawn to read the book till the end. However, also people who are entrenched in the Emunah will benefit from the clear knowledge of the basic principles and will be more motivated to serve Hashem.

Yisroel Wiesel

(RABBI) YISROEL WIESEL

BS"D

APPROBATION

Adon Olam—A Search for Meaning is much more than an exposition of the famous liturgical poem Adon Olam. Through its pages the reader will journey on an astounding tour of Jewish wisdom. Whether you are a novice or a Torah scholar, you will encounter here some of the most fascinating concepts about G-d and life that you could ever want to understand. In this work the author weaves all these concepts together with masterful artistry.

I have two suggestions for those contemplating reading this book. Don't be fooled and don't be apprehensive. While this book is written in the form of a novel, don't be fooled by the enjoyable story, and mistakenly put it down, thinking that you want something of more content. And for those who think they might not yet be ready for such depths, don't be apprehensive. This work uses the novel form to enable all its readers to digest these deeper teachings about faith in a pleasant and delightfully adventurous way.

Whoever you are, I feel that this book will help you to grow immensely, in your faith. I wish you all as much growth in reading this work as I have had.

RABBI AVRAHAM SUTTON

2 Cheshvan 5744
October 6, 2013

Translation of Rabbi Linder's Approbation

Moshe Uri Linder
Rabbi and Moreh Tzedek
In the Neve Yaakov Mizrach neighborhood
Jerusalem

B"H, Menachem Av, 5773
Approbation

My dear friend, HaRav HaGaon R' Zalman Weiss shlit"a, is full of faith and trust in Hashem, as well as pure notions and deference to sages; he spends his time with the three pillars—Torah, Avodah and acts of loving-kindness. Most of the day he sits and studies, and the rest of the day he is busy with a Heavenly pursuit, and in addition, he draws [to Torah] those that are far. He has thought to publish some thoughts, acquired from pure wellsprings, to disseminate them for the good of the public; to clear the path and remove the thorns from lacking hearts.

A quick person, he has collected material from many books and authors, from great people and famous educators, and has succeeded in gathering lofty sayings about the great and holy song, Adon Olamim, written by early sages. All are put together in his book, presented in a concise and orderly fashion, and the end result is sweet as sweet can be.

The book was written in a language that is foreign to me; but since I know the author shlit"a and his thoughts and discourse, and he has told me the contents of a large part of the book, and discussed the great majority of it with me, and these are indeed good, pleasant things, and great rabbis, who have read the entire book, have given their approbations, and praise it, therefore I join them in an approbation that the book is all good and unblemished, the goal being to strengthen the foundations of the pure faith and correct concepts. Undoubtedly, anyone who reads it will benefit from it immensely, and come out greatly strengthened.

Sincerely, and with blessings for great success,
His friend and admirer,

Moshe Uri Linder
Rabbi and Moreh Tzedek,
59 Zevin St., Jerusalem

OHR SOMAYACH אור שמח
TANENBAUM COLLEGE

BS"D

בס"ד

9 Kislev / 5773

Haskama

I have known the author of this book, the avreich Rabbi Zalman Weiss, for many years.

Having read most of the book and checked it in terms of proper *hashkafa*, I can say that the material within it is accurate and proper.

I recommend *Adon Olam—A Search for Meaning* to all those who are beginning to delve more deeply into the Torah outlook on life, and wish to gain a profound understanding of Jewish faith.

Mendel Weinbach
Rav Mendel Weinbach
Rosh Yeshiva, Ohr Somayach
Jerusalem

In Appreciation and Dedication

Towards the end of his life, the great Chofetz Chaim is quoted as having said, "Hashem, what can I give You? You have given me the Mishnah Brurah and many other books, but what do I have to give You?" Although he had dedicated his life to the hard work of producing these great works that have helped, and continue to help, our people to serve our Father in Heaven, he knew that all of the talent, genius and strength, etc., needed to produce these works came directly from Hashem. From the Chofetz Chaim we should all learn that truly everything that we have produced is really a gift from Hashem.

Throughout the many years of writing *Adon Olam: A Search for Meaning* time and again it became clear to me that all of my successes were directly from Hashem. There are no words of thanks that could properly express the depths of appreciation and gratitude I have to the Master of the Universe for having enabled me to be part of this great project.

Many messengers were sent to help this project come to fruition, and to them also many thanks are due.

First, the person who actually gave me the impetus to write this book: As I was preparing many students for their conversion to Judaism at the Rabbinical Court (*Beis Din*) of Rabbi Nissim Karelitz in Bnei Brak, many questions on faith came up that I did not always have the answers to. Rabbi Yisroel Dov Wiesel of Bnei Brak, a judge on that Beis Din, was always to be counted upon to have the best answers. Over the years these answers became a central part of my teachings for these students. It was Rabbi Wiesel who years ago told me to put what I was teaching my students into the form of a book. Moreover, he was not only the impetus of the book, but read and re-read the forming text to be sure of the propriety of its contents.

Rabbi Mendel Weinbach, may his memory be for a blessing, *Rosh Yeshivah of Yeshivas Ohr Somayach* in Jerusalem, instructed me precisely what to write and what not to write. Until almost the very end of its composition, every step of the way, his hands were in this book. Just weeks before his death he read through the nearly-finished work and signed an approbation for it. This book is his 'baby' as much as it is mine.

Rabbi Moshe Uri Linder of Neve Yaakov has spent years teaching me most of the information needed to write this work. He guided me as to what many of the deep concepts found here mean. He also cautioned me as to what needed to be left unstated but, rather, merely inferred.

A special thanks is owed to Rabbi Daniel Lehrfeld, Rosh Yeshivah of Yeshivas Beis Yisrael of Jerusalem, who graciously gave me the means, as well as a place to learn and compose this work.

My wife Channah Malkah has scrutinized the text all along, until the book finally came out as well as it has in its present form. From her I have learned that if at first you don't succeed, do it the way your wife told you to.

Mrs. Bracha Bender was instrumental in helping to form the plot of the novel, and helped me write it.

Daniel Weiss proofread the book.

Mrs. Yael Goldwasser was the one who took the rough draft of this book and turned it into a much more readable text, in addition to editing and doing proofreading. I am very grateful to her for all of this, as well as for her constant insistence on maximum clarity.

Alon Golub provided valuable technical support.

Rabbi Professor Glaberson and Rabbi Doctor Eliyahu Berlin helped me understand many scientific concepts needed for the composition of this book, which I had till then only understood in a rudimentary way.

Yerachmiel Goldberg took the text apart as needed, and also added much to the mathematical calculations and thoughts within the science sections of this work.

The staff of Menorah deserves special appreciation. From the beginning, Ashirah Yosefah made it clear that she and her staff were viewing their involvement in ADON OLAM not merely as a business venture, but first and foremost, as a mission to heighten the world's awareness of Torah and true faith (emunah).

Chaim Natan Firszt's keen editing eye quickly spotted problems and proceeded to smooth them out successfully. Gal Narunsky put heart and soul into designing the book's layout. Yochanan Jones designed the cover that captured the book's essence.

It was a pleasure to hand over my 'baby' to this highly professional and open-minded team.

Last but not least on this list, I cannot thank my students enough. It would be safe to say that this book is a result of their contributions, namely, their incessant questions, which drove me to search for complete answers, and, eventually, to write them up in this form.

There are many others whom I would like to express my appreciation to, but they are too numerous. Please realize that even if your name was not mentioned, your efforts are appreciated.

A donation was made in memory of the donor's parents l'iluy nishmas Naphtali ben Mordechai Erika bas Baruch.

From long before the inception of this work, there was one very special man and his wife whose support was always readily available to me. His encouragement, and that of my mother (may she live many more long and good years) got me over many seemingly unconquerable hurdles in life, including the writing of this book. Their helpful suggestions and heartfelt concern persuaded me that, with Hashem's help, I could in fact reach the end goal, but when I did, that special man was no longer amongst the living.

Towards the end of this work's composition, my father, Leonard Weiss (Laibel ben Noach) died a sudden death. I dedicate this book to his memory. May it be the will of the Master of the Universe that this book will help many of God's children grow closer to His service. In that merit, may my father's soul have an elevation and merit to sit under the wings of the Divine Presence in the World to Come.

Rabbi Zalman ben Laibel Weiss

Disclaimer

The author of this book has devoted years to the study of the ancient liturgical composition ADON OLAM. Rabbinical authorities guided him to present the results of this study in the format of a novel that would promote the absorption of deep ideas. The rabbis feared that if it was not written this way, the average reader would not be drawn to it.

Please note that the translation of the text of ADON OLAM in this book encompasses the deeper meanings of the words and is, therefore, quite different than a simple, literal translation. The reader will come to understand these meanings as the book unfolds.

Presenting esoteric and biblical truths by means of a novel involves certain drawbacks. For example, while many prominent figures in Jewish history are depicted in the following pages, it is important to remember that it is really impossible to fully conceive the thought processes of such great people. The novelization of any historical, biblical figures in this book is not to be seen as a portrait; rather, it is an attempt to bring alive the author's understanding of these individuals' ideals. The author claims absolutely no definite knowledge on their actual perspectives, thoughts, feelings, or words.

Whenever such literary tools appear in the text, a note will refer the reader to this Disclaimer in order to maintain integrity.

Another important point relates to the last section of the book, Section Five. There are a great many different opinions as to the nature of the End of Days. What is presented here is a composite of some of the accepted notions, as authorized by the rabbis who were consulted on this matter by the author, namely: Rabbi Mendel Weinbach, z"l, Rabbi Yisroel Wiesel, and Rabbi Moshe Uri Linder.

Note to the Reader

This novel was written for the Torah scholar as well as those beginning to search the depths of Judaism. As such, the author was sensitive to the fact that some of the latter readers might not be familiar with the Hebrew language or with the text of the liturgical composition ADON OLAM, upon which this novel is based. Most Hebrew words in this book have, therefore, been translated into English. Since the footnotes will usually only translate these terms once, therefore a glossary has been provided to enable the readers easy reference to these terms as the book continues. Terms translated many times in the text will not appear in the glossary. Hebrew lettering is used solely for the text of ADON OLAM, so that the reader will be able to quickly pinpoint those words that are from the actual text thereof. Some Hebrew terms do remain, but where they appear, the words have been transliterated into English and are italicized, together with footnotes which provide the reader with an English translation or explanation.

A narrator was created to help guide the reader through the depth of the information presented. This character, called simply ADON OLAM, is the "omniscient soul" of the ancient liturgical composition ADON OLAM. In the course of the novel, the narrator will present many events in world history while simultaneously helping to process the information contained in these accounts. The narrator speaks to the reader, the "Searching Soul," who sometimes knows neither how nor where to search for meaning.

Whenever this narrator presents a new scene to the Searching Soul, or shows a clearer understanding of the information just presented, the text changes to *this typeface*, indicating that the particular sentence or paragraph is outside the storyline. Accordingly, the text remains in the present typeface when the narrator is merely informing the reader as to who is speaking, or giving some detail about a scene or event within the storyline.

Note that the simple translation of *Adon Olam* is "The Master of the World" which is a reference to God. The author was concerned that many of the sentences in this novel with the words *Adon Olam* might be misunderstood as referring to God when they are not. Therefore the ancient liturgical composition ADON OLAM always appears in SMALL CAPITAL LETTERS, as is the narrator, who shares the same title. When referring to God or just to the words "Adon" and "*olam*", these words appear as they normally would.

The story refers to an imaginary rabbi, Chacham[1] Ovadiah Yashar, and his scholarly work, *The Hidden Master*. (This book has never existed.) The passages quoted from *The Hidden Master* were written by the author, Rabbi Zalman Weiss. However, quotes from other sources presented as being within *The Hidden Master*, as well as throughout this book, are all authentic.

We hope that you not only enjoy reading this work, but that upon its conclusion you will have grown closer to God as you search for deep meaning in life through the words of ADON OLAM.

---

1   Literally: Wise man. This term is commonly used in the Sephardic communities of Jews to describe the greatest rabbis of their generation.

". . . The Supreme King—
He is wrapped in a light that
can illuminate night as day.

And know, that even though
a thick cloud conceals Him,
the light still dwells with Him . . .
forever shall he reign."[2]

From the morning prayers of the second day of Rosh Hashana.

SECTION ONE

ADON OLAM:
The Personal Master

אֲדוֹן עוֹלָם אֲשֶׁר מָלַךְ, בְּטֶרֶם כָּל יְצִיר נִבְרָא
לְעֵת נַעֲשָׂה בְחֶפְצוֹ כֹּל, אֲזַי מֶלֶךְ שְׁמוֹ נִקְרָא

~

Adon Olam asher malach, b'terem kol yetzir nivra
L'eis na'asa b'cheftzo kol, azai Melech shemo nikra.

~

The Infinite Master of the hidden world,
Who has reigned before all Creation and subsequent formation,
Was enabled to be called King only upon
His will making everything come into being.[3]

Allow Me to Introduce Myself

I KNOW YOU. I've seen you around and have been waiting for the right moment to speak to you. Believe it or not, I was written nearly 2,500 years ago just for you.

I know there are many Jewish concepts that confuse you. You feel that there is more to Judaism, much more than you presently understand. You are yearning to connect with a bigger picture, but you don't have any idea how to find it. Sometimes you are frustrated, because you don't even know what questions to ask.

I know your feelings and I know your questions. I have known the questions of searching souls like yours throughout all the generations. Your grandparents sang my words. Your ancestors taught me to their children. I was carried throughout history into every Jewish city and home. Through the tortures of Auschwitz I was faithfully recited. In the fires of the Inquisition, Jewish men and women whispered my words. I am still sung today from England to Yemen, from Australia to Kazakhstan. There is no sect of Jews that has not heard of me.

I have all of the answers that you have been looking for.

. . . Oh, you want to know who I am? You probably think of me as a children's song. I am that prayer you have heard sung in synagogue since your youth. They call me ADON OLAM.

Ah, I see your incredulity. Do not be fooled by my simple appearance. When you come to understand the secrets that I hold, all your confusion will vanish. I was written to be the answer when there was nobody left to give it. I was written to light a path for our people through every kind of darkness that would envelop them.

I know this may sound strange, but some of the greatest men in history imbued my few short stanzas with wisdom beyond space and time. I am alive, Searching Soul. No matter where you have come from and no matter what you have gone through, my words are instilled with a secret message especially for you.

Is this too extraordinary to comprehend? Imagine that you owned a computer that would never need to be updated. The technical advancements built into it would never be outdated, never be surpassed. Its programmers preempted any advancement that could ever be created. Your computer would never become obsolete. It would never arrive at an equation that it could not solve. Such a computer would only dimly mimic the power that our holy sages instilled into my words. I have lasted through the most grueling eras, yet my ability to answer our people's questions will never be exhausted.

Now, after all the millennia, it is finally your turn to receive these answers, now, when you need me the most, and my authors knew that you are worth helping. So take my hand, Searching Soul. Trust me to guide you. There are answers to questions that now seem unanswerable. Your transformation through my words will leave you whole and finally able to call yourself a true servant of God (Hashem)[4].

We are about to embark on a mission that will close all of the breaches between you and your Creator. Do you dare? Even when a heart has lost the courage to hope, the truth is still out there, waiting. I am now waiting for you.

---

4   Literally: The Name. It is a reference to the Ineffable Name of God. This has become the traditional way that Jews refer to God, and this term will be used frequently throughout the book.

Braving the Storms

*S*EARCHING SOUL, *my authors knew of the difficulties that would challenge your faith, and my words were composed to help you not only survive the storms, but thrive. Together we will dissect my words until they become your key to the mysteries of the universe.*

Like so many, you have many unanswered questions about Jewish faith. You examine even the most basic tenets closely, as you search for clarity in your confusion like a blind man sifting for colored jewels among worthless stones. You often feel lost and frustrated. Sometimes you may even find it difficult to hold onto your practice in the face of the unknown. Or perhaps you are among those who hold on without knowing why, going through the motions of a living Torah[5] yet feeling dead inside.

Which is worse? Both leave life empty. You, like so many others, yearn to truly understand the truth, yet you are overwhelmed by what appear to be contradictions and dead ends.

My authors had your jewels. They untangled the confusion and polished the diamonds. Now I will start to reveal my secrets to you, but let's you and me take the scenic route, where I will introduce you to a few other searching souls much like yourself.

The issues that bothered them were already addressed in my words. Pay close attention to how these young men you are about to meet, like you, were never satisfied with mediocrity. The more they learned, the more questions they asked, and the more unexpected an-

---

5   The Torah is the Five Books of Moses. This term also refers to the entirety of Jewish law and other holy Jewish texts.

*swers they received. As we will relive their personal
adventures, you will receive the answers to both your
asked and as yet unasked questions. As your soul will
become intertwined with theirs, you, like these young
men will unlock the wisdom of the ancient sages and
will become a possessor of answers.*

It's Been a Year

THE REST OF the *yeshivah*[6] has just left for the morning
classes, leaving just two figures in the empty study hall.
Yehudah Stark and Ovadiah Yashar sit together with an antique
copy of an Arabic book, whose title is translated as *The Hidden
Master*, lying on the small table between them.

Yehudah is a broad-shouldered, light-skinned man in his
thirties. His appealing features would easily characterize him to
all as handsome. The *yeshivah* hired him two years ago to become
the student counselor because of his magnetic personality. He
commands confidence without saying a word. He is the kind
of man that the young men at the *yeshivah* want to emulate.

Ovadiah, with his fragile looking posture and olive skin,
looks at the old, worn leather-bound book. As he looks up from
it, his intense black eyes cast a haunting look at his friend and
mentor and tears well up in them. Yehudah sees the sadness
and uncertainty, but is silent.

"Where did you get my father's book from, Yehudah? I left
it in the safe in the *yeshivah* office."

"When you came to the *yeshivah* ten months ago," Yehudah
replies quietly, "you told the Rosh HaYeshivah[7] that you were on
a mission to learn this book. You and he knew that you were
not yet ready. Since this book is written in Arabic and since he
knew that I am the only member of the staff who knows how

6   Religious academy for studying Torah.

7   Literally: head of the Torah academy. This figure is usually much more than just a principal.
     He also helps guide the students in their religious growth.

to read and speak Arabic, I became the logical person to help you, so the *Rosh HaYeshivah* gave the book to me."

"Come to think of it, how do you know Arabic? You are Ashkenazic,[8] with light-brown hair and hazel eyes. I'm missing something."

Yehudah smiles. "In Columbia University I took up International Affairs with an emphasis on Middle Eastern Politics. So it was natural for me to take Arabic as my language requirement. I liked it so much that I double-majored."

"So that's why you went into the intelligence corps in the Israeli Army." Ovadiah's tone expresses awe.

"Shhh. We don't speak about that. Anyway, back to our subject. Three months ago the *Rosh HaYeshivah* entrusted me with this book, as he felt that the time was nearing for you to start your journey toward fulfilling that mission. Seeing that it is based on ADON OLAM, he sent me to a rabbi who is very familiar with the depths of this subject, so I would learn enough to be able to truly help you. Last night the administration staff met to discuss the matter, and we all feel that the time has come for you and me to finally learn *The Hidden Master*."

Yehudah's voice is gentle as he continues: "I know that today marks the first year anniversary of your father's death."

The tears that were hanging onto Ovadiah's thick black eyelashes begin to stream down his cheeks. His voice breaks. "It wasn't just a death; it was a murder."

"I know that, Ovadiah. We all do, and I know that nothing can ever completely heal the searing pain that you must be feeling." Ovadiah nods wordlessly, as Yehudah goes on. "But I hope that maybe you and I will together be able to fulfill your father's last plea."

You wonder what plea they are speaking of. Come along with me—we are going a year back in time, traveling to the Yashar household on Long Island—and I'll show you.

8   A Jew of European descent.

His Last Plea: *Adon Olam*

THE CAR DOOR SLAMS in the driveway. A boy, only eighteen years old, walks into a large, comfortable suburban home on a cool morning. His hands are red with the weight of the grocery bags he is carrying, but the sight he sees changes this everyday errand.

Blood is sprayed like water over the hallway. The boy's hands open instinctively, like a baby dropping a toy. Groceries forgotten, he runs along the trail of red.

His footsteps and wild eyes lead him to a man's body strewn carelessly across the floor. The boy kneels down, gasping against an onslaught of tears, choking on his own sobs, as he looks down on his dying father.

The man's last words are whispered to his son, desperately, longingly, "Ovadiah, never forget . . . Adon . . . Olam . . ."

That unforgettable day, a diamond dealer's lust for wealth overcame his respect for human life. Binyamin Yashar, Ovadiah's father, had been discarded on a criminal's way to unearned wealth.

Now, a year later, *The Hidden Master* is sitting between Yehudah and Ovadiah.

Ovadiah reminisces: "It was just a few weeks before Dad's murder that he said to me: 'My son, in the words of the short poem ADON OLAM you can find the answers that can override the tide of pain and loss that Jews have suffered throughout the centuries. We haven't survived the strangest and most violent of national histories in all of humanity unscarred. The balm for those scars can be found here in *The Hidden Master*, the book that your grandfather wrote.'

"'You never met my father, may he rest in peace. He died as an old man just before I left Morocco, which was before I even met your mother. He was among the most important rabbis of our people. He wrote *The Hidden Master* for people like me, people who didn't yet understand the depths of their faith. For decades after his death I didn't even open this book's holy pages. A few years ago I picked it up and read it. You may have seen the difference it has made in my life. Maybe one day we will learn it together. Nothing would make me happier.'

"Now, Yehudah," Ovadiah says, "I sit here with lots of pain, and lots of scars. This book is closed to me. Not only do I not know any Arabic—so I cannot even read the words—but my grandfather was a wise rabbi and my father told me that there were many deep and even mystical ideas inside his book. I was not raised with any of the tools to understand this book. Until a few months ago I never even dreamed of setting foot in a *yeshivah*."

Curious, Yehudah asks, "So how did you find this place?
"Laibel Weiss."

"Who is he? Tell me about him."

From Shivah[9] to Yeshivah

*C*OME WITH ME, *Searching Soul, as I again take you back a year ago to the incidents of the last morning of Ovadiah's father's shivah when Laibel Weiss walked into Ovadiah's life . . .*

An unfamiliar man with a long white beard walks in. Ovadiah is sure he has never met him before. A gruff man, in his seventies, he sits down heavily on the couch. He wears the black suit and fedora of the ultra-orthodox Jews.

"My name is Laibel Weiss," he says, as he hands Ovadiah a small velvet sack filled with black leather straps and boxes. "I don't know quite how to say this, but your father was somewhat of a closet Jew. These here are his *tefillin*.[10] He would have wanted you to wear them." Ovadiah doesn't yet know what to do with *tefillin*. Laibel's sorrow is thick, obvious. "I learned Torah with your father

9   The week of mourning following the burial. During this week the immediate family members do not leave their home and guests visit and comfort the mourners.

10   Phylacteries. Leather boxes that contain certain sections from the Torah. They are worn by Jewish men when they pray the daily morning prayers.

every morning for the past five years. We also learned your holy grandfather's book, *The Hidden Master*. Every word changed him so much. He told me that the falsehoods that he had accepted through time were being melted by the fire of these words. I've wanted to meet you for a long time, Ovadiah, but he didn't want to make waves in the family peace."

The old man sighs and rests his elbows on his knees. "Such a tragedy for your family. Terrible. Terrible." After a long silence, he looks up at Ovadiah. "I heard that his last words were 'Adon Olam'. While he was dying he was trying to point you in the direction of life. I cannot be silent now. I cannot leave Binyamin's hopes shattered. A *yeshivah*, you ever heard of such a thing? Where you go to learn Torah? The morning of his death we spoke of sending you to a *yeshivah*."

Laibel then scribbles the name and telephone of a *yeshivah* in Jerusalem on a scrap of paper from his pocket just as Ovadiah's mom emerges from the kitchen to see the strange visitor. Her blue eyes widen fast. Ovadiah realizes that she recognizes this man. What else had Mom and Dad hidden from him? Laibel rises to greet Estelle Yashar and the conversation between Laibel and Ovadiah ends. Mr. Weiss and Mrs. Yashar sit quietly together for several minutes as Ovadiah watches, agog. Who is this Laibel Weiss?

As Laibel is about to leave, he beckons Mrs. Yashar over to a corner near the door. In the quiet house, his whisper is hard to ignore: "I am so sorry for your loss, Mrs. Yashar. Your husband was a very special person, a very fine man. But now is a new time. Please forgive me for what I am about to say . . ." He hesitates before continuing. "Mrs. Yashar, please don't stop your son the way you stopped your husband."

Now come, let's return to Ovadiah and Yehudah in the empty study hall.

"So, Yehudah, less than two months later I caught a plane to Israel and this *yeshivah*, and here I am. I came to the *yeshivah* with one suitcase and this old book. I hoped that some day I would be ready to understand its concepts and find someone to teach me. The *Rosh HaYeshivah* said that he would find me someone but that I needed some time to grow first as a Jew. You have no idea how much I've been looking forward to this moment."

Between Ovadiah and Ovadiah

OVADIAH LOOKS DOWN at the book and places his right hand on it. Yehudah's hazel eyes are questioning. "Excuse me for being forward, but if you are the grandson of . . ."

"I know what you are about to ask. Everyone has the same question. My grandfather was one of the spiritual leaders of his generation and I was raised secular. What happened between the great Chacham[11] Ovadiah of Morocco and Ovadiah Yashar from Long Island? I am not exactly sure what happened in Morocco. Dad didn't speak much of his past or his family. I don't even know if there is anyone left from his family. All I know is that as a young teenager he left religion behind him. He came to America and married a non-religious Ashkenazic girl. So I was raised in a completely secular environment, but then things changed. For the last few years of Dad's life I saw him here and there sneaking a moment to read, or should I say devour, this old book that lies in front of us now.

"Mom wasn't at all interested in changing her way of life, but Dad was hungry for something he had lost. The last year before his murder, Mom stopped thwarting Dad. Maybe that was Laibel's doing. Slowly but surely, Dad kept bringing more and more Judaism into his life—and into mine. He started to speak to me differently. We actually started to speak about Hashem, and commandments. I started to notice a real change in him. Whenever he looked up from this large, old book, he looked . . . happy! As I told you, I did not know Arabic, knew nothing of what was inside this old book, but I could tell that

---

11   Literally: Wise man. This term is commonly used in the Sephardic communities of Jews to describe the greatest rabbis of their generation.

whatever it was had become, perhaps had always been, the center of his world. The light of my father's life all seemed to have come from this old worn book.

"In the last few months he kept saying that he would teach me so much more at the right time. 'Some day I will get the guts to change it all,' he said. 'Maybe I will even send you to *yeshivah*,' he said, 'but not today, not yet . . .' Nobody knew that the right time would never come."

Ovadiah starts to cry, and Yehudah gently places his hand on his shoulder.

"So, buddy, I see that a lot is riding on this book. O.K., pull yourself together. We have a lot to do. Ready?"

"I guess so."

Yehudah's commanding, yet gentle, tone, once again has its magical effect. Ovadiah is now ready to embark on the journey.

Let's Get Started

"LET'S START learning about ADON OLAM. The first two words are *Adon* and *olam*. Do you know their Hebrew translation?"

"Of course! *Adon* means Master and *olam* means world."

"Master of the World. That's a good enough translation for now. Do you know who the first person was to ever call Hashem by the name *Adon*?"

Ovadiah is hesitant. "Maybe it was the first man, Adam?"

"No. You are off by only two thousand years or so."

Ovadiah smiles, abashed. "Oh. Sorry. So who was it, and why did that person decide to use that name or description for Hashem when no one else had done so before him?"

"Let's open your grandfather's book and let him answer for you. Remember what your father told you about this book. It was written to help all people understand even the greatest depths of Judaism. To capture the interest of his audience, Chacham Yashar sometimes chose to embellish the texts of various Torah sources with some of his own words in order to speak out profound concepts in stimulating ways. Many times he even used biblical and other historical figures as tools to demonstrate deep concepts and teach us, his readers, ideas we would not have understood otherwise. So he begins . . ."

Adon: The Avraham[12] Revolution[13]

THE FURNACE GLOWS fiery red, and a slow sneer spreads over the bristled face of King Nimrod, leader and trailblazer for tyrants and megalomaniacs for all of history to come.

"So it has come to this, eh, Avram? You fool. What? Do you think that your God will save you now?"

Avram stands silent as a wall. He does not honor Nimrod's question with a response. He sees no reason to waste his breath on this power-hungry idolater.

"I mean it, Avram. You will not survive this. I am the king of this land, the king of your world. I decide whether you live or die. If you do not bow down to my authority, you will be put to death in the furnace before us."

The crowd of onlookers goes wild, hooting and howling in enthusiasm for the drama of death and domination that promises to unfold before them. Will Avram take the challenge? Will he forfeit his life for his monotheistic dreams? Because that is all they are, think many members of the crowd: dreams. Nothing more. Nothing to count on.

"I will not bow to you, Nimrod. I bow to no one but the true King, the Master of the Universe, *Adon Olam*. I'd rather die for His truth than live for your lies. Throw me into the fire if you wish. I am a wall!" Avram's confident voice echoes off the empty plains surrounding them.

---

12   This is the way Abraham's name is said in Hebrew. As you will see in the next few paragraphs, Avraham's name was originally Avram; only later in his life was it changed to Avraham.

13   Please refer to the Disclaimer.

*His words will be repeated by his descendant, King
Solomon, thousands of years later when the wisest of
all men composes the Song of Songs. There[14] he writes
that Israel as the bride promises the Almighty as her
groom that "I am a wall . . ." —She will be loyal to Him
forever, unmovable as a wall against the tides of time.*

Now, nostrils flaring and eyes ablaze, the humiliated Nimrod gestures
to the henchmen at his side. Grinning cruelly as the boors lift
Avram from where he stands, the dictator whispers, "Into the
furnace," with a pleasure bordering on mania.

The crowd gasps as Avram repeats his declaration moments before
disappearing among the flames: "*Adon Olam*, Master of the hidden world, for You alone I am a wall!" Surely the man has lost his
mind. How could Avram declare such unbending commitment at
such a moment? He is about to die! His skin will be eaten alive,
every nerve-ending consumed; he will be screaming in agony,
the fire surrounding him.

But there is yet another surprise. Only a minute or two later, with a
quiet and joy that seem to emanate from a world far beyond the
natural, Avram emerges unscathed from the furnace. Not a hair
of his head has been singed. The vicious celebratory screams and
dances of the Nimrod-worshipping, idolatrous crowd are stopped
cold as the hero steps once again into the blue-skied daylight.

"My Master, *Adonoi*, for You alone I am a wall . . ."

Personal MASTERpiece

YEHUDAH LOOKS UP from *The Hidden Master* into Ovadiah's excited eyes.

"Yehudah, the way you teach it, I feel as though I'm really
there."

"That's not me; that's just the way your grandfather embellished the *midrash*.[15] Chacham Yashar wanted to start with

14 Song of Songs 8:10.

15 Rabbinical homiletical interpretation of the Torah.

this particular *midrash* about Nimrod and Avraham[16] because this event and the word *Adon* have everything to do with one another. *Adon* is the ultimate expression of Avraham's relationship with Hashem."

"But, Yehudah, how does this word express Avraham's relationship to Hashem better than any other name of Hashem that He was called before?"

Yehudah reaches into his bag and takes out a book, *Rav Schwab on Prayer.*

"Here, let me read you this explanation:"[17]

The world had to wait until our father Avraham discovered that the Holy One, blessed be He, should be addressed as **Adonoi**. What did he discover, that none of his illustrious ancestors—Methuselah or Noah or Shem—knew?

To understand this, we must analyze the true meaning of an **adon**, a master. A master has a personal relationship with his servant. Whenever the servant performs his duties, he is directly serving his master. By way of contrast, a **melech**, a king, has only a very general relationship with his subjects, because he has an entire nation to govern, and very few people know him personally. We refer to the Holy One, blessed be He, as **Melech HaOlam**, King of the World, in all of our blessings, and a blessing is not complete without this reference.

However, we preface this appellation with "**Baruch Atah Adonoi**", blessed are You, our personal Master, meaning that we recognize the Holy One, blessed be He, as our Master before referring to Him as the King of the universe. When addressing Him, we recognize first that He is "our personal Master," with whom we each have a personal relationship—literally, He knows **me**! Then we acknowledge that our Master is the King of the World.

So, while the earlier great righteous people recognized Hashem as **Melech HaOlam**, the Universal King, it was only our father Avraham who recognized that the **adon** of the world is really **Adonoi**, each individual's personal Master . . . that each individual has a personal relationship to the Holy One, blessed be He . . . .

16 Shir HaShirim Rabbah, chapter 8, sections 9 and 10, with the Eitz Yoseph commentary.

17 In the quotes from Rabbi Schwab, many Hebrew terms used by him are translated into English in order to facilitate an easier read for those not familiar with them.

Therefore whenever a person says the word, **Adonoi**, my Master, no matter how small he thinks he is, he is in direct contact with God . . . .

We can now understand why our days start and end with ADON OLAM, which expresses the most basic concept of our prayers, that no matter how insignificant we may be, no matter how full of shortcomings we are, we still have the right to approach the Holy One, blessed be He, directly. The **Adon** of all Creation is **Eli**, my personal God.

"So Ovadiah, that's your answer in a nutshell. Avraham's relationship with Hashem was personal. His love for Hashem compelled him. As he acted when faced with the fiery furnace, so he continued to act throughout his life. And this was the legacy that he passed down to his offspring after him. And that's the message that ADON OLAM starts with. This is the Jews' starting point: proper service to our personal Master (*Adon*) must be a compelling, never-ending service. But that was just the introduction. Ready to begin to find out why else the illustrious authors of ADON OLAM chose to start their time-transcending message with *Adon*?"

Who Authored ADON OLAM?

"I'M ALL EARS. But first could you tell me who authored ADON OLAM? I heard somewhere that ADON OLAM was composed by a liturgical poet in the Middle Ages."

Yehudah cringes at the very idea.

"Not quite, buddy. The holy words of ADON OLAM were given to us in an intensely concentrated and precise form. They were written in order to guide the Jewish People toward the Creator every day, no matter when, no matter where, and no matter what would happen to them throughout the ages. No, Ovadiah, the liturgical poets whom we call *paytanim*, were righteous men, but ADON OLAM was not written by these men. It is much more than a liturgical poem. Rather, it is the masterful work of our ancient sages, who were the wisest of men. ADON OLAM was written approximately 2,500 years ago by the members of the Great Assembly."

"Really? I don't know much, but I do know that that's a heavy statement to make. What's your source for it?"

"Rabbeinu[18] Pinchas of Plutsk."

"Rabbeinu who?"

"Pinchas of Plutsk. Although many have not heard of him, he was one of the Vilna Gaon's[19] most loyal and exacting disciples. When he begins his comments on ADON OLAM in his book, *Siddur Sha'ar HaRachamim*,[20] we find one of the great secrets Rabbeinu Pinchas unearthed—the source of ADON OLAM. There he expresses his position that ADON OLAM's authors were none other than the members of the Great Assembly.

"In the Vilna Gaon's approbation to this book he refers to one of Rabbeinu Pinchas's comments on this very same verse of ADON OLAM, where the illustrious authors are disclosed as the members of the Great Assembly. It seems clear that the reason that the Gaon's awareness of this shocking claim did not deter him from giving his approbation was because Rabbeinu Pinchas gleaned this hypothesis from the Vilna Gaon himself."

They Slaughtered What?

"IN OTHER WORDS, the Vilna Gaon didn't say so directly, but it was understood from something else he had said. What did the Vilna Gaon actually say, then, Yehudah?"

"The Gaon teaches us of an incident presented in the Tal-

---

18   Literally: Our Rabbi.

19   The Vilna Gaon (Eliyahiu ben Shlomo Zalman Kremer, 1720–1797) was an important rabbi in Lithuania. He was known simply as "the Gaon" because of his great wisdom. Although this term "Gaon" usually refers to the Torah giants of the second half of the first millennium of the Common Era, Rabbi Eliyahu's knowledge and wisdom was considered far beyond the wisdom that had been seen for many centuries. Thus he was given the title Gaon.

20   *Siddur Sha'ar HaRachamim*, page 69. The translation of the title is *The Prayer Book: The Gates of Mercy.*

mud[21] where we are told that the first generation of the Great Assembly was dealing with a generation that was losing its struggle against the Evil Inclination to worship idols. In order to save that generation and future generations of Jews, the Great Assembly decided that they had no choice but to, so to speak, slaughter the spiritual forces which created the Evil Inclination toward idol worship, because they feared that otherwise the masses might eventually become so divorced from Hashem that there would be no going back. It was an emergency situation."

Ovadiah is tickled by this. "That sounds like a good idea. Why didn't Moshe Rabbeinu[22] or any of the other earlier leaders of our people slaughter this force in the earlier generations? It would have solved so many problems!"

"Well, Ovadiah, it is not all as simple as that. The Vilna Gaon explains[23] that by suppressing the influence of the forces of evil, the forces of good must be equally weakened. If not, he explains, the world would have been knocked off balance. You see, Ovadiah, this balance is quite important. If these forces of good and evil are not equally balanced, then free choice would not exist—and without free choice our physical world would have no reason to exist either."

"Why? Wouldn't the world be a better place without forces of evil? Why do we need free choice?"

"Later on, as we study more of your grandfather's book, we will learn the answers to both your questions. Meanwhile, let's finish with this, so we can get back to our discussion of Avraham and Adon."

Ovadiah acquiesces reluctantly. "O.K., Yehudah, go on."

"'Ze l'umas ze asa HaElokim'—'God has made the one as well as

---

21   The Talmud is an encyclopedic rabbinic work containing thousands of pages. It was composed during the first few hundred years of the first millennium of the Common Era. It contains all aspects of halacha (Jewish law), as well as much aggada (non-legal teachings that deal with moral and philosophic issues), and encompasses many facets of Jewish thought and faith. Here the reference is to the Talmud's Tractate (volume) of *Yuma*, page 69b.

22   A term of respect for Moses. Literally it means Moses, our Teacher.

23   In chapter 30 of his commentary on *Seder Olam*, an authoritative book containing the timeline of Jewish history.

the other.'[24] There is a balance in the world which must be kept; if a bad influence is neutralized, then a corresponding good influence must go, too; otherwise, the world's equilibrium will be disturbed. The Vilna Gaon posits that when the members of the Great Assembly slaughtered the Evil Inclination toward idol worship, prophecy needed to be removed from the world as well. In other words, he viewed it as a simple cause-and-effect equation. When Hashem granted the request for the removal of this force of evil, He simultaneously closed certain channels of good—in this case, prophecy—so that the proper balance for free choice would not be disturbed. And so, the first members of the Great Assembly, many of whom were the last prophets, knew that as an outcome of their prayers to remove the Evil Inclination toward idol worship, Hashem would cause prophecy to come to a close very soon."

"But, Yehudah, what does that have to do with Rabbeinu Pinchas's claim that the members of the Great Assembly were the authors of ADON OLAM?"

"Everything! Remember, Ovadiah, that prophecy had been a reality of life since the first man walked the earth until their generation. It was among the most ancient dependable channels to connect with the Creator. How could Hashem's Holy Nation remain holy without its prophetic link to their Creator? Our nation was about to go from something like one thousand to zero. It would eventually reach the point when there would be no Temple standing in Jerusalem, no prophecy and dispersion of the Jews among the heathen nations. Something had to be done, and someone had to take the responsibility to do it. So the Great Assembly, the Sanhedrin that was convened at the beginning of the Second Temple period, got to work on their many projects that would secure the survival of our people.

"Having learned these teachings from the Vilna Gaon, Rabbeinu Pinchas was given the beginnings of the grounds to conclude that ADON OLAM was one of those colossal projects. With the Vilna Gaon's approbation of Rabbeinu Pinchas's words we now come to view ADON OLAM as both an ancient

24 Ecclesiastes 7:14.

and central work which was composed, like their other projects, to aid the spiritual survival of the Jewish People. As we continue, let's keep in mind this driving force behind all the works of the Great Assembly."

The Sanhedrin's Key

OVADIAH IS IMPRESSED. But he wants to know more: "What were the other projects of the Great Assembly and what drove them to achieve these undertakings?"

"They wrote texts and passed edicts that have influenced Jewish lives for millennia. Their words sculpt the rhythm of our days even now. To start with, they authored and canonized many of the books of the Holy Scriptures and the daily prayers as we have them today. For example, the Books of Ezra, Nechemiah and the Scroll of Esther have been attributed to them, and they were the ones who composed the *Shemoneh Esrei*,[25] which is the most central component of a Jew's daily prayer. These writings were in progress during the 130 years of this great Sanhedrin.

"Let's try to think what must have been on their minds nearly 2,500 years ago, and then we will better understand why ADON OLAM was written."

Yehudah leans back for a moment and stretches before continuing:

"What would it mean to them that the period of prophecy was coming to a close? As I already pointed out to you, this was no small change, and it happened merely forty years after the inception of the Great Assembly, when Ezra, the son of Seraya, the last prophet, closed his eyes for the last time. They knew that from then on the world would be devoid of prophecy until the future coming of the Messiah and Israel's final redemption. Their people's harsh history would unfold, and yet there would be no prophet to steer the masses back to the path that they would (could) stray from.

---

25   Literally, "eighteen"; a fundamental Jewish prayer, recited three times a day by religious Jews.

"With the future unknown, they knew that they must leave their people fortified for anything that may occur. They knew that they needed to find a way to reach the people when they—these great sages—would no longer be there. They knew that they must compose the text that would dissolve confusion, before their people would be swallowed up by confusion for all time. They knew that the lack of prophecy would leave breaches in faith that their people could not yet even fathom. Without prophecy they would have only shards left of the Judaism that once was. They knew that they must give the people many tools for putting the shards back together, tools that would endure no matter how many times the vessels would be shattered."

"And my grandfather knew about all of this?"

"Of course! *The Hidden Master* informs us that with ADON OLAM we can search for—and find—meaning in our existence. Your grandfather states that 'those who come to possess its messages will be enabled to become true servants of the Almighty Master of the World, true servants of the *Adon Olam*, and so will understand the purpose of their existence'."

What's the Big Secret?

"BUT, YEHUDAH, I don't get it. If ADON OLAM is so important, why was its significance to our people kept such a secret until the times of the Vilna Gaon and Rabbeinu Pinchas?"

"It wasn't. Not by a long shot. I told you that the *Rosh HaYeshivah* sent me to learn *The Hidden Master* with a rabbi who was well-versed in ADON OLAM. During our first meeting this rabbi referred to a source[26] that compounded the statements of Rav Shrira Gaon[27] (906–1006 CE), his son Rav Hai Gaon (939–1038

---

26   *Mateh Moshe*, page 31.

27   In this case, the term Gaon is referring to those great rabbis of the Gaonic period, which was in the second half of the first millennium of the Common Era.

CE), and Rabbi Yehudah HaChasid (1150–1217 CE), producing the following paragraph:

> Whoever pays attention to and understands the beginning of ADON OLAM, is guaranteed that his prayers will be heard, and that the Satan will not fight against his prayers. There will be no Satan or mishap in his prayers on Rosh Hashanah and Yom Kippur, and his enemies will fall before him . . . (and) his Evil Inclination will be at peace with him. And about such a person King Solomon, may he rest in peace, states, "When a man's ways please Hashem, He brings even his enemies to be at peace with him."[28] And it is possible that this is the reason that the tradition has become widespread to say [ADON OLAM] before all blessings and praise.

"So, Yehudah, from the words you just quoted it seems that no one should even open his or her mouth in prayer without first understanding ADON OLAM."

"Correct. That is exactly what my rabbi concluded.

"Also, I want you to notice their emphasis of: 'the **beginning** of ADON OLAM.' The truth is, Ovadiah, that all of ADON OLAM's messages are in that first stanza. Theoretically, it would have been enough to have only that stanza; but for most people this way of presentation is much too condensed, so the concepts need to be reiterated a few times, in greater detail, in order to be fully appreciated. By the end you'll understand it all much better."

For a few moments Yehudah leans back with his hands behind his head. He looks into the 19-year-old's face before him and sees a clear resemblance between the elderly rabbi he had been sent to learn with, Rabbeinu Reuven, and the young Ovadiah Yashar, Rabbeinu Reuven's nephew . . . .

Come with me Searching Soul, back to that meeting three months ago . . . .

We Never Knew

THE ELDERLY Rabbeinu Reuven Yashar sits in his study, speaking with Yehudah Stark.

"Young man, seven months ago your *Rosh HaYeshivah* told me about my nephew Ovadiah and this book that you have just handed to me. It was at that time that he informed me of my long-lost brother Binyamin's demise. Until that moment I never knew what had happened to Binyamin. I always prayed for him, but never knew where he was. The pain at hearing of his death was shattering.

"Yehudah, the *Rosh HaYeshivah* and I agree that your participation is necessary to help Ovadiah, my brother's son, become the best Jew he can be. In order to help you understand who Ovadiah is, let me first tell you something about Ovadiah's father. Our mother, may she rest in peace, died when Binyamin was a baby. Binyamin was raised by our father alone, with great care and devotion. But all that nurturing didn't seem to help. Our father saw Binyamin slowly slipping away from the path of his forefathers.

"The times in Morocco were changing. It was not the same religious community that I was born into twenty years prior to Binyamin. Our father, as the leader of our people, was worried about the new generation that Binyamin found himself in, and he was especially worried about Binyamin. He spent years writing this book to meet the new challenges, Binyamin's challenges. He finished it not so long before he fell ill and died; this was forty years ago. Young Binyamin never had the chance to learn from his loving father the words that could have changed his life. After the *shivah*, Binyamin gave me a hug and with a few tears said, 'I have nothing to hold me here in Morocco any more. I have no reason to stay with the ways of the past.' I knew that I could not convince him to stay. I couldn't offer him anything, so as a last effort I handed him my father's personal copy of *The Hidden Master*. He promised me that some day he would read it.

"Yehudah, the *Rosh HaYeshivah* and I don't think that I should expose myself just yet to the lad. He needs to grow to become a good Jew on his own. By growing with his friends he will internalize much more than if I would get involved. The pressure that would be created by my presence might hinder his growth. I will eventually meet him, but for the time being let's learn together, you and I, so that you can grow with these words and give them over to Ovadiah when the time comes."

Let Them Speak

"O.K.," SAYS YEHUDAH to the still-attentive Ovadiah, "now that you know about the authors, it's time to return to Avraham calling Hashem *Adon*. You'd better get relaxed (settled), because I have a lot of information to pass on to you about why the members of the Great Assembly chose to start ADON OLAM with the word *Adon*.

"As you saw with the *midrash* about Nimrod, *The Hidden Master* uses unconventional methods to bring biblical figures and their messages alive to the reader. Before I tell you about the next scene, please keep in mind that Chacham Yashar did not claim that these biblical figures actually said the words that he wrote. In this scene, he brought us back to the times of Ezra the Scribe's[29] Sanhedrin, the times of the Great Assembly, and let us hear the discussions being held by its members. Imagine being there two thousand years ago on the Temple Mount where Chacham Yashar depicts our ancient sages (as saying) . . . .[30]

"It is not only the ramparts of Jerusalem that we must rebuild. The soul of our holy nation must also be raised from the ashes. We need to compose words that will hold them strong so that they will never suffer spiritual annihilation. How should we start our message to the ages?

---

29   This is the same personage as Ezra the son of Seraya, mentioned previously. He is also known as Malachi, the last prophet.

30   Please refer to the Disclaimer.

"Obviously we should start with the source of our faith. Fellow prophets and sages, we must start our eternal message for all future generations by clearly defining how, from its very inception until now, our faith has vastly differed from those that came before and all those that are to come. Therefore, the expression of Avraham, the father of our faith, the first Jew, is the only one whose words are appropriate for such a message.

"There have been others who claimed to be monotheistic, but it was only our forefather Avraham who revealed to the entire world what that belief really entails. He was beginning something completely new. His beliefs held our people strong until now, and it is those same beliefs that will be needed in the future.

"Whatever challenges our people will have, Avraham's expression will speak to them. Our people are about to meet up with other errant faiths and tainted views of monotheism that could pull them into the storms of confusion. We must give them clarity. So, like Avraham, we must start our message to them by referring to Hashem as *Adon*."

"But, Ovadiah, Adon is by no means the only name or expression that these illustrious authors used to describe our relationship with Hashem. Look at the text of ADON OLAM, and you will see that Hashem is referred to by many different names or expressions. He is referred to as *Adon* ~ Master, *Melech* ~ King, *Cheftso* ~ His Desire, *Shemo* ~ His Name, *Tifara* ~ Splendor, *Echad* ~ One, First and Last, My God, Living Redeemer, Rock, Banner, Refuge, My Portion, Healer, Helper, the Tetragrammaton, and, finally, the Sephardim[31] refer to Him in the last words as *Shem Norah*, Awesome Name."

"That's some list. But what did you mean when you said that they used these names or expressions to describe our relationship with Hashem? And why not just use one name, like *Adon*?"

"Names are actually descriptions. Each of these names describe to us the ways that Hashem interacts with us. When you know how Hashem is relating to you and how you should

---

31 This refers to Jews whose ancestors stem from either Spain, Portugal, or any Middle-Eastern country, as opposed to Ashkenazim, who are Jews of European descent.

be relating to Him, then you can understand so much more about the *olam*, the world, and why He created it, and what your role is as His servant. The jumbled and tossed pieces of your life begin to make sense when you know all this.

"So let's go a little further with the concept of Avraham calling Hashem *Adon*, the first name I mentioned."

Yehudah jumps up and gathers a *Gemara*[32] and a few other books from the shelves of the still-quiet study hall.

"The Gemara states:[33]

*'Rabbi Yochanan said in the name of Rabbi Shimon bar Yochai, "From the day that the Holy One, blessed be He, created the world, there was no one who called the Holy One, blessed be He, **Adon** until Avraham came and called Him **Adon**, as is stated, 'And he [Avraham] said: My **Adon**, **Elokim**,[34] how [in what way] shall I know that I shall inherit it?'[35]"*

"Adon literally means Master. What does that tell us about Hashem, about ourselves and about our relationship with Hashem? Avraham's generation referred to him as Avraham Ha'Ivri, which is the source of the word, Hebrew. This word literally means "the one on the other side," because it was like the entire world was on one side of a river and Avraham was on the other. You have to have a little historical context here. Let's go back to Nimrod for a moment. Why was he trying to kill Avraham?"

"Beats me! Why do tyrants behave like that anyway?"

"Nimrod had a definite agenda. At that time, Nimrod had convinced almost the entire populated world to follow him in a rebellion against monotheism. He used this as a tool for his own gain. He wanted to be the only ruling power, but knew that if there were one all-powerful Adon, Master, then the world would have to act according to the Master's Will and

---

32 Tractate, or volume of the Talmud. This term also is used to refer to the Talmud in general.

33 Tractate *Brachos* 7b.

34 One of the names of God.

35 Genesis 15:8.

not his. Avraham was the only one spoiling Nimrod's plans of world domination. We learn[36] that Hashem called Avraham "singular in his world" because he was the only one who really recognized—well, we'll explain exactly what he recognized as we go along. But look, here's that midrash:

> When the wicked Nimrod threw our father Avraham into the fiery furnace, the archangel Gavriel declared before the Holy One, blessed be He, "Ruler of the World, allow me to descend and cool off the fire and I will save the righteous one from the fiery furnace."
>
> The Holy One, blessed be He, replied, "I am singular in My world, and he is singular in his world. It is proper for the Singular to save the singular."

"And don't think that Avraham's efforts stopped at the furnace. Just 25 years after the furnace incident, Nimrod began building the Tower of Babel—we learn[37] that Avraham was 48 at the time—and that Avraham was right there making fun of the people building the tower and cursing them in the Name of his God.[38] Basically, Avraham was instigating a revolt."

What About Noah?

"BUT, YEHUDAH, aren't we ignoring somebody—or a few somebodies? We know that Avraham wasn't the first man to dedicate himself to God. I mean, for example, what about Noah?[39]"

"You're some astute guy! But before I go on I'll actually up the ante on your side. Did you know that Avraham wasn't even the first prophet? Adam, Seth, Enosh, Methuselah and, yes, Noach and Shem and Arpachshad and Chanoch—these were all not only men of God, but were actually prophets."

36   The Gemara in Pesachim 118a.

37   Seder Olam.

38   Yalkut Shimoni on Noach, 61.

39   Referred to from here on as Noach.

"That section you brought from Rav Schwab referred to this."

"I see that you've been paying attention. Since they were prophets, it seems to be a safe assumption that they believed in and worshipped the single Almighty God. The Torah itself states that "Noach walked with God."[40] You should also know that not once but twice we are informed that Chanoch walked in the ways of God.[41] Not only that, but the *Midrash*[42] informs us that Noach actually stood up, like Avraham, and castigated the generation that was following Nimrod during the rebellion of the Tower of Babel. So far, Noach seems to be just as much a servant of Hashem as Avraham, right?"

"Exactly! So what was the difference between them? If calling Hashem *Adon* symbolizes a very different relationship with the Almighty Master of All, then what was it about Avraham that was different and that made him the first to call Hashem *Adon*, Master? What was different about his relationship with Hashem as opposed to that of all of these other great men? What then does the name *Adon* symbolize to us? And why, accordingly, did the authors of ADON OLAM choose to start their message to Avraham's descendants with this word?"

Yehudah smiles and says nothing, waiting for Ovadiah to think for himself. Ovadiah continues hesitantly.

"It must be that if the first Jew is the first one to call Hashem *Adon*, this name somehow shows the special and distinct character of the relationship of the Jews to Hashem. That must be why ADON OLAM starts with this word, but I don't yet see any difference. Is it some small nuance?"

"Actually, Ovadiah, the difference is massive, but before we begin to see just how revolutionary Avraham's life was, I want to make it clear that the righteous people who lived before Avraham were also really righteous. I mean, Hashem Himself called Noach a righteous and perfectly faithful man[43]. When

---

40   Genesis 6:9

41   Genesis 5:22 and 24.

42   *Bereishis Rabba* 31:3 and *Sanhedrin* 108.

43   Genesis 6:9

was the last time that God Himself said something like that about you?"

Ovadiah grins ruefully. "Not lately."

"Keep clearly in your mind, Ovadiah, that these people were connected to Hashem beyond anything that we can even conceive of. Yet the varied midrashim[44] seem to actually put down Noach. The midrashim used extreme language in order to magnify for us what at first seems an imperceptible difference between these two righteous men, Noach and Avraham. Upon examination of this information we come to the realization that Avraham achieved a clarity and a depth of connection with Hashem that nobody had ever come close to achieving before him. Through the midrashim we come to discover that the gap between the earlier righteous individuals and Avraham was actually vast, while still retaining our understanding that the others mentioned were giants of righteousness."

"So, Yehudah, what exactly **was** the difference between Avraham and the others you listed?"

"Let's look together at Ethics of the Fathers 5:3.[45] Here our sages tell us that 'Avraham's righteousness was so great that he received the total reward that would have gone to the ten previous generations, had they not been sinful.' But the previous mishna[46] implies no such reward for Noach."

Ovadiah reads the next mishna on the page and seems confused.

"Yehudah, I just don't get it. Why didn't Noach deserve the same reward as Avraham?"

Yehudah looks down at The Hidden Master and begins to translate Chacham Yashar's embellished rendition of Genesis 18:23–33 . . . .

---

44 This is the plural form of the word Midrash.

45 This is a Tractate in the Mishna (see following note).

46 Each smaller subsection of Ethics of the Fathers and all other tractates of the Greater Mishna are called simply a mishna. The complete Mishna is the first written compilation of Oral Torah Law. This massive work was compiled during the Tanaitic period and eventually became the seed which developed into both the Babylonian and the Jerusalem Talmuds.

Precious Ten

AVRAHAM'S MIND and heart are working furiously.[47] The Almighty has just informed him of His decision to destroy the city of Sodom. Avraham knows that the Almighty has revealed this information to him for a reason. The cogs continue to turn quickly, when suddenly it all clicks into place. Clarity has dawned and Avraham acts immediately.

"Perhaps there are fifty righteous men in the midst of the city. Please don't destroy the city if there are fifty who will call out Your Name. I long for the whole world to recognize Your Kingship. Even these fifty are precious . . . .

"Behold now I have commenced to speak to the Lord, although I am dust and ashes. Perhaps the fifty righteous men will be missing five. Will You destroy the entire city because of a missing five?

"The people of Sodom are evil, but maybe all hope is not lost. If at least twenty good men can be found to influence the city in the right direction, this group of people may still be trained in Your service . . . .

"Please, let the Lord's wrath not be kindled, and I will speak yet this time, perhaps ten will be found there . . . Just ten . . . If only there is at least a quorum of ten, Sodom may yet join in Your service.

"You know it is not Sodom I pray for," says Avraham. "Not Sodom for the sake of Sodom. You are the Source of everything. Nothing and no one has any meaning if not attached to You. I pray for Sodom so that its inhabitants will come to serve You. I pray for Sodom for I want the whole world to serve You."

What a Difference!

"IN THIS RENDITION, Ovadiah, many words were added to the original Torah text so the readers could best understand the difference between Avraham and the other righteous ones before him."

47   Please refer to the Disclaimer.

"I still don't see the difference. I already knew that Avraham searched for every possibility to bring the world closer to Hashem, but isn't the same thing true about Noach?"

"Not in the same way as Avraham. We are told[48] that when the Holy One, blessed be He, said to Noach that He would save him in the ark, Noach did not request mercy for the other inhabitants of the world, and they were all destroyed."

"I don't understand. How can that be? We know what superhuman efforts Noach expended to save the creatures in the ark. I don't get it."

"Don't get confused, Ovadiah. The midrash is not denigrating Noach, but rather just trying to pinpoint for us the difference between these two giants. Both were being confronted with the very difficult option of praying or not praying for the wicked. What was it about Avraham that made him pray for the wicked when Noach let them go to their deserved doom?"

Would You Pray For Evil?

"ACTUALLY, YEHUDAH, I kind of understand Noach. Why would anyone want to pray for evildoers? After all, Hashem had just told Noach that He was fed up with these people. Why should Noach pray for them? So why does Ethics of the Fathers inform us that Noach didn't receive the reward that Avraham received?

"The Talmud[49] has your answer. It tells us that 'Avraham Avinu[50] caused the mouth of every passerby to call out His (Hashem's) Name.' Avraham would not rest until the whole world would praise Hashem. And what The Hidden Master points out to us here is that this included even the wicked of Sodom.

"Avraham felt constantly compelled to turn even the lowest

48   Zohar on Genesis, 67b.

49   Tractate Sotah 10b.

50   Literally, Abraham our Father. This term—Avinu—is used to show respect for our forefathers Avraham, Yitzchak and Ya'akov

of evil people toward Hashem's service. This was the loving-kindness of our father Avraham. This is why he was called Ha'Ivri, the one on the other side. The other righteous people before Avraham Avinu did reprove their generations, but Avraham wouldn't give up when the reproof fell upon deaf ears. He went further. He used loving-kindness to win the world over so that all people would eventually become Hashem's servants. Avraham sought out opportunities to show the heathen world around him Who was their Master and to Whom they owed homage."

Yehudah pauses for a few moments to turn some more of the old brittle pages of *The Hidden Master*. The musty smell of the brown pages fills their corner of the empty study hall. As Ovadiah breathes in the smell, he thinks of how happy his father was as he read this musty old book and of how glad he is to finally be fulfilling his father's last wish. Yehudah turns one last page and looks up at Ovadiah.

"Here it is, I found it. In his rendition of the next *midrash*, Chacham Yashar creates a clear picture of how, for Avraham, serving Hashem was the entire definition of personal life. As you listen, imagine you were there, near Avraham Avinu's tent, nearly 4,000 years ago."

Don't Thank Me[51]

AVRAHAM IS SITTING outside his tent, on the lookout. He is overjoyed to see a group of travelers appear in the heat of the day. They are hot, tired, hungry, and thirsty. Running toward them, he welcomes them warmly, as he does any traveler who approaches his four-doored tent.

Inviting them in, he serves them a feast worthy of kings. Several hours later, when they have eaten and rested and are about to go on their way, they say:

"Thank you, Avraham, for your hospitality. We appreciate your kindness, your food and drink on this hot day. You and your household have worked very hard to care for us, and we would like to honor you for your efforts."

"Ah, my dear friends, your kindness is enormous," responds Avraham, "but please don't thank me. It would be a lie for you to thank me, and it would be a lie for me to accept your thanks. All that we have in this world is from *Adon Olam*, the Master of the Universe. I am merely His servant. It is Him that you and I both must thank. It is not to me that any honor and gratitude should be shown, but to Him. He is the One Who made the food, He is the One Who gives me the strength to help you, and He is the One Who brought us together."

"But, our dear host, you are the one that toiled to help us, not your God. We want to thank you!"

"My honored guests, if you do not intend to thank Him, then don't thank me, but instead pay me, but I don't want your money. I'd rather that you acknowledge Hashem instead. Hashem is the Source of all kindness. He created the world and all that is in it. Remember that it is only to Him that we all owe our thanks. Remember that He alone is your Master, your Adon."

Somewhat puzzled by all they have heard, the guests depart. A seed has been sown. Avraham *Avinu* has helped yet another few people to embark on their search to recognize Hashem.[52]

One day, though, his guests are of a different sort. They are angels, and they come on a day that is particularly hot and uncomfortable; what's more, they come three days after Avraham *Avinu's* circumcision, when his pain is the greatest. And Avraham is unaware that they are angels. Nevertheless, he runs to greet them, like he would anyone else . . . .

It Doesn't Stop There

YEHUDAH LIFTS his head up from *The Hidden Master* to look at Ovadiah. He sees that he is ready for the message. "From the verses that follow, we see that Avraham wanted to create the same scenario with these holy guests, as with

---

52   Based upon *Midrash Rabbah, Vayera*, end of 54.

others, even though he had many excuses why not to run toward them on that day, especially since he was experiencing prophecy when he first noticed them. Can you list some of the rationalizations he could have used to stay put?"

"Yeah, sure. He was old, he had just had surgery, and not only that, but we learn that Hashem purposely made the day hot so that nobody would want to pass by Avraham's tent like they usually did. We know that the 'guests' were not men but angels. No one else was out that day. Hashem was not demanding from Avraham to do anything. Quite the opposite! It clearly would have been understandable had Avraham taken a break for a day or two."

Yehudah's eyebrows shoot up. He is impressed with this beginner who seems to have gathered quite a bit of information over the past few months.

"O.K., Ovadiah, let's put all the pieces together. For Avraham, service to Hashem was all-encompassing. It was a step beyond that of Noach. As we said already, Avraham caused every passerby to call out Hashem's Name. Avraham simply would not stop until the whole world recognized Hashem. This claim was not made about Noach. After Noach finished his year-long ordeal in the ark, he actually planted a vineyard and got drunk from its produce. He viewed life as still having moments for the self. Avraham's outlook on the world did not allow him to relax as Noach did, for he felt compelled at every moment to find more ways to bring the world to its goal of serving Hashem.

"But that isn't all. Avraham wasn't willing for this type of service to stop with him. And that's why the Sodom story opens with Hashem telling the angels that, 'I know him (Avraham), that he will command his children and his household after him, that they shall keep the way of Hashem . . .'[53] The Ramban[54] teaches that 'I know him', means 'I know his greatness and exaltedness and because of that he will command his children to do what is correct before Me. And therefore I

---

53 Genesis 18:19.
54 Rabbi Moshe ben Nachman. A famous Torah commentator from Gerona, 1194–1270.

will make him into a great and wondrous nation so that they will serve Me . . .'"

So God's a Racist?

OVADIAH IS SILENT for a few moments, struggling with something. Yehudah sits quietly, waiting for him to get up the courage to speak his mind.

"Well, Yehudah, I must admit this has been an incredible two hours, but something in all of this bothers me. From what we have learned about the word *Adon* it seems like—excuse me for even saying it—it seems that the word *Adon* is portraying Hashem as a racist. Since *Adon* expresses the special relationship with Hashem that Avraham forged in the world, and the relationship that he bequeathed to his descendents, the Jewish People, consequently it seems to be ignoring the rest of the world! Well, excuse me, but don't they count? Don't they also deserve the opportunity to serve Hashem in this complete way? Hashem made them just like He made you and me and Avraham. Don't they have an obligation to have a relationship with God? I thought the Torah tells us that the rest of the people in the world also have commandments. It just can't be that ADON OLAM is implying that Hashem is a racist; we must be missing something. I'm confused."

With a clanging alarm, the bell rings to signal the end of the morning session of classes. All around them, students are starting to converge upon the now not-so-empty study hall, to continue learning with their study partners. Yehudah and Ovadiah look up from the small mountain of books strewn over the desk between them. Their time for today is up.

"I have to teach your roommate, Shimi, now, so I have to go. We'll be in touch. And about your questions, they are good ones, but I don't think I'm the best person to answer them. There's someone we all know who can answer them better than anyone. Stay put and I'll send him to you. In the meantime, is it O.K. if I take *The Hidden Master* with me? Before we meet I need to go over a few points with a rabbi."

"Please take it, Yehudah. And thanks for helping me start to fulfill my promise."

"You should know, though, that we've just scratched the surface!"

Left alone with his thoughts, Ovadiah pulls out his wallet and takes out the last picture of his dad.

"I've started, Dad. I promised you at the graveside that somehow I would find out about ADON OLAM. I've started . . ."

Suddenly a large and muscular hand impacts upon Ovadiah's shoulder. Let me introduce the owner of this hand to you. Avraham Ben Avraham, Avi for short, is a twenty-five-year-old righteous convert. His six-foot-seven bruiser body and chiseled European face with blond hair and clear blue eyes always brighten up the days of those who surround him. He was born in Düsseldorf, Germany, and, as I will tell you later, something sent him searching for meaning, searching for the truth. After he finished his degree in comparative religions he went searching even more. Eventually he found Judaism and ended up coming to learn with Yehudah before his conversion. He is one of Yehudah's first students, but today their relationship is more that of friendship than of teacher and student. Because of his vast knowledge of other faiths and ideologies, Avi has become Yehu- dah's right-hand man in their joint efforts to enable other young men who come from varied backgrounds, to reach their highest spiritual potentials. And it's my hope, Searching Soul, that as you get to know him, he will help you do the same . . . .

"*Guten tog*, Ovadiah. I didn't forget you, buddy. I remembered that today marks the first anniversary to your father's death, yartzheit, so I came by your room before morning prayers, but

Shimi said you had left early in a really down mood. You still look down. Can I sit with you?"

"Thanks for your concern. Please do."

Avi sits down in the chair Yehudah has just vacated. As usual, Ovadiah can't help but pity the piece of furniture now being subjected to Avi's huge bulk, and the thought makes him smile in spite of himself.

Ovadiah continues: "You're not the first to come looking for me today, Avi. All the guys came—Shimi, Natan, Shalom. You all remembered. I really appreciate it. And Yehudah just spent two hours with me starting me on my dream."

"I know. He and I were speaking about his meetings with that Rav[55] of his for the past few weeks. Anyway, Yehudah said that I have the answer to your question. What's the question? I hope I have the answer."

"I kind of thought that he would send you. I mean, who else would he send? Yehudah just explained the meaning of the word *Adon*, how Avraham *Avinu*'s relationship with Hashem was different from that of any other human being before him. You know about this?"

Avi's sparkling eyes grow serious as he nods in assent.

"So, what is your question?"

"Ah, well, I was just wondering about non-Jews? Don't they also have commandments from Hashem? What's the difference exactly between their service to Hashem and ours?"

Avi leans back comfortably. He's on home turf.

"First of all, you're right that they also have commandments, and therefore it is a good question. If both have commandments from the Commander, what makes one's service qualitatively different from the others?"

"Exactly." Ovadiah is pleased with this rewording of his question.

"There are seven commandments, called the Noahide laws, and they apply to all people. When a non-Jew fulfills these commandments, he has met all his obligations. However, there is a big difference between the relationship that following the seven Noahide laws create with Hashem and the relationship that following the 613 commandments that were given to the Jewish People create with Hashem. During my studies of world religions I never saw any religion that spoke of or aspired to the depth of service that every Jew is required to achieve."

Ovadiah still looks puzzled.

"O.K.," says Avi, "I will let King David explain a bit more.

"There is a verse in Psalms[56] where he says, 'Stay away from evil, and do good, seek peace and run after it.' To make a long story short, the seven Noahide laws only deal with the first quarter of the sentence, 'stay away from evil.'"

"What do you mean? I did not see that in the list of the seven."

"Let's take a look at them together, then. Six of the seven are negative commandments. They instruct the person to stay away from destructive behavior: do not steal, do not commit adultery, do not kill, do not eat the limbs ripped off of a live animal, do not curse Hashem, and, six, do not follow any idolatrous belief or practice or have anything to do with aiding idolatrous behavior. The seventh commandment is to establish courts of law, just in order to uphold the first six. So number seven is the non-Jew's only positive commandment, but it's really just an instrument used to keep the first six. Yaah, I mean, yes?"

Ovadiah nods, and Avi goes on.

"This Noahide list is just about staying away from evil. These are the only commandments that are obligatory for anyone who is not Jewish. In contrast, we Jews have 248 positive commandments and 365 negative ones. We see from this mixture of positive and negative commandments that for the Jew it is not enough to just 'stay away from evil.' We must also, as King David said in that verse, 'do good'. It isn't enough to just avoid destroying the world; rather, the Jew has to positively and constantly be involved in active service of Hashem. The Jew does this by following not just the negative commandments but also the positive ones.

"In the third part of the verse from Psalms we are told to 'seek peace.' Well, the translation of *shalom* as peace in this verse is not so good. *Shalom* and *shleimus*, completion, are from the same root. Really what the Jew is supposed to go after is completeness, wholeness, and perfection. No finite being can be complete, whole or perfect while being within finite limitations. So, Ovadiah, where can we who are finite creatures find completeness, wholeness, and perfection?"

Ovadiah is proud that he can answer that question: "These can only be found with the only complete, whole, perfect Being—with Hashem."

"So the Jew is being commanded to become a part of the perfection of Hashem. Where is the *Derech Hashem* (Way of God)?"

Avi leaps up to grab a book off a nearby shelf and crash-lands back into the chair.

"Here[57] you see the wisdom of the Jews. I love this statement:"

> *True good exists only in God. His wisdom therefore decreed that the nature of this true benefaction be His giving created things the opportunity to attach themselves to Him to the greatest degree possible for them . . . they can be considered part of God's perfection as a result of their association with Him.*

"What the Ramchal[58] is explaining here is that attachment to Hashem is the completion that King David informed us that we must pursue. That is why he said not only to stay away from evil and do good, but also to take it one step further: We're supposed to actively go after real *shleimus*, real completion. It is through emulating the Creator by obeying all of His commandments and trying to behave like Him (so to speak), like Avraham did, that we create attachment to the Source of all of the worlds, the only thing that can ever really be perfect: Hashem."

"Worlds? What is this, science fiction?"

"Ah, you haven't gotten to that yet with Yehudah—seeing through trees? Well, how do they say? Fasten your seatbelt. You will soon see. Just leave it to Yehudah."

---

57   *Derech Hashem*, Section 1, chapter 2, paragraph 1.

58   Rabbi Moshe Chaim Luzatto (1707–1746), author of many books, including *Derech Hashem* (The Way of God), which will be quoted extensively in this book.

"Seeing through trees?"

Avi smiles mischievously, leaving Ovadiah still bewildered.

"Anyway, King David continues the verse by telling us that once you understand how to get to *Shleimus*, completeness, then you must 'run after it.' The seven commandments are the way to keep out of trouble, but they are just the basics of acting like a decent human being. This cannot really be called making Hashem's Will your will.[59] A person doesn't just sit around avoiding murder all day, *Yaah*? This is not running after completeness. The six-hundred-and-thirteen take us beyond our limited sense of self. They allow us to become greater than we ever thought we could be. How does Rabbi Yehudah ben Teima say it?[60] 'Be bold as a leopard, light as an eagle, swift as a deer, and strong as a lion to carry out the Will of your Father in Heaven.'

"I heard a class[61] on the second chapter of the *Nefesh HaChaim*,[62] where he explains that the seven mitzvahs allow every human being to achieve personal *tikkun*, but they don't bring *tikkun* to the world."

Ovadiah wonders about this new concept. "Tikkun?"

"*Tikkun* means rectification—to fix what's imperfect. People purposely aren't born perfect, you know. Keeping the seven commandments of Noach turns a person from an animalistic being that runs after anything that he feels like doing—including indulging in the stupidities of lust or anger—into a decent person. That's actually quite a big thing, when we see how people behave today. But it isn't enough for someone who calls himself a servant of Hashem and who relates to Him as his personal Master, *Adon*, like the descendents of Avraham do. We're meant to be more than decent human beings. There are other religious legal systems in the world, as I well know, but

---

59   Ethics of the Fathers 2:4.

60   Ethics of the Fathers 5:23.

61   Rabbi Kluft, a modern-day lecturer who has given a series of hundreds of lectures on the book *Nefesh HaChaim*.

62   This is the title of a book written by Rabbi Chaim of Volozhin (1749–1821), who was one of the greatest students of the Vilna Gaon. As is common practice, Rabbi Chaim of Volozhin is often referred to by the name of his most famous book.

I found none that makes one's every meeting with the physical world into a means of connection to our Master—until I studied Judaism."

"Yehudah was right. If anyone could explain this, then it's you. But can non-Jews attain that close relationship with Hashem also?"

Not Just a Feeling

"WHAT'S THE PROBLEM, Ovadiah? I converted, didn't I? That special relationship with Hashem is available to anyone who truly desires it. But there is another side to it as well, which I think is the reason there are so few converts. The recognition of Hashem as personal Master is not just a cuddly feeling of warmth and closeness. It is that, certainly, but it also brings with it awesome responsibility. When you see that your connection to the Infinite needs to encompass your entire concept of reality, your petty goals must melt before this. It isn't just 613 'dos' and 'don'ts'. It's not just some sort of spiritual triathlon. It's a complete repositioning of all your thoughts, desires and actions. If you truly realize that coming close to Hashem is the only thing that matters, then you will not be content to just live a quiet little life anymore. You will do whatever it takes to reach out and help the whole world come close also. I have no doubt that this is the most fulfilling thing that any human being could possibly do with his life, but it is not easy."

"So, Avi, you told me that you and Yehudah were discussing his learning of *The Hidden Master* together. Is this the main point of ADON OLAM, the difference between non-Jewish thought and Jewish thought?"

"ADON OLAM is so central to Jewish thought. Yehudah and I have been learning little pieces of it together for the past two years, even before we got your grandfather's book. When the administration told him to take this book and learn it well, he was ecstatic. ADON OLAM has been on his mind for years. He has been using its messages to help guys here at the *yeshivah* through their tough times. Your grandfather's book is like the cherry on top of the ice cream for Yehudah. So, back to your question: ADON OLAM contains a lot more than just the difference between Jewish thought and non-Jewish thought. It teaches us to not only put our personal desires aside momentarily, but to change our view of those desires. Its goal is to mold us into seeing beyond them to a bigger picture, a more encompassing picture, a picture where God's Will is the only thing that is real. When you understand ADON OLAM you will see that life is not what you thought it was. Life—real life—is serving Hashem, emulating Hashem. Anything else is just a living death."

Ovadiah is dumbfounded at this last statement. "Living death? What's that???"

"You'll soon understand."

"But when will I understand all this stuff already?"

"When we go to the woods."

"The what???"

Olam: Off to a Hidden World

HELLO AGAIN, Searching Soul, it's me, ADON OLAM. I have come this time to tell you that if you think that you understand the makeup of your physical world, I suggest that you think again. My next words will expose the world that you live in to be completely different from what you may have imagined until now. By delving into the depths of the rest of my first stanza, your eyes and mind will be given the tools to see through the physical facade and to voyage through hidden dimensions where you have never ventured before. My first stanza reads

אֲדוֹן עוֹלָם אֲשֶׁר מָלַךְ בְּטֶרֶם כָּל יְצִיר נִבְרָא
לְעֵת נַעֲשָׂה בְחֶפְצוֹ כֹּל אֲזַי מֶלֶךְ שְׁמוֹ נִקְרָא

~

Adon Olam asher malach, b'terem kol yetzir nivra
L'eis na'asa b'cheftzo kol, azai Melech shemo nikra.

I'll translate that for you as:

The Infinite Master of the hidden world,
Who has reigned before all Creation and subsequent formation,
Was enabled to be called King only upon His Will
making everything come into being. [63]

Don't worry. I didn't expect you to understand that just yet. Let me ease you into possibly some of the most difficult concepts you may ever fathom. Come with me now as Yehudah Stark takes Ovadiah and his friends on an expedition to a hidden World.

It's a week later, when Yehudah finds Avi in the lunchroom and pulls him aside. "Shalom Aleichem! [64] Feel like making a bonfire in the woods again?"

"*Wunderbar!* That night is still one of the highlights of my life!"

Yehudah waves him away. "Back then, I was just starting to teach guys here at the *yeshivah;* I've learned so much more since."

"We both have."

"Right. Now it's time to use all of the knowledge that we have gained to help a few other guys understand what's hiding behind the world—we're going to show them how to see through the trees."

"I'd love to help with it! And I was expecting it besides. I even mentioned it to Ovadiah recently."

---

63   In order to understand why the Hebrew was translated in this manner, please refer to the Disclaimer.

64   Literally "Peace be upon you." This is the standard way that Jews greet each other.

"Great. I'll invite the guys, and you and I will set up some props in the woods. We'll need to bring flashlights, some thermoses of Turkish coffee, marshmallows, matches, rappelling equipment, and a waterproof camping lantern too. The guys will have a big night coming, so I'll tell them to take a nap after lunch tomorrow. It's all been worked out with the *yeshivah* administration."

"You can count on me. Who is coming, Yehudah?"

"Ovadiah, Natan, Shalom, and Shimi."

Allow me to introduce you to the three new members of the group.

Natan Nagar is one of the yeshivah's most delving book-worms. He and his long-term college buddy, Shalom Shapiro, came to yeshivah together after they had finished their university studies. As with many close friendships, they are so vastly different from one another that one wonders how the relationship came about. Natan, a slender, tall, and very dark Yemenite, is the cerebral genius type, always seeming to be reading something. His favorite spot is in the corner of the study hall, where he spends hours making sure that he remembers and categorizes every detail of what he learns. But he stays within the confines of the cold didactics of his learning, ignoring some spiritual holes—or, should I say, craters—that he has never explored.

*Shalom is quite the opposite. Short and redheaded, he's no slouch, but is much less impressed with dissecting information and placing it in the proper categories than is his friend Natan. His real quest is the **why**. His typical response to any statement is: "O.K., but why isn't it the other way around?" Digging for truth is what drives him.*

Through their search to fill in their holes, and find truth, I hope that you will find something to fill your own holes and discover the truth as well.

Avi muses: "That's an interesting combination of guys. I get why Ovadiah is coming. But how did you come up with the rest?"

"I thought," explains Yehudah, "that Natan should come because, although he is brilliant, he isn't reaching his potential as a Jew. In our many talks and excursions together, I have noticed that he seems to miss the deeper meaning behind much of his practice. Until I learned *The Hidden Master*, I was only able to make small dents in his way of thinking. Lately, he has been feeling an emptiness that he has not been able to fill. I am sure that ADON OLAM, with all its newfound richness, will fill that emptiness.

"As for Shalom, with all of my efforts until now, he still hasn't been able to buckle down and learn. He has too many unanswered questions. Nothing I have taught until this point has been enough to quench his thirst for truth. ADON OLAM answered some of his 'whys' in the past, but not enough. *The Hidden Master* is just what he needs. I think it will put everything together for him."

"But, Yehudah, what does Shimi have to do with this group? He doesn't fit in at all."

"Oh, yes, he does, Avi."

They're speaking of seventeen-year-old Shimon Parsi, Shimi for short. Tall, dark and lanky, he is a recently enrolled student in the yeshivah. Unlike the others, Shimi was somewhat forced into the yeshivah. His parents hoped that a few months in this atmosphere would help to bring the wayward youth back to his senses. Having been over-pampered, Shimi is a spoiled skeptic. He seems to care more for pleasures than for knowledge or truth.

"I chose to bring him specifically because of his apathetic, if not sarcastic, approach to the truths of our faith. He needs to know that he doesn't know all of the answers, and that the answers actually do matter to him. So, Avi, together you and I are going to have ADON OLAM open his mind to be able to receive new wavelengths. ADON OLAM has something to offer everyone, even the Shimis out there."

"Never a dull moment when you're around, Boss!"

Yehudah can't help smiling. "See you tomorrow."

Hidden World

IT'S JUST AFTER evening prayers, and Yehudah, Avi, and the curious—if not bewildered—young men are walking down the lamp-lit street toward the forest that nestles below the neighborhood.

Yehudah makes use of the time for something of an introduction: "I'm sure that you've all heard from Ovadiah that we have been studying *The Hidden Master*. I realized that there is a lot in there for all of you, even those who have learned a smattering about ADON OLAM with me before. So I decided to include you all in this adventure. Tonight I am going to show you how ADON OLAM can change your lives. The vague and ambiguous can become clear. I will show you that many seemingly irrelevant statements that you have all heard quoted until now can become the foundations that will strengthen your faith. Give me your ears, your minds, and your hearts, and by tomorrow morning, when we come back up this hill, I am sure that you will feel as if the whole world has been reinvented before your eyes.

"As we make our way down toward the woods, let's try to understand why ADON OLAM's authors chose the words that they did. Ovadiah, I'll let you start. Tell the guys why they chose to open with the word *Adon*."

"I'll give it a try, Yehudah. To make it short and as simple as possible: *Adon*, which means personal Master, speaks of the Jews' unique relationship with the Almighty. Avraham *Avinu* was the first to use this name for describing his relationship with Hashem. Jews, as the descendents of Avraham, must never stop striving to recognize Hashem—and to have the whole world do so as well. Our love and devotion to our personal Master demands nothing less than our never-ending service of Him. To the Jew, Hashem is not just a distant king whose edicts we must obey. Rather, He is the personal Master whom we yearn to get closer and closer to with our every breath, and it is this yearning that defines our relationship with our *Adon*. That, in a nutshell, is why *Adon* was picked as the first word of ADON OLAM."

Avi is impressed. "Pretty good, little guy." Ovadiah grins back at him shyly, and thankfully.

Yehudah leans over a fence overlooking the pitch-black valley.

"Just like the night hides the forest, so too, the physical world hides the nature of Hashem's relationship with us. This hiding is totally intentional. Actually, the physical world was created for the sole purpose of hiding Hashem behind thick clouds. This is why our sages chose the next word to be **Olam**. Shimi, what is the translation of *Olam*?"

"You know what it means, so why are you asking me?"

Yehudah can't resist poking him. "Come on, you promised that you would participate!"

"O.K. *Olam* means world."

"Correct. But, as usual, in the Holy Tongue, there is a lot of meaning beyond face value. As you guys know already, every Hebrew word has a root—two or three letters, usually shared by other words as well, with all of these words having a common thread of meaning. Sometimes we can learn more about one word by investigating other words of the same root or of a similar root, and comparing their meanings. Natan, maybe you can tell us what the root of *Olam* is and what other words use that root? Maybe this will shed a little light on why this word was picked."

"*Olam* is derived from the root *alam* ~ עלם, which is the root of the word *ne'elam*, which means **hidden**. *Olam* also means **infinity**."

"Very good, Natan. So, guys, it seems that the *Olam*, or world, is a reference to something both infinite and hidden."

Shalom pipes up: "But the physical world is neither hidden nor infinite. Anything physical is by definition finite—it has a definite beginning and a definite end. It has boundaries. Something that is infinite has no boundaries—no beginning and no end. So it does not seem that the term infinite has anything to do with our physical world. Physicality is also graspable, visible—not hidden. Why would the Holy Tongue use this word, which seems to be the opposite of the physical world, to describe our world?"

Yehudah is pleased to see that the guys are on the right track—and bouncing off of each other just the way he thought they would. He goes on:

"When the authors of ADON OLAM chose the word *Olam*, it wasn't a simple choice. But, without the depth and multiple meanings of this word, none of their messages to the generations would have been complete. Tonight, as we unfold all those meanings and those hidden in the rest of the first stanza of ADON OLAM, all of you will start seeing things very differently than you had before. Brace yourselves, because you are about to see that nothing you have ever physically experienced is actually as it seems."

Now, Searching Soul, as we follow Yehudah and his friends, you will begin to see how my words enable you to peel back the limited clouds of physicality that hide an infinitely greater spiritual reality behind them. By now, they are walking down an ill-paved road, into the valley. The tall buildings of the outlying Jerusalem neighborhood are behind them, and soon the pavement ends. Beyond it, all they can see are the shadows of trees illuminated by the silvery light of a full moon.

Yehudah's voice breaks the silence once more. "Shimi, what are the words of the first verse of ADON OLAM?"

Shimi, in a tone showing his stubborn disinterest, rattles off the Hebrew verse quickly:

אֲדוֹן עוֹלָם אֲשֶׁר מָלַךְ בְּטֶרֶם כָּל יְצִיר נִבְרָא.
לְעֵת נַעֲשָׂה בְחֶפְצוֹ כֹּל אֲזַי מֶלֶךְ שְׁמוֹ נִקְרָא.

~

Adon Olam asher malach beterem kol yetzir nivra,
L'eis na'asah becheftzo kol, azai Melech shemo nikra.

Yehudah picks up and continues: "And who remembers that English translation I asked you guys to memorize for tonight?"

Ovadiah is the first to answer. "Yeah, Yehudah, you translated it like this:

'The Infinite Master of the hidden world,
Who has reigned before all Creation and subsequent formation,
was enabled to be called King only upon His Will
making everything come into being.'"

"What do you all think those first few words mean—Infinite Master of the hidden world?" Yehudah's sideways glance toward Avi goes unnoticed by the others, but is not wasted upon him. Avi is indeed quick to pick up his cue:

"Well, the Master part, I think Ovadiah summed up pretty well. We must relate to Hashem like Avraham did. He is our personal Master always, not just one part of our life. Our whole sense of being, our very identity, must be that we are servants of Hashem. That's the Master part of it, but I'm not sure what exactly infinite or hidden are alluding to. Does it mean that God is hidden? Infinity is everything. There can be nothing outside of the Infinite, so where is the Infinite Master hiding?"

Yehudah hastens to explain.

"The world itself is hidden and simultaneously hiding the Infinite. Or you could think of it this way: The essence of the physical world itself is just as hidden as God. You think that what you see is what you get? Think again. Tonight we're going to uncover this hidden world of ours and see it for what it really is. To do that, we will use astronomy, biology, chemistry, quantum physics, and lots of Torah. By the end, you will learn how to see through these trees."

"I'm not as worried about seeing through the trees as I am about bumping into them." Shimi's sarcastic tone elicits quick smiles, but nothing more.

The small band has just left the road—or should we say that the road has left them? There's nowhere to go now but backwards or into the woods. Yehudah leads them down a steep incline toward what sounds like rushing water.

"My rabbi led me through *The Hidden Master* and now I will lead you. Just consider me your tour guide through the wonderful worlds of ADON OLAM. Follow carefully. Taking a step in the wrong direction can be very dangerous."

Shalom, after grasping the damp trunk of a small tree which stops him from skidding down the incline, can't help asking: "Hey, Yehudah, are you referring to the trail here or to ADON OLAM?"

A Most Limited Kingship

A FEW MINUTES later the friends have arrived at the banks of a quick-moving stream, winter runoff from the Judean hills. It has rained during the day, and so there is rushing water in this normally dry gorge. Though too small to be called a river, it is too wide to jump across. In the small clearing in front of the water, the guys find boulders to sit down on.

Shalom is the first to speak.

"Before you take us into this new hidden world, I have a question. The next words after *Adon* and *Olam* describe how Hashem reigned before Creation. Upon what did he reign before everything was formed and created? If nothing was there, it seems like a very limited Kingship to me.

"And why does ADON OLAM then state that after Creation His Name was called *Melech*/King, why not *Adon*/Master, like Avraham called Him? After all, this is how the sentence began.

Was there or is there still something lacking in our knowledge of the word *Adon*?

"And why does the stanza end by saying that only at the time of Creation He was called King? After all, the stanza began just a few words before, by stating that He was already King before Creation!"

Shimi is not impressed by this list of questions.

"You think too much. It's just a poetic device. After all, it's just a song. Not every word has to be understood so deeply."

Yehudah gives Shimi a friendly clap on the back.

"I guarantee you that after we finish our hike you will never say that ADON OLAM uses extra words for poetic purposes.

"The Sulam[65] is quoted[66] as having said that all kabbalistic thought is rendered down into the five—or seven—short stanzas of ADON OLAM. No word is wasted. Give me a few hours and all of Shalom's questions will evaporate."

5 = 7

NATAN LOOKS up quizzically.
"Why five or seven? Do we have some type of a rabbinic dispute as to how to break up the stanzas?"

"No, it's different versions: the Ashkenazic and the Sephardic ones. In the Ashkenazic one, there are five stanzas, and all Jews have them and agree upon them. According to the standard Sephardic tradition, however, there are another one-and-a-half stanzas. And according to the Yemenites, there is yet another half stanza beyond those of the Sephardim. Many Moroccans, including the Baba Sali[67] and his colleagues—Ovadiah's grandfather being among them—also included the extra half-stanza that the Yemenites do.

---

65   An authoritative translator of the Zohar from the original Aramaic into Hebrew.

66   R. Moshe Uri Linder heard this directly from his uncle, who was the son of the *Sulam*.

67   Rabbi Israel Abuhatzera, zt"l, (1890–1984) known as the Baba Sali, was a leading rabbi of Moroccan Jewry, and a world renowned kabbalist.

"None of these additional statements contradict the traditions of the shorter texts. In fact, the additional concepts in the longer versions are alluded to in the shorter versions, but the allusions are sometimes quite hidden. The longer versions clarify some of the most important, yet hidden, messages of ADON OLAM. 'Both these and those are the words of the living God.'[68] They all have the same messages for us. I am going to explain the text with all of these additions to enable you to see the fullest picture possible."

Physicality of the Spiritual

YEHUDAH GETS UP from his stone and is about to lead the guys across the stream when Ovadiah stops him in his tracks.

"Just one more question. When you say that Olam means that the world is hidden and hiding the Infinite, are you referring to the physical world or to some spiritual concept?"

Yehudah is all too happy to answer: "I'm glad you asked that. The author's purpose in composing this first stanza was for us to recognize that physicality is just an altered state of the infinite and totally spiritual will of Hashem. ADON OLAM starts by explaining the spiritual roots of the physical world."

"What??? I don't quite get it. Is there really a connection between the two?"

"Yes Shimi, there is. This may sound incredible, but very soon you will understand. Come with me across the stream where, like in *The Hidden Master*, we will first deal with this through the realm of science."

Over the River
and Through the Woods

YEHUDAH JUMPS onto a wet and slippery boulder, and grabs a rope that is stretched across the stream.

"We're going to cross this roaring stream with the help of this rope. Don't worry, it's taut and dependable. Earlier today, when Avi and I were setting up all of the props that you will see tonight, it began to rain, so we added the rope to help you cross. Without rain, it's a dry riverbed.

"So, guys, it's over the river and through the woods, to another world we go. As we cross, think of the words of Chacham Yashar who tells us to think about how many Jews have passed through the torrents of this physical world before you. Each tried to forge their own way, through their own tests, their own raging waters. Some accomplished their mission, while others got washed away. I won't go into it all now, but as Ovadiah can tell you, it was the Great Assembly who gave us ADON OLAM as a rope to hold onto amidst the rushing waters of our lives in exile, without the benefit of prophecy. What we are going to be learning together is not just an ancient liturgical poem. It's an instruction manual to help us cross the violent flow and not get washed away."

Heads nod, as a more serious atmosphere begins to permeate the group. This is not just a night of adventure, but of spiritual growth. Even Shimi's curiosity seems to be aroused. "Hey Ovadiah, what's all this about the Great Assembly?" he asks.

"I'll tell you on the other side. Let's cross first."

The group gathers on the far side of the stream. Ovadiah teaches them what he learned from Yehudah about the Great Assembly.

"Little guy, you have quite a memory." Avi continues to be impressed.

They go on. Yehudah now takes a sharp right to begin an ascent, dodging trees and dense underbrush. As they make their way over a thin trail, Ovadiah notices a weathered wooden sign hanging from a rusty nail on a nearby tree trunk. He squints in the moonlight to make out the words "PATHWAY TO THE HIDDEN WORLD". The tiny path they follow rises at a sharp incline, and the rocky terrain makes each step precarious. Flashlights appear, and heavy breathing takes over as they climb.

Then Yehudah stops just as abruptly as he started. All turn right to follow Yehudah into a terraced plane where they sit down on the damp, cushiony bed of fallen pine needles and grass.

Astronomical Astronomy

"OVADIAH, you asked earlier which world I was talking about, the spiritual world or the physical world. The Torah shows us that they are not separate. I will say the next few sentences slowly, so that you can digest them, one by one:

"The first stanza of ADON OLAM alludes to a chain of four worlds, or levels of reality.

"We, who are in the final world of the four, the physical state that we now experience, are purposely blinded to our spiritual Source.

"The members of the Great Assembly wrote this first stanza to enable us to accomplish our mission here of removing the blinders and seeing what is hiding beyond the chain."

There is silence for a few moments. Then Yehudah continues brightly:

"But, as I promised before, let's talk some science before we get into the Torah's explanation of the chain. We will begin with the large and get to the infinitesimal. Astronomy. Everybody lie down."

Without a word, the guys settle on their backs on the moist turf, looking through the now-sparse trees, up at the clear night sky above them. Yehudah speaks softly.

"As you look up into the stars you can make out constellations. There are thousands of stars visible to the naked eye.

Each of them is light-years away. By the way, each light year is a distance of 9,454,300,000,000 kilometers. Most of those stars that you see are much larger than our sun. The diameter of our small sun is 1,391,980 kilometers across. Just to help you get a sense of scale, 1,299,437.3 earths can fit into the sun. If you were walking at approximately six kilometers per hour without stopping for a minute, it would take seventy years to encircle the sun."

Yehudah lets that sink in, then continues:

"Pretty impressive, huh! Brace yourselves!

"Imagine that we shrank the size of our sun to the size of a grain of sugar, which is approximately one millimeter. If we were to collect all of the suns (stars) in the astronomically known universe and place them all together in one spot, they would cover the surface of South America approximately 30 centimeters high. Keep in mind that in "sugar grain distances" the next nearest star (sugar grain) to our sun, 4.2 light years away, is about 28 kilometers.[69]

"Maybe I can help stop your heads from spinning. Let's put it this way. If all of the people of the world each had approximately 1,090,000 sacks of sugar at their disposal, and if each one of them simultaneously started to count them by dropping one grain of sugar per second, it would only take 50,000 years to complete the process. Don't hold me to it. I could be a few grains or years off."

"Such large numbers really make me feel insignificant," blurts Shimi.

"*The Hidden Master* adds to your feelings of insignificance. It quotes Psalms,[70] which uses the word *Olam* to refer to infinite time, just like Natan told us. There it states; 'Me'olam ve'ad olam atah El. From everlasting to everlasting You are God.' Hashem's existence never started and never ended, or as ADON OLAM tells us in the third stanza, Hashem is בלי ראשית, בלי תכלית ~ *bli reishis, bli tachlis*. Without a beginning and without an end."

---

69   The author is well aware that the calculations are for descriptive purposes only. Spherical stars do not fit together like a glove, nor are all of the stars even close in size; and of course, there are other factors that are not included here.

70   Psalms 90:2.

Significant Insignificance

While the rest of the group takes in the awe-inspiring beauty of the sky, Ovadiah's mind wanders toward different territory. He is thinking to himself, *I felt this insignificance from the moment that those horrible clods of earth pelted against my father's pine coffin. I know that each human being is less than a speck in the universe and in time.* As he begins to speak, his voice is husky. He addresses no one in particular.

"Who can tell me the largest number they can think of?"

As usual, when it comes to information, Natan is quick on the draw.

"Well, the largest number ever named in mathematics is the googolplex. That's a one followed by more zeroes than there are elementary particles in the known universe."

Shalom interrupts Natan: "Yeah, I remember that class. We took it together, didn't we? If a person were writing two zeroes per second, writing out all the zeroes in a googolplex would take billions upon billions of years."

Now Ovadiah lets out a question that has been bothering him for over a year: "Compare your googolplex to infinity, Natan, and what do you get?"

"Zero."[71]

"Yup. Anything finite compared to infinity does not exist at all. I'm looking at the stars and thinking that it's not even that we are microscopic in space. Compared to infinity, we are actually nonexistent. Hashem is Infinite. And since His infinity is not limited to space but also encompasses time, of what significance are our 120 years of life on this earth compared to the infinity of Hashem? None. It's as if we never existed.

"So, of what significance is our life or even the existence of the whole Jewish People? Does it matter at all? What does the entire sum of the cosmos matter? Compared to infinity, the finite space and matter of the whole cosmos are nothing.

---

71 In mathematical terms, any finite number (a) divided by x, as x approaches ∞ (infinity), equals zero.

Psalms[72] says it best: 'Hashem, what is man that You take knowledge of him, or the son of man, that You make account of Him? Man is like a breath, his days are like a shadow that passes away.' So does anyone have an answer as to why we have to go through the difficulties of life if, in the end, our short lives never mattered?"

Shimi feels shaken by Ovadiah's statements. His interest is more than aroused. *I really want to know the answer to this,* he thinks.

By now, several guys have sat up in their places. Looking at the stars isn't going to cut it while their friend Ovadiah is having an existential crisis. Avi lays a beefy arm around Ovadiah's skinny shoulders. He speaks softly.

"This is about your father, isn't it?"

Ovadiah looks at Avi with tears in his eyes, but his tone is defiant.

"Well, I mean, maybe, but I still have my questions."

Through the silvery moonlight, Ovadiah sees Yehudah turn toward him.

"Ovadiah, how can you possibly feel insignificant if Hashem made all of the stars in the universe for you?"

"For me? What do you mean? That is absurd."

"Now I am going to tell you all something really significant. Listen carefully, guys. There is a Gemara[73] which describes the Jewish people as worrying that Hashem has forsaken and forgotten them. Hashem responds to them by explaining the organization and enumeration of all of the stars in the universe, and Hashem says, "And all of them I created only for you, and you say that I have deserted you and forgotten you?'

"By the way, the number of stars that the Gemara informs us of equals 10 followed by eighteen zeros. One of our great commentators from hundreds of years ago[74] says that this number needs to be multiplied by the number 600,000.[75] This brings

---

72 Psalms 144:3–4.

73 Brachos 32b.

74 The Rama Mi'Pano.

75 This is the number of Jews who left Egypt, each one with his own special horizon of vision.

the total to 6 followed by twenty-three zeros. NASA estimated the number of stars in the universe to be 10 followed by twenty-one zeros. A few years ago an Australian observatory reached twenty-two zeros. Maybe if they learn a little Torah, they will eventually arrive at the correct number that we have had for hundreds of years.

"Although compared to Hashem this universe of stars is insignificant, you see nevertheless how significant Hashem's love is for us by the vastness of what He created for us.

Yehudah sits down next to Ovadiah and places his hand on his shoulder. "Ovadiah, your questions are excellent. These are the questions raised in your grandfather's book. He tells us that they are exactly what the Great Assembly was dealing with when they wrote ADON OLAM. We will be answering some of your questions tonight, and more of them as we go through the rest of ADON OLAM. For now, I can tell you that your life certainly has significance, more than you can possibly imagine."

Science is Not the Enemy

TIME FOR a break. Yehudah motions to Avi to open the first thermos of hot Turkish coffee. Everyone relaxes for a bit as they enjoy this most welcome hot beverage on this cool night. Once finished, they throw the collapsible mugs back in their backpacks. Amid the small ruckus of standing up and brushing themselves off, Yehudah sets off again, up the small mountain, speaking easily as most of the rest huff and puff.

"Before we get deeper into science, please remember that there are many people who want to deny the existence of God. They will use any excuse to prove that they are justified in their vendetta against God and religion."

Avi interjects here:

"In the process of my Comparative Religions major, I had an entire course on "Intellectual Atheism." I read plenty of books and articles that commonly twisted the data so that it would seem to say whatever they wanted it to say. Usually, if you take an honest look at the facts, you'll find that the contradictions these people claim are basically made up. I had another course called 'Science and Religion in the Modern Era'. In that course I learned how, throughout the modern era, new scientific discoveries are common and scientific theories change. Along with these changes come new and more sophisticated 'scientific' rebuttals to the beliefs of the Torah. Through my years in university, it became clear that although science does develop or change its theories, Torah does not change its standpoint. No matter what scientific thinking comes and goes, Torah is for keeps."

Yehudah nods and continues: "Avi's point is well taken. We'll be making use of some scientific knowledge tonight, but that doesn't mean that you should get too upset if some day you find someone using some new scientific find, different from what we will be saying, as an excuse to deny Hashem. Many religious people will tell you that science is a threat to Torah, but people like that probably have not studied much science. The truth is that the more you know about science, the more you see the presence of Hashem in the world. With the help of science we can look at a tree and see Hashem. Science has shown that intelligence lurks behind even the most low-level forms of life, to a mind-boggling extent. Through its study it becomes more and more obvious that every detail of our world is intentional and well thought-out.

"Come on guys, don't look so tired, the night is young and anyway we are almost at the summit. Just another two minutes."

A Tree of Ostrich Eggs

THE GUYS HAVE reached the top of the hill and have stepped out of the sparse mountain woods. Now they face a wide, tree-strewn plateau. Is it an orchard? A few meters away, something silvery-green catches the moonlight. As they get closer, Ovadiah and Shimi make out a tree unlike any they have seen before. It is a gnarled olive tree, with roots bulging out of the earth everywhere around it. Its branches twist and curve into the clear night sky and thousands of small almond-shaped leaves mimic the stars with a dull light. The boys advance toward it, marveling at the sight.

They all gather around it, and Yehudah says, "In his books *Rejoice O Youth* and *Sing You Righteous*, Rabbi Avigdor Miller speaks about the magnificence of a tree. You see a trunk and some exposed roots and branches, but what you don't see is the billions of cells coexisting in an intricate dance, all working together to keep this tree alive.

"Rav Miller explains that Hashem could have made the trees from, say, just a few hundred cells. Cells could have been much larger. After all, the Ostrich egg is large but it is just one cell. Why did Hashem choose to use such amazingly complicated structures and fantastically high numbers of cells? He could have created biological structures that are much less compli- cated. The amoeba is just one cell, yet it moves, eats, secretes and reproduces. Why not make the tree out of larger, more independently acting cells that could co-exist like protozoan colonies?

"Rav Miller suggests that maybe Hashem's reason for making the tree so complicated was so that we could start to under- stand, in a small way, the concept of infinity; even though, as we discussed before, billions are still very much finite. But now let's come down from the stars and think of this: all around us there are finite objects called trees, and even if we spent an entire lifetime we would not have enough time to count the cells of even one of them, let alone understand their precise 'cooperation' that creates the life of the tree."

Webs of Life

"LET'S LEAVE biology aside and look at chemistry for a moment. Shalom, you got your Masters in organic chemistry. Could you explain to us the webs of life? Believe it or not, this will give us an insight into the world of ADON OLAM."

"Sure thing, Yehudah. When you study science, you start to see the wisdom of Hashem. One example is the way science explains how inert matter became living organisms like this tree. A huge number of things had to take place in order for life to begin, and they all happened exactly right. It was statistically (almost) impossible for that to happen by chance, and it can't be simulated in a laboratory. It makes no sense that everything went so right—unless you believe in God. Basically, science has shown *how* life got started, happened, but the fact that it happened at all is basically a miracle. Let me explain, and guys, hold on to your *yarmulkes*[76]. Here comes a different view of things than you are used to.

"Yehudah wanted me to explain the webs of life. The organic molecule is a web of many atoms 'combining' to form a structure that allows life to be present. These atoms are 'attached', but not really. This attachment is not an actual physical connection, but rather forces that hold the atoms in a very complicated position. The highly complex positioning of one atom next to another with a web-like appearance, is called 'folding patterns' by scientists. Let's discuss for a moment how complicated these folding patterns are in the makeup of a simple protein molecule."

The guys shift in their places, wondering where this is all going, and what webs have to do with it all. Shalom continues:

"Without protein there is no life. Proteins are made from amino acid molecules.[77] Escherichia coli cells, among the simplest of these structures, can make a complete, biologically active protein molecule, containing 100 amino acid residues,

---

76   Religious skull-cap. It is actually an acronym *yarei mi'Kel*, meaning fearing God.

77   Information from Lehninger, Nelson and Cox, *Principles of Biochemistry*, Worth Publishers, page 182.

in about 5 seconds. Yet calculations show that at least 10 to the fiftieth years would be required for a polypeptide chain of 100 amino acid residues to fold itself spontaneously by a random process in which it tries out all possible combinations around every single bond in its backbone until it finds its native, biologically active form. Other calculations[78] have shown that the time it would take for the smallest of the proteins to randomly fold into its native conformation would be 10 to the 87th seconds. This is unimaginably more than what these scientists claim is the age of the world. Yet our bodies are able to live because, as we said, this happens within about 5 seconds. What I want you to understand from all of this is that protein folding, and therefore life, cannot be a completely random, trial-and-error process. When I was learning this in university, it started to occur to me that Hashem's hand must be controlling at least these folding patterns. In the complications of these structures and their delicate folding patterns, we start to see the masterplan behind Creation.

"But this is just the beginning of the amazement. One night, while Natan and I were in our dorm room studying for finals, Natan told me something that gave the whole world a new perspective. Natan, show the guys just exactly what physicality isn't. Right now your bodies seem to you to be a solid object. But that is not really true."

Physics-ly Not Physical

N ATAN BEGINS: "Shalom's information makes you understand just how complicated the structures of life are, but it was during my studies for my Masters in Physics that my eyes were opened to the deception of physicality. Let's take a look at an atom. You all think that the atom is a couple of protons and neutrons with some electrons spinning around them. Well, not really. The pictures in high school physics books

78 Donald Voet and Judith G. Voet, *Biochemistry*, second edition, page 194.

are misleading. What people don't usually understand is that, distance-wise, the proton is something like a fly in the middle of a large football stadium and the electron is like another fly at the periphery of the stadium flying around it. The only thing that attaches the external fly to the internal one is some sort of force or power. All of the space in between is empty. If, and I do mean if, we consider the neutrons, protons, and electrons to be particles, then if we remove all of the space in between these 'particles' there is not very much stuff at all.

"The subatomic matter of that tree that we're looking at, with its billions of unfathomably complicated cell structures, takes up the same amount of space as a few grains of sand. The tree's perceived massive volume is created by the subatomic "particles" being distant from each other, while still being held together by forces and energies."

Natan pauses to give everyone a chance to picture the stadium, the flies, and how they could all really be the size of a few grains of sand. Then he goes on:

"But let's take another look. Maybe there aren't even those few grains of matter. We now know that neutrons and protons are made of even smaller particles, whose structure is unknown. And are they really particles at all? What is matter?"

Einstein's in ADON OLAM?

WATCH, Searching Soul, as Natan redefines physicality and opens for us a window into a new world for you, the world of ADON OLAM.

"It was Albert Einstein who came up with the famous equation that E (energy) = M (mass or stuff) multiplied by C (velocity of light) squared. Let's see what we can do with this equation to enlighten us about what we are presently learning. If we use a little math and wish to define not energy but mass or stuff, the equation would look like this: M (mass) = E (energy) divided by C (velocity of light) squared. Mass therefore is really just a relationship between energy and velocity of light. $M=E/C^2$.

"Energy is not physical; it is a type of force or power. Velocity is also a type of force/power relationship and is equally not physical. So these two non-physical concepts working together somehow equal what we call physical stuff!"

Shimi, who has been listening intently, says, "Freaky, Natan, really freaky."

Yehudah, who has been leaning on the ancient olive tree, says: "Kind of makes you wonder what if anything you are really leaning on. Well, bravo to both Shalom and Natan. What you all might not know is that what Einstein said and what modern science professes, is clearly alluded to in the words of the holy Zohar where it states that . . ."

> If people would know all of the **powers** that Hashem had instilled into the world they would know the powers of their Master in His great wisdom, but Hashem hid it from them only to make sure that they would not err, and that they would not trust in their wisdom and forget Hashem.[79]

Yehudah muses aloud, "Hmmm . . . The powers Hashem instilled into the world. Scientifically, those powers are the entire makeup of the world as we know it. So, it seems that modern science, too, holds that powers, forces and energies, and their reactions make up matter."

Natan interjects, "But that's not all, guys. Today science seems to conclude that energy itself is not even a constant. You have heard of 'the theory of conservation of energy'. Well, energy is no longer considered to be conserved or constant. There seems to be an ongoing creation of energy. Therefore, somebody must be creating it constantly. The constant creation of this energy is what makes and maintains the world. If this were not so, physical existence would instantly come to an end.

"Look at the tree. What's there? Matter? What's that? Energy, force, or a relationship between the two? If energy is not a constant that is conserved, then Who is sending these forces which create the world? These were the questions that Shalom and I formed that night while we were studying for finals. Actually Shalom came up with most of the question. Eventually we came to *yeshivah* to find the answers."

The boys are silent, absorbed in these questions-to-end-all-questions. Yehudah continues, "But all that we have described until now is in the third dimension. Have you ever thought about the idea that there is something *beyond* the third dimension?"

Beyond the Third Dimension

YEHUDAH LEADS the guys a few meters away from the tree.

"So now you see that the tree is not really what it appears to be. Its matter is actually just a relationship of energy and forces, which themselves need to be constantly recreated, but so far we have only taken a closer look at the physical. Physicality and all of the tests that come along with it are only in the third dimension. Where is the spiritual realm, and how can we relate to it? My high school geometry teacher explained it to me like this:

Searching Soul, let's go back in time to Yehudah's high school. His geometry teacher is in the middle of a lesson:

"O.K. class, this is not a religious school, and I am not trying to push any specific religion upon anyone, but there is something very interesting that geometry has to offer that I think will affect your spiritual lives, if you open your minds. Think for a moment of the theoretical line, which is in the first dimension. Since it is limited to the parameters of length, it has no existence as far as the plane, which is in the second dimension, is concerned. For if I would put an infinite amount of width-less lines together I would never arrive at even the smallest plane, which is made up of length and width.

"The cube, which is in the third dimension, similarly sees no reality in the plane. For, just like in the previous example, an infinite amount of planes that all have no thickness or height, will never equal even the smallest of cubes, which has a defined length, width, as well as height.

"This line of reasoning, pun intended, follows into the further dimensions. To the fourth dimension, something bound by the parameters of the third dimension does not really exist. Time is thought to be the fourth dimension. What if we assume that God is beyond the limits of time?"

Young Yehudah Stark raises his hand and is given permission to speak.

"Hey! I'm Jewish, and my dad taught me this Torah concept that totally sounds like what you're talking about. It's really cool. See, Jews refer to God by this four-letter Name which we never actually say out loud. It's written with the Hebrew letters *yud* and *hei* and *vov* and *hei*, but what's awesome is that these letters make up a combination of the words: was, is, and will be. God's Name is describing Him as being above the boundaries of time."

The teacher sees a need to contain this outburst of spiritual thought:

"I will have to think more about that. However, just to counter your theological zeal, Mr. Stark, if we assert that the Creator created other dimensions beyond our own, dimensions beyond what we could ever discover, this also means that God is beyond the lower strictures of these boundaries that He Himself created, just like the line is not real to the plane. Therefore physicality, and all of its tests, being in the third dimension, can be of no importance to God."

Yehudah responds: "Unless—"

But the teacher is adamant: "No more. Now, back to geometry."

Back to the present and the woods for you, my friend.

"Unless what?" Shimi wonders.

"Unless the third dimension is infused with a bridge that simultaneously links and breaks through all boundaries to bring us into a direct and unbounded relationship with the Infinite Creator Himself." Yehudah finishes the thought.

By now, Shimi is entranced: "This I've got to hear."

No King and No Ants

I T'S 12:30 AM, and the yeshivah guys are following Yehudah through high grass. Suddenly the grass becomes unnaturally sparse and short. Yehudah points with his flood-flashlight toward an enormous colony of knee-high anthills:

"Chacham Yashar tells his readers to imagine that they are in the most beautiful palace that the world has ever seen. He paints the picture of the most powerful flesh-and-blood king of all time sitting right in front of them on his royal throne, but then Chacham Yashar tells his readers to look down.

"On the floor in front of the king are millions of ants. What are these tiny little ants doing? They're bowing down and prostrating themselves to the mighty king. They think he's terrific, but what does the king do in response? He tells his cleaning service to sweep them away. These ants are loyal servants bowing in admiration and service to the king, but the king just sees them as a bunch of insignificant insects."

Again, it is Shimi who speaks up:

"I think I know where you're leading us, Yehudah. We all understand why ants are not important to the king. It's like us and Hashem. We are as small and therefore as insignificant as the ants in His eyes."

Not so, thinks Yehudah, *but I have to be careful—one false step or word, and he'll lose interest again.*

"Excellent, Shimi! You're right that we're small, but there is a difference between the parable and the reality we're talking about. Both the king and the ants have arms and legs. They both have eyes and mouths. They eat and drink. Each was born and one day will die. The king and the ants have plenty in common because they both exist in the third dimension of space, and their time in this world is limited.

"Hashem is beyond the third dimension, infinitely beyond time and any other limitations or boundaries that we exist in. He is so much more than just really big or strong, and, compared to His Infinite Existence, we do not exist."

Yehudah looks for a moment at Avi and continues: "This is what the Rambam[80] tells us in his Thirteen Principles of Faith[81]: 'I am faithful in my complete faith that the Creator, blessed be His Name, is not physical and cannot be grasped by that which applies to the physical, and He has no similarity to anything whatsoever.'

Avi, who got the hint, picks up the narrative:

"Guys, when I was studying comparative religious philosophies, I studied the Rambam on this issue. It was at that point that I started to understand the vast chasm between Judaism and the other world religions. Judaism has an allergy to any boundaries being put on Hashem or on any part of Hashem in a way that no other 'monotheistic' religion has. It started to bother me when I saw many books group Judaism together with these other faiths as having a similar belief system, placing Judaism on par with some other faiths. Some texts would refer to these other faiths as sharing the same 'ethic' as Judaism. Upon studying this principle of the Rambam, it became quite apparent to me that writers of these texts and the world at large don't really understand what Judaism claims."

Yehudah interjects: "If we follow the Rambam's principle, then it seems that my geometry teacher was correct. Billions of people who are bound by the third dimension could not mean anything and should have no reality in front of Hashem."

Shalom cannot hold his questions in anymore.

---

80   An acronym for Rabbi Moshe ben Maimon. Born in 1135 in Cordova, Spain and died in 1204, in Cairo, Egypt. He was a great Talmudic commentator, halachic authority, codifier, and philosopher. Also known as Maimonides.

81   The Thirteen Principles of Faith are based upon the Rambam's commentary to the Mishna of Sanhedrin Chapter 10. These articles deal with the three primary categories of belief: The nature of belief in God; the eternal, unchangeable truth of the Torah; and reward and punishment.

"How do we connect with that? How do we serve like that? All our normal terms of divine service fly out of the window. If Hashem is like a big king and we are like ants, at least we can have some grasp of what we are up against. I understand why the other world religions felt the need to create gods that have boundaries. Without these boundaries, serving the Infinite seems to be meaningless. Compared to infinity all is literally zero, but to create a bounded god, for example, one who is born and dies, means that he or it is finite. That is a false god. So if we are to be truthful what are we left with?"

Everyone waits with baited breath for Yehudah to answer.

"Avi was offended by Judaism being compared to the world's other religions, because we are not merely a religion. Rather, Judaism is the only means of connecting with reality. It is truth in the face of falsehood. As we look at giant trees, at a large mountain, or at the powerful crashing of waves, we sense grandeur, and, as Rav Avigdor Miller told us, that grandeur should lead us to feel an awe of Hashem's infinity, as compared to these finite things. But, in view of the science and geometry that we just learned, the worth of these impressive physical sights evaporates along with our own sense of significance. We realize that we are seemingly infinitely less important than these ants in front of us."

Ovadiah now asks, "But the Torah which was given to us by Hashem demands that we serve Hashem. Our service must therefore be significant in Hashem's eyes, but how can it be?"

Raising Us Out of the Dust

YEHUDAH STAYS SILENT as they leave the anthills and enter a very heavily wooded area. The moonlight is barely visible through the tall, thick trees. He sits everyone down on the moist, spongy ground, covered with a thick layer of pine-needles. The enormous size of the trees and the vast valley in front of them makes the nocturnal visitors feel like dwarfs. Then Yehudah begins to speak:

"Insignificant? Not quite. Actually you are most significant. You just have to open your eyes to the worlds that ADON OLAM is about to show you. Although you may all be sitting on the ground, you can be raised beyond the heavens. Psalms[82] tells us that,

> '. . . His glory is above the heavens. Who is like the Lord our God, Who is enthroned on high, and yet looks far down to behold the things that are in Heaven, and on the earth! He raises up the poor out of the dust, and lifts the needy out of the ash heap; that He may set him with nobles . . . .'

"As we now open up the spiritual worlds that ADON OLAM illuminates for us, you will learn how to use your limited, third-dimensional lives to actualize Hashem's Torah and through it to create a bridge between all dimensions and become significant. Hold on tight as we break out of our low limitations and rise past the finite to infinite meaning."

Exposing the Roots

YEHUDAH POINTS OUT the large gnarled roots that undulate in and out of the surrounding pine-needle-strewn soil.

"Look at these tall trees. Their ability to withstand the winds and not fall over is due to their roots. Their roots are the source of nourishment that enables them to continue life. In fact, these roots are their source in every way. Without understanding the roots of the tree you simply do not understand the tree.

"Few ever dare to understand the real roots of our physical world and why it is here, but that is exactly what the Great As-

---

82   Psalms 113:4–7.

sembly did approximately 2,500 years ago. Prophecy was about to leave the world. Because they knew that soon no one would be left to do their job, these most holy Sages decided to expose once and for all the secret spiritual roots of our physical world.

"ADON OLAM was composed by them to open your eyes to how your finite physical existence stems from spiritual roots and therefore shouts of ultimate purpose and significance. It is from these roots that our physical world constantly receives the input, the nourishment that allows its physical existence.[83] These spiritual roots are the source of all physicality. It seems clear that our Sages of yore knew when they wrote ADON OLAM that if we, the later generations, did not understand these spiritual roots, we simply would not understand this physical world. But with them we can understand why we are here and how to utilize this existence and to reach beyond. As we delve into these roots, Shimi and Shalom and all of you, your significance will become apparent.

"To understand **why** we exist, the Sages first chose to expose **how** we exist. For this they needed to reveal concepts from Kabbalistic[84] thought to the masses of the generations to come. But how would the average person understand these great depths? How would the messages be understood correctly? They needed to be careful and concise with their words: אדון עולם אשר מלך בטרם כל יציר נברא ~ Adon Olam asher malach b'terem kol yetzir nivra ~ Master of the hidden world, Who has reigned before all **Creation** and subsequent **formation**.

"Guys, it's time to discover the chain that the world is dangling from."

Do We Dare Look at Kabbalah?

INSTINCTIVELY, everyone looks upward, expecting to see a chain, or at least the end of one, as Yehudah continues:

83 Nefesh HaChaim 1, 2.

84 Rabbinical mystical literature.

"So where did the cosmos, the trees with their complicated cell structures, the web of organic molecules, the amino acids, the atom and its sub atomic parts all come from? We now understand that forces, powers and energies somehow make up 'matter', and that energy is not completely conserved. So there must be an input of energy and power, to keep the world going—but where do these energies and forces come from? The Zohar[85] informs us that Hashem looked into His Torah and from there created the world. How this happened, or, should I say, happens, is learned from Kabbalah.

"As we heard in the name of the Sulam, ADON OLAM is a condensation of all of Kabbalistic (secretive or mystical) thought. Usually, Kabbalah is left for the Torah Scholars, but ADON OLAM was composed by the members of the Great Assembly not just for the wise rabbis but also for the laymen. Its few stanzas are completely intrinsic and necessary for every Jew in his daily life."

Now it's Natan's turn to ask:

"Yehudah, one of the first things that the rabbis at the beginner program at the *yeshivah* taught us was to stay far away from Kabbalah Centers. I understood from them that we don't need Kabbalah but rather we just need to know how to practice the laws, and we ought to leave mysticism behind."

And Shimi chimes in once again:

"The study of the Zohar and Kabbalah seems to be looked at by the *yeshivah* world, as a subject for weirdoes who want to enter the twilight zone. One of the rabbis told me that these so called Kabbalah Centers actually have as teachers and students non-religious Jews and even some non-Jews who claim to know Kabbalah. I was also told to stay far away, and you are telling me that Kabbalah is necessary to understand Judaism. What's going on?"

Avi answers: "The rabbis at the *yeshivah* are correct, Shimi. A beginner should not try to become a mystic. Partaking of Kabbalah Center classes and books with their distortions will not enhance your Judaism at all. They are using mistranslated

---

85   On *Parshas Bereishis*, which deals with the first section of the book of Genesis.

Jewish texts to form their own religion. And the 'faith' that they have formed does not even resemble real Torah Judaism. Unfortunately, today many Torah novices go to Kabbalah Centers. This is a travesty. If you try to learn Kabbalah or Zohar when you are still a Torah novice, you may distort the meaning of Torah, including the Kabbalah itself, ripping it into misunderstood shreds."

Yehudah now takes over. "Avi's correct, but I do not mean that you should learn Kabbalah, nor was it the intention of the members of the Great Assembly that everyone should do so. Yet Chacham Yashar explains to us that ADON OLAM opens with a few very basic Kabbalistic concepts that are ultimately necessary for understanding the depth of the basics of Jewish faith."

Shimi still looks puzzled, but nods.

The Arizal Opened That Which Was Closed

"So," SAYS YEHUDAH, "let's start with ADON OLAM's next words. אשר מלך בטרם כל יציר נברא ~ Who has reigned before all Creation and subsequent formation. Shalom asked earlier this evening, 'Over whom is ADON OLAM saying that Hashem reigned? How can there be a *Melech HaOlam*, a King of the world, without there being a world over which to reign?' These were the same questions that the Arizal came to answer."

"Who's the Arizal?" asks Shimi. By now no one is surprised at his sudden surge of involvement.

"He lived in the years 1534–1572," answers Yehudah, "and enlightened the Jewish world to the secrets of the Zohar that had remained hidden and elusive for so many generations. He taught all of his teachings orally to his student, Rabbi Chaim Vital (1542–1620). From Rabbi Vital's books, *Otzros Chaim* and *Eitz Chaim*, we come to understand the depth in the meaning of the Zohar's statement that the Holy One, blessed be He, 'looked into the Torah and created the world.' And it is through Rabbi

Vital's teachings that we can start to understand the depth of the world as depicted by the illustrious authors of ADON OLAM.

"Rabbi Chaim Vital uses physical terms to explain completely non physical, spiritual realities. He states that, 'In the examples I will bring there is no up or down, no right or left, no before or after or time sequence. All words and expressions that I will bring relating to these parameters are therefore only written in order to allow information to enter the physical ear to understand a reality far beyond us, from where all Creation came.'"

"I don't get it . . . at least not yet." Shalom is stumped by this avalanche of unfamiliar ideas.

"That's o.k. Don't worry about it right now. Just keep looking at the nighttime forest. Soon it is going to appear to you as an altered form of Torah. Your neurons are about to be shaken up, so hold on tightly. We're about to take flight!"

When the Beginning Has No End

YEHUDAH CONTINUES:
"Rabbi Vital writes of the well-known, but seldom understood, concept of the Ein Sof.[86] Ein Sof means the Infinite One, Who is without beginning or end, Who, as ADON OLAM states in its first stanza, existed בטרם כל יציר נברא ~ *B'terem kol yetzir nivra* ~ **before any form was created**—before all Creation and subsequent formation. The Ein Sof is the starting and ending point of all realities. The Vilna Gaon's student, Rabbeinu Pinchas of Plutsk, explains that when the members of the Great Assembly wanted to describe this concept of Ein Sof they chose the alias ***Adon Olam***."

"How do the words, *Adon Olam*, refer to the *Ein Sof*?" Natan likes connections to be clear and precise.

"It's a *gematria*."

"Oh, yeah, we've all heard about *gematria*—that weird playing with words and numbers. I don't believe it actually means anything," Shimi blurts out, unimpressed.

"*Gematria* is not just a game. In the Hebrew language, every letter is assigned a number, based on its place in the alphabet. Sometimes this is very significant. *Gematria* can indicate that there's more to a text than meets the eye.

"For example, Rabbeinu Pinchas explains that **Adon** in *gematria* has the same numerical value as **Ein**; **Olam** numerically equals **Sof**.[87] So the words *Adon* and *Olam* are parallel to the words *Ein* and *Sof*. The members of the Great Assembly were, then, informing us that *Adon Olam*, the Master of the hidden world, reigned before any form was created. We now understand, through *gematria*, that it was the *Ein Sof* that reigned before any form was created."

"Let's try to picture what *Ein Sof* means, and only then can we understand what It was reigning over. Imagine a formless, non-physical and completely spiritual infinite reality which existed before the lowly state of the physical. It not only encompasses all but is all. There is nothing other than It, whether spiritual or physical. It is the only existence from which all spiritual and physical existences are derived, and it is where they are still contained. Since it is infinite, nothing can exist outside of it."

Natan holds his head; he looks dazed. His didactic mind just got a jolt. He feels that he will never be the same again; and he expresses what has just hit him:

"So this means that the physical is actually contained within the spiritual. The higher reality that rules over physicality is the spiritual."

Ovadiah, whose dark eyes are opened very wide with amazement, speaks up as well:

"This must be what our Sages of yore meant when they stated that the Holy One, blessed be He, is referred to as 'Place', because the physical world is not the place of Hashem, but rather Hashem, Who is completely spiritual, is the 'place' of the physical world."[88]

87   *Siddur Sha'ar HaRachamim.*

88   *Bereishis Rabbah 68:9.*

A Well-defined Confusion

SHIMI IS NOW totally into it. He desperately wants to understand what was just said: "Hey, there seems to be a hole in your logic. What does it mean that the spiritual, which occupies no place, is the place of the world?"

"Well put," comments Shalom. "This is a well-defined confusion if I ever heard one."

"ADON OLAM can clear up your confusions," says Yehudah calmly. "We just learned that scientifically the physical world is not quite what we perceive with our eyes. Everything physical is really just varied forces acting upon each other. Yet, to our eyes, physicality seems very different from the forces and powers that lead to its existence. As Natan told us earlier, the word *olam* (world) comes from the same root as *ne'elam*, or hidden. The authors of ADON OLAM chose the word *olam* in order to show us that the physical appearance of the world is used to hide the physical world's spiritual roots, which are actually powers exuding from the *Ein Sof*. These powers are hinted at in the combination of the two words *Adon* and *Olam*, Master of the Hidden World, Who is the *Ein Sof*.

"To understand how the physical comes from the spiritual, the Arizal will lead us through the four consecutive worlds, or stages of reality, alluded to in the first sentence of ADON OLAM."

"Is this the chain that you were referring to before?" asks Ovadiah.

Astute little guy, aren't you, Yehudah thinks to himself. Aloud, he says: "Follow me as we are going to use these four worlds to find our roots and understand what we and our physical world really are. Let's start our descent through the worlds of ADON OLAM. Buckle up and prepare for entry. Hold on to your *yarmulkes*. The entry could be a little rough."

Are You Spiritually Thick?

IN THE MIDDLE of the thick woods it is dark, but, as the trees sway, occasional glimmerings of moonlight do make their way through to the small group seated on the cold damp ground. Listen carefully, Searching Soul, to Yehudah who now gets up, as he delves into one of my major points:

"ADON OLAM leads us through a path to show our physical existence to be screaming of its hidden spiritual Source. The Zohar states:[89]

> **In the beginning**, *when it arose in His Desires, may His Name be blessed, to make the worlds that would run via His Kingship and Sovereignty, He chiseled away an "**apparent**" abyss (a void) in order for there to be a "place" to instill (l'**ha'atzil**) into it all of the worlds, with the light of the Ein Sof (the Infinite) blessed be He.*

"This apparent abyss is inside, made from, and constantly dependent upon the Infinite, totally spiritual, Source of all, Hashem. Since there is nothing and nowhere that is not Ein Sof, therefore it is impossible for there to be a void of Ein Sof. This is why the abyss is only referred to as an apparent abyss. The abyss is obviously not a physical concept, but rather it is defined as the ability for the Infinite Spiritual Source of all to hide His existence from Creation."

Shalom, as usual, has a 'why' question: "But why should the Infinite Spiritual Source of all hide in the first place?"

"Without this abyss there can be no Creation, for if Hashem did not 'hide' His Infinite Essence from Creation, then nothing could be conceived of as separate from the Ein Sof. All would be defined as part of the infinity of the Ein Sof. The Arizal tells us that the apparent abyss is totally spiritual in its nature, yet he calls it a 'place'. What he means to tell us is that if there wouldn't be a spiritual concept of Hashem hiding His Infinity then there would be no 'place'. no way to conceive of creating anything that is seemingly independent of His existence."

89   Genesis, Masok Mi'Devash 185.

"Seemingly independent existence? So you really mean to say, Yehudah, that there is nothing outside of the existence of Hashem?" asks Natan, who is still working through his thoughts on the matter.

"Remember, the Torah itself tells us that 'there is nothing other than Hashem.'[90] Where could we exist if Hashem is taking up the entire 'place'? But while hiding behind this spiritual illusion, the *Ein Sof* remains like an unseen backdrop, which is totally filling the abyss. The purpose of Creation is to listen as Hashem beckons us to pull away the clouds that hide Him. And so, Ovadiah's grandfather entitled his book *The Hidden Master*. We exist only in order to expose Him as the only and Infinite Source of all. When we use this physical existence to show that the only existence is Hashem, then our every action becomes eternally meaningful."

"Where do you see this four-world system that you are speaking of in the words of ADON OLAM?" Natan is, again, seeking clear connections.

"ADON OLAM opens with some strange terms that speak of the Kabbalistic concept of a series of four distinct 'worlds', or spiritual states. This series is the chain upon which our world is hanging and is described as occurring inside the apparent abyss. Each of these four stages creates a further barrier to understanding the spiritual Source from where it originates. With the creation of each successive 'spiritual world' comes a further estrangement from pure spirituality. Eventually this series of 'worlds' creates the illusion of physical independence from our spiritual Source. These worlds are not called Jupiter, Mars and Saturn, for as I just said, they are spiritual in nature. Only the last world, number four, is what we, for the moment, call a physical state.

"But don't be so convinced of your physicality. You will soon understand through this chain of worlds, that physicality is just a different, or spiritually 'thicker' product of the previous spiritual states as they spiral down. The 'thickening', as Rabbi Vital calls it, is not a physical thickening. Rather, it is the il-

90   Deuteronomy 4:35.

lusion that there is a furthering or abstraction of the product from its Source. But remember—all is still happening within the Source, inside the apparent abyss which is still in the *Ein Sof*. So let's go for a trip out of this world."

Out of This World

YEHUDAH CONTINUES, "So, ADON OLAM says that Hashem reigned before any form was created. Anyone reading these words should be wondering over what Hashem was reigning before any form was created. As Shalom noted before, if there were no forms created, then this seems like a pretty limited kingship. Well, Shalom would be correct unless . . ." Yehudah's pause begs a response.

"Unless what? Get to the point already." Shimi's crass speech doesn't manage to hide that he is actually quite fascinated by the concept.

"Unless He was reigning over something out of this formed and created world. And that, my friends, is exactly what ADON OLAM is telling us. One of the messages of ADON OLAM is the same as that of the Zohar which I mentioned a few minutes ago. You all remember that the Zohar said that Hashem 'chiseled away an **apparent** 'abyss' in order for there to be a 'place' to instill (l'ha'**atzil**) into it all of the worlds'. ADON OLAM is telling us that what Hashem was reigning over before any forms were created was something called *Olam Ha'atzilus*."

"L'ha'atzil—Ha'atzilus. Hey, they have the same root," Natan points out.

"*Olam Ha*—what did you say? I'm still in this world. You want to bring things a little closer to Earth so I can understand?" Of course that's none other than our tactless Shimi.

"Instead of bringing it down, let's bring ourselves up. '*Olam Ha'atzilus*' is a Kabbalistic term referring to the highest and first world of those four spiritual worlds that we just spoke about.

It is the world before Creation.[91] It is not a physical world, but rather a completely spiritual state of existence, which is *eitzel*-near Hashem, hence its name, *Olam Ha'atzilus*, which, as Natan correctly pointed out, shares the same root as *l'ha'atzil*, and also as *eitzel*. Since this is the spiritual world, or state, nearest to the Spiritual Essence of Hashem, let's just call it 'the Nearby World'. It was to this Nearby World that the Zohar tells us that Hashem instilled, or revealed His Will and Plan for Creation.

"Revealed? What do you mean by revealed?" questions Shalom. "And why is it called a world if it is not physical? Why is a spiritual state referred to as a world?"

"Remember that the Nearby World is the first rendering down of Hashem's completely spiritual Essence. Its creation enables the formation of the first barrier to its totally spiritual Source. Now we can appreciate what Natan explained to us earlier this evening, that the word *Olam*, world, can also mean 'hidden.' An *olam* is a barrier which hides its Source. This spiritual state of the Nearby World is created in order to become a barrier, the first barrier in a series of four, which hides its Source. With the creation of the first barrier, Hashem's Essence is just starting on its way to becoming hidden. This hiding is what enables the Nearby World to be conceived of as 'outside of Hashem' and thus to become the first creation."

Ovadiah needs a little help. "I still don't get it. How again does hiding bring about creation?"

"It's all based upon perception," says Avi. "If there is something that can be perceived as being outside of Hashem, then that thing has been created, or removed from being perceived as part of the Infinite Oneness of Hashem. The perception of being other than Hashem's Infinite Essence comes about through spiritual barriers to the Infinite Spiritual Source of all. When you reveal something, it has to be revealed to something which appears outside of you. With these barriers in place, which

---

91 The information for the next two subchapters, "Out of this World" and "On the Verge of Physicality" has been drawn and adapted from the text of *Rav Schwab on Prayer*, Mesorah Publications, pages 6–7.

hide Hashem's Essence, Hashem can begin to set creation of 'the other' in motion."

"Couldn't have said it better myself. Thanks, Avi." And Yehudah continues. "Now that you understand how Creation is launched into existence through the first barrier of the Nearby World, let's take a look at what the contents are of this first spiritual barrier. Kabbalistic terminology explains it like this: The Nearby World is the spiritual 'vessel' to which Hashem revealed His plan for the rest of Creation."

All this has been building up in Natan's mind, and now he shouts out in excitement, "What a mind blow! Now a lot more makes sense. What a trip!"

"Well, when you come home from the trip, would you mind letting us in on the details? We would all appreciate it." That's Shimi, of course.

"I just understood that evidently the Nearby World is the world over which ADON OLAM tells us that Hashem **reigned before any form was created**. Think of it this way, guys: Since this Will and plan that was revealed to the Nearby World is the basis for what would continue to be rendered down, eventually creating a physical world, then of course the Master, the **Adon**, had to reign over and control this first world, **olam**. So that's what it means when it says that Adon Olam, the Master of the first hidden World, reigned over this first hidden world before anything else was formed or created."

"O.K. Natan, seems like you got that down pat. So now, Yehudah, get to the point. How did this plan for Creation make spirituality into our physical world?"

"No shortcuts, Shimi. Before we get to our world, which is world number four in the series, ADON OLAM tells us that we first have to deal with worlds numbers two and three. I'm going to take ADON OLAM's lead and not go into too much detail. You aren't all supposed to become Kabbalists and understand too much of what these worlds really are. Rather, you are supposed to have a rudimentary knowledge in order to understand what Shimi calls 'the point.' So let's go through the next two worlds really quickly."

On the Verge of Physicality

"TAKE ANOTHER LOOK at these immense trees which tower over us. Scientifically we already showed them to be different from what your eyes perceive. Now as you follow me through the next few worlds of ADON OLAM's first stanza, these trees, the world around them and your own selves will take on a much higher meaning. Come with me," dares Yehudah, "as you learn to see through the trees and discover what is really behind them, and what you really are.

"The next two spiritual stages or worlds rendered down from the Nearby World are mentioned in the continuation of the stanza, where it states that *Adon Olam*, the Master of the first Hidden World, the Nearby World, is the One אשר מלך בטרם כל **יציר נברא** ~ *Asher malach beterem kol* **yetzir nivra** ~ Who reigned over that world before all **Creation** and subsequent **formation**. *Nivra* (created) is a derivation of the Hebrew root *bara*. What was created was *Olam Ha'***Beri'ah*** (The World of Creation) which is also derived from the root *bara*. 'The World of Creation' is the first spiritual product of World number one, the Nearby World. It can be more simply referred to as the next, thicker, form of the previous spiritual state of hiding. And as we now know, that apparatus of hiding is what we call a spiritual world."

"Wait a minute." Shalom can't hold it in anymore. "These worlds, or hiding devices, are getting spiritually thicker—for what reason, again?"

"Even I got that." Shimi says pompously. "Hashem makes these spiritually-thicker worlds so that we can buy into the deception that we are independent. Shalom, Hashem is everything. Nothing is outside. There are no independent existences. There are just 'worlds', hiding devices. This spiritual deception is what enables creations to conceive of themselves as existent, as other than Hashem."

Avi is taken aback at Shimi's insightfulness. "Shimi, I admit I didn't think you had it in you."

"Until tonight, neither did I. But don't get too impressed,

Avi. I've gotten this far, but why is Hashem using this chain of hiding devices? Your guess is as good as mine."

"By the end of the night, the guesswork will be unnecessary," says Yehudah. "But we're not there yet. First we need to go on just a little further. Remember, we're approaching the 'point'.

"So now we are about to encounter the third world. Following 'the World of Creation' is a further thickening or abstraction, described to us in this first stanza of ADON OLAM, through the word, *yetzir*: *Olam Ha'**Yetzirah**, '*The World of **Formation**'. This is the next spiritual state, where the Holy One, blessed be He, structures and forms the concepts which will eventually exist 'physically' in the fourth world, in *Olam Ha'asiyah*."[92]

The Point Made Simple

YEHUDAH PAUSES a moment, and then proceeds to sum matters up didactically:

"Let's make things simpler. We now understand that Hashem's reign began even before the existence of the World of Formation and the World of Creation. So three worlds have been hinted at so far in the first stanza of ADON OLAM:

אֲדוֹן **עוֹלָם** אֲשֶׁר מָלַךְ בְּטֶרֶם כָּל **יְצִיר נִבְרָא**

~

*Master of the first hidden world [the **Nearby World**·1],*
Who has reigned over that first world before all Creation [the world
*of **Beri'ah**·2] and subsequent formation [the world of **Yetzirah**·3]*

"Through these three eventually came the next and final stage or world—*Olam Ha'Asiyah*—which is related to in the next words: לעת נעשה ~ *L'eis na'asah*."

---

92   Don't get confused: although in ADON OLAM the word *nivra* comes after *yetzir*, this is just due to the grammatical construction. We're talking about The World of Formation (Yetzirah) coming into existence through the World of Creation (Beri'ah), which existed before it, and not the other way around.

"L'eis na'asah can be translated as 'At the time of making'. The word asiyah comes from the root oseh or asah, to make or conjure up into 'physical existence' that which before existed only spiritually. Through this last barrier, the spiritual is to become one stage more thickened, one stage seemingly more separated from its Source, till it actually appears to not resemble the spirituality that it originated from at all. Olam Ha'asiyah is the final stage. It is our seemingly physical world and its sur-rounding cosmos."

So What?

"SO WHAT?" All are shocked by this completely out-of-character remark coming from Natan, who has done some more thinking.

"I understood what you said, Yehudah. I have it all outlined in my head. I could even repeat it. But so what? Who really cares about this? Why would this help anyone better understand his or her relationship with Hashem? And therefore why did the authors of ADON OLAM need to put this chain of worlds in their text? Why does anyone need to know about the existence of this four-world chain?"

Shalom holds his chin and turns to Yehudah, "It's a good question. Out of character, but a good question."

"Got any good answers, Yehudah?" wonders Ovadiah.

"I don't have the answers, but ADON OLAM does. ADON OLAM states that this World of Asiyah, the physical World, was made from Hashem's cheftzo, His Will. ADON OLAM's words לעת נעשה בחפצו כל ~ L'eis na'asah b'cheftzo kol, mean that after the first three worlds, when the time came to make the fourth world of this series, which is physicality, it was made through His Will, cheftzo, which we have learned is the directing force of all of these four worlds, the content of the Nearby World."

"Now hold that thought because I have a shocker for you, which will answer Natan's meltdown, I mean question. Kabbalistic thought explains that Hashem's revelation of His plan for Creation to the spiritual forces of the Nearby World, world number one, is called **Torah**. Now, think for a moment of what our holy Sages meant when they said that not only was Torah created before the world,[93] but that Hashem reigned over or looked into the Torah and from it created the world.[94] So Natan asked 'So what? . . . Why does anyone need to know this?' Our Sages handed us the knowledge of this four-world system in order to paint for us a clear picture that was and still is very necessary for all of us to possess.

"That picture shows us that physicality is based solely upon Hashem's Will, His Torah. Creation of the physical from the spiritual is the 'thickening', the perception of being far from Hashem, our Infinite Source. But Hashem is Infinite, and there is nothing outside of our Source, nor is there any way to distance ourselves from the One Who encompasses all."

"This is all very theoretical," notes Ovadiah. "I'm with Natan. How are we supposed to use this knowledge to get closer to Hashem? How can we relate to that which is worlds of barriers away from us? How can we peel away impenetrable clouds that were set up by the Infinite?"

Yehudah, who, as usual, is not fazed, responds, "The only channel that can penetrate the clouds that hide Hashem from us is His Torah, from which we, our world, and all of the barriers of the four-world chain were derived."

The Unbroken Beam

OVADIAH, who is now sitting on a thick root which protrudes from the forest floor, asks, "I don't yet fully get it; that was really deep. Before you go any further with that thought, Yehudah, I am still missing something. What is the nature of what Hashem is thickening that becomes physicality?"

93   Tractate *Shabbos* 88b.
94   *Bereishis Rabbah*, Ch. 1.

"Lights and breaths," says Yehudah, as he beams his flash-light through the darkness of the nighttime forest. "You all see this beam of light. Ovadiah, put your hand for a moment in front of the beam. Good. What do you all see?"

"Nothing," says Shimi. "If you wanted us to see, you would have brought us out here during the day. What are you getting at?"

"It's the same thing with breath, Shimi. If I put my hand in front of my mouth, then the breath is blocked."

"And so?"

"And so, if you stop the connection to the Source, then the effect—the lower worlds—ceases to be. The Arizal informs us that the whole nature of our world is similar to the concepts of lights and breaths. Our existence is based continually upon our constant connection to our Source."

Torah Constantly Creates Anew

SHIMI JUMPS in a cathartic panic: "Wait a minute. It's just like the endangered theory of the Conservation of Energy that Natan mentioned before. In reality, the constant creation of energy is what makes and maintains the world. Without the constant input of new energy from a source we would instantly cease to exist. Are you really trying to tell me that we Jews knew this since the times of the revelation of the Torah?"

"Yes. In fact, the members of the Great Assembly, the same group responsible for ADON OLAM, related to this concept when they composed the text of the blessings before the read-ing of Shema Yisrael.[95] They wrote there: 'And in His **Good** He renews every day constantly the acts of Creation.' We are

---

95   This is a central Torah text (Deuteronomy 6:4) which is also a central part of the daily
     prayers. It proclaims the Oneness of God.

told that the word **Good** is commonly used as a reference to the Torah itself.[96]

"So when the members of the Great Assembly told us that 'in His Good He renews every day constantly the acts of Creation,' that means that the Torah is what renews Creation. *Olam*, the hidden world, the Nearby world and Torah are all one and the same. 'Every day constantly' refers to this Creation reoccurring every split second, and we, like the beam of light and the breath, are just the continuation of the Source. Without the constant input of spiritual energy from the Torah our physical state would immediately cease to exist. Hashem is constantly recreating the World through Torah. Now, let's look once again at that previous quote from the Zohar:

> If people knew all of the **powers** that Hashem has instilled into the world they would know the powers of their Master **in His great wisdom**.

"That input being instilled is the Torah."

"It seems clear to me now," says Natan, "that our physical world is not as separate from Hashem as I thought before. Actually, we are not separate at all. Physicality is merely the 'materialization' or the spiritual thickening of, or seeming distancing from, Hashem's Will. As you just quoted from ADON OLAM, Hashem makes בחפצו ~ *b'cheftzo* ~ through His Will, כל ~ *kol* ~ everything. What is there and here and everywhere is just Hashem's Will, *cheftzo* which makes all, *kol*. I am beginning to see through these trees. It seems to me that what the authors of ADON OLAM are telling us is that we need to live knowing and acting like we know that all existence is just Hashem. All is His Will transformed into spiritual thickenings or barriers to understanding, and our job is to pull back these barriers and expose Hashem as the only reality. This is why we were created, isn't it?"

Shimi has also been thinking. "So let me get this straight. Physical 'particles' are just rendered-down forms of the forces coming from their Source. Stop the input of this force and our

96   Proverbs 4:2, Brachos 5a, Ethics of the Fathers 6:3.

physical world ceases to be. This is clear science. What ADON OLAM is telling us is that the input is a spiritual reality called Torah. So without the Torah there is no physical world. I heard my rabbi saying something similar to this in school. The rabbi told me that if Jews stop learning Torah for a minute then the world will cease to exist. I thought that he was crazy. Now I am starting to understand that maybe I ran away a little too soon."

With this observation Yehudah tells them that it's time to continue on their journey. So they get up, somewhat cold and damp, and resume walking, this time downhill.

Solidifying the Disconnection

"NOW I THINK I understand what the Midrash is telling us." Ovadiah begins summing it up in his own way as they walk along. "**The Holy One, blessed be He, looked into the Torah and created the world**.[97] Hashem used His Will in order to create. The Torah, His Will, is the breaths and the lights that Yehudah said the Arizal was referring to. What this Divine Will created was successively thicker spiritual realities, different forms or spiritually altered states of Itself.

"We feel so far away from Hashem, yet we are really inside of Him. The first stanza of ADON OLAM seems to have been written to inform us that we are four worlds away from our Source, yet we are within Him. If we do not seek the connection, then we have solidified the disconnection."

Shalom breaks into the discussion: "These all sound like very high thoughts, but I don't understand why we need these four worlds. Why couldn't Hashem have just created the world, presto, without four worlds? Hey, Avi, you studied world religions. Do any other religions have a need for these different spiritual stages, or are the Jews the only ones with such complications?"

Empty Faith

AVI IS DEEP IN THOUGHT. Something's brewing. His mind is putting together many pieces of a puzzle that have been scattered and disconnected till this moment.

"The answer is," he says finally, "that there is no other such 'theory' in any of the world's other religions. They simply state that their god or gods in some way created the world, either alone or with or against other spiritual beings. But I am so glad that you asked that question. In thinking of the answer I just realized how the simplicity of their belief systems proves their falsehood. Remember earlier on, when Ovadiah asked Natan to compare the googolplex to infinity. Do you remember what he got?"

"Zero."

"From this we all learned that the infinite is incomprehensibly different from the finite. Therefore, something finite, which is comparatively insignificant, cannot grasp the Infinite Essence of Hashem. We can only grasp that which is related to ourselves in our physical terms, hence the abundance of idolatry throughout world history. Any other religion's claim to understand or relate to the Essence of the Infinite Creator without the bridge to the Infinite that we have just discussed is by definition false.

"There are religions that claim monotheistic beliefs. Some of their followers understood this problem and therefore either limited the forms of their gods, or naively believed the claims of false prophets who could not answer the question of how to bridge the finite and the infinite. Obviously, neither of these options solves the problem. As for those who created limited, mortal gods, we already discussed how ridiculous and obviously false it is to attempt to compare the finite with the infinite in any way. The bridge cannot be created by use of anything false.

"It is so clear to me now that this four-world system described in the first stanza of ADON OLAM is a starting point in searching out deep meaning in our faith. It might seem complicated, but it contains some of the ABC's of Judaism. Without it, confusion can deter us from relating to Hashem truthfully. These few short words at the beginning of ADON OLAM are meant to help us begin to relate more meaningfully to the Infinite, the *Ein Sof*, which Rabbeinu Pinchas told us is the *gematria* of *Adon Olam*. This four-world system builds the bridge between the finite and its Infinite Creator, and that is why ADON OLAM, which was written to help us understand our faith, must start by describing this four-world bridge. Faith without this bridge now seems comparatively empty."

Unkelus's Message

"BUT, AVI, where do you see the four-world system being described as a bridge?" Shalom wants to know.

"In those same first words of ADON OLAM, of course. The Torah was not only Hashem's means of creating us, but also the means for the finite to reconnect with its Source via those same channels, through which we were created. Just backtrack. This was Unkelus's message."

Shimi has again run into an unfamiliar figure, or, at least, one he doesn't remember learning about. "Unkelus? Who's that?"

"You probably remember hearing about the wicked Titus from Rome who destroyed our Holy Second Temple. His nephew was the righteous convert Unkelus. His is among the most authoritative commentaries of the Torah. Many times throughout his commentary he translates 'Hashem', or pronouns referring to Hashem, as Torah. Until this moment I was boggled by this. I asked my rabbis in *yeshivah* and they referred me to a multitude of *midrashim* and passages in the Zohar where Hashem and His Torah are referred to as one and the same. I never understood the significance of all this until Shalom asked if any other religion had such a concept of this four-world bridge.

"Unkelus is saying that you can connect to the Infinite, but only through the proper channels. Hashem and His Will are One. Hashem and the Torah are One. You, the finite, cannot even speak of the Essence of Hashem, Who is the Infinite, for you cannot even begin to really know the Essence of God. None of us can, but—if you call Him Torah, you are relating to Hashem's Will, which is actually the Source from which you've come. And so, Unkelus often translates nouns and pronouns relating to Hashem as Torah. Since you are derived from this four-world system, starting with the Torah (the contents of the Nearby World), which is Hashem's Infinite Will, you somehow have the ability to relate to Hashem via the same channels through which you were derived."

When Through His Will *All*, Then *All* is His Will: Our Purpose in Creation

OVADIAH IS STILL not satisfied: "But I still don't get it. Why did Hashem do this? Why create the world by way of the Torah, or why create it at all? The question of significance is still there. Of what significance are we? We are finite. So how can we have any meaning in a world created by the Infinite? Is it all a game? What is this existence about? What are we about and why are we here?"

They are now back at the small but roaring stream, coming at it this time from the other side, Ovadiah speaks up again:

"Stop a minute, everybody. When we were here earlier tonight, Yehudah, you told us to think of the rushing water passing in front of us and of how so many Jews have already passed through this world before us. Some of them managed to accomplish their missions, and many others just got washed away to a seemingly meaningless end. I hoped that tonight I would learn why I am here and how to avoid getting washed away.

"But I'm not there yet. Even though I understand that the Torah is the means of creating the world, I don't understand how the stories and the commandments of the Torah as we see them in writing are His complete and Infinite Will. How do the finite words of the Torah encase the Infinite Will of Hashem? And how do these finite words that I can carry in a single scroll have the ability to connect me meaningfully to the Infinite? As Jews, we know that our job here is to become as close as we can to Hashem, but I do not yet understand how learning a seemingly finite book could possibly forge our closeness with the Infinite, nor do I understand why this would be Hashem's purpose in Creation!"

Shimi is heard muttering to himself: "What a lot of questions. How does he come up with all of them? But they're pretty good ones . . ."

Using a Stone to Identify the King

"LET'S FIND the answers in the next statement of ADON OLAM," Yehudah responds, "'לעת נעשה בחפצו כל אזי מלך שמו נקרא ~ *L'eis na'asah b'cheftzo kol azai Melech Shemo nikra* ~ At the time that His Torah made everything, only then could His Name be called King. This line could also be read as 'Only at the time when through (or from) Hashem's Desires or Will everything (kol) was made, could His Name be called or identified as King.'

"These words lead us to understand much more than just **how** the world was created. They are showing us **why** it was created. The message is that the physical world was created so that from amidst the clouds of physical existence, we could strive to identify Hashem as King.

"We've already dealt with the words לעת נעשה בחפצו ~ *L'eis na'asah b'cheftzo*; now, let's look closely at כל ~ **kol**. *Kol* translates as 'everything' or 'all'. But these words are not just saying that everything physical came from His Will. Rather, they inform us that only once physicality finally came into being through the Torah, could Creation see that **All** originated from His Will."

Ovadiah interrupts: "But why is this possible only in the fourth, physical state? Were the other previous spiritual states of existence somehow unaware of their origin?"

Shalom joins in as well: "I second Ovadiah's question. Can't the identification of Hashem as King come from one of the other spiritual worlds? Can't the angels, who are in one of those spiritual worlds,[98] also identify Hashem as King? The angels are higher than us. Surely they can identify Hashem. Aren't they from a less blinded and less hidden world?"

"I see that we need to understand what ADON OLAM's words 'calling His Name King' or 'identifying Him' mean." Yehudah bends down and picks up a few rounded stones from the banks of the stream. "Shimi, you have good eyesight. Could you identify which of these stones is rounder than the others?"

Shimi eyes them all in the moonlight, and points to one of them: "That one."

"To identify something, you need to 'pick it out of a crowd'. If there is only one existence, with nothing else around, then there is not only nothing from which to distinguish it, but there is no separate existence by which to identify it. If this stone were everything, this wouldn't only make it impossible for there to be other stones, it would mean that the stone was never-ending. There would be no airspace around it. Shimi would not be able to see it because nothing outside of it that could identify it would exist. This means that there would be no Shimi.

"Identification is alluded to in ADON OLAM by the word נקרא ~ *nikra*, which translates as 'calling'. First you identify something, and then you can give it a name. This, my friends, is the purpose of the four-world system that ADON OLAM il-

---

98   Kabbalistic sources 'place' the spiritual existence of the angels as being in the spiritual world of Beri'ah, world number two in the chain of four.

luminates: to identify Hashem and then to call His Name King. The system starts with a seeming void, which spirals down to create an apparently physical world from where Hashem's creations can choose to identify Him."

The Heroic Choice?

SHALOM IS in a quandary. "So Yehudah, let me get this straight. ADON OLAM exclaims that only after the creation of the physical world do we have the ability to call Hashem King. This 'calling Hashem King' is simply the ability to identify Him as King. I get it. I really do. Since Hashem is Infinite, then until there is this mirage of physicality there can be nothing which discerns itself as other than Hashem, and therefore there can be no way of identifying Him. But what I still don't get is, what's the big deal about being enabled to choose to identify Hashem as King? Just because we are seemingly separate from Hashem doesn't mean that any great heroic choice is being made to recognize Him as our Source."

Natan wants to clarify Shalom's questions further: "What's bothering Shalom, and I think the rest of us too, is that Yehudah is telling us that the purpose of Creation is this choice. The choice doesn't seem so astounding, and so what great purpose has been affected by our creation?"

"In simpler terms, what's the big deal?" Shimi is blunt, as usual.

And Yehudah responds: "What's the big deal? The answer lies in ADON OLAM's next word, כל ~ *kol*, which means **everything**, absolutely **EVERYTHING**. When we will learn the second stanza of ADON OLAM—ואחרי ככלות הכל ~ *Ve'acharei kichlos hakol*, which translates as, 'at the end when **everything** is finished', we will learn about a very different meaning of the word כל ~ *kol*. In the meantime, in the first stanza, we are dealing with the opposite end of the picture—not the end but rather the beginning, and the purpose of everything."

When Everything Becomes Evil

A S THE GUYS START to walk along the banks of the winding stream towards their next undisclosed destination, Yehudah gives over a startling message.

"Let's start tackling this phrase by clarifying the meaning of the word kol. The members of the Great Assembly use this word kol, everything, in a few places. Does anyone know of another example besides here in the middle of the first stanza of ADON OLAM?"

Natan is, of course, quick on the draw: "We all do. It appears in the morning prayers, in that same first blessing before the recitation of Shema Yisrael that we quoted earlier. There the members of the Great Assembly wrote 'Who forms light and creates darkness, makes peace and creates **everything** (hakol).'"

"That's a perfect example, Natan," notes Yehudah. "Our Sages borrowed most of the words that you just referred to from somewhere else. Let's take a peek at the verses that they were quoting and see if comparing them to the text of the blessing can cast light on what else is hidden in the word 'everything'.

"Isaiah states[99]: 'I am Hashem, and there is none else. I form the light, and create darkness: I make peace, and create **evil**.' You all see that except for one word, the blessing is a direct quote from Isaiah."

"But why did the members of the Great Assembly change the word 'evil' that appears in the verse to the word 'everything'?" wonders Shalom.

Shimi is somewhat alarmed: "Where the verse uses the word **evil**, the authors of the blessing use the word **everything**. Is their change in the text implying that everything is really evil?"

"Yes and no." Now that Yehudah has raised the eyebrows of the entire group, he continues: "So let's look more attentively at these same authors' use of this word **everything** in their text of ADON OLAM, so that through it we will see just how evil everything really is."

99   Isaiah 45:6–7.

Why Are You Here?

THE WINDING STREAM widens until there is no more path to walk on, but Yehudah doesn't flinch, and just keeps leading the group straight ahead through the water as if there was no stream. As the guys carefully splash through this now wide but shallow, trickling brook, Yehudah continues: "Now, I am going to give a more complete answer to Natan's earlier question of 'Why does anyone need to know about this four-world chain?' Until now, we have gained an understanding of why we need barriers from our Infinite Creator in order to be considered 'other' than Him. But now, through better understanding ADON OLAM's choice of the word kol, we are going to begin to understand not how, but rather why we were created. With this information you will all start to understand how to avoid getting washed away by confusions, as so many others have."

"So kol simultaneously means both 'everything' and 'bad'. Yehudah, that seems like a strange combination of meanings. Usually I can understand the link between the varied connotations of words. Here I am coming up with nothing." Natan shrugs.

"It's the link that connects these wide-ranging meanings that defines our reason for being."

As usual Shalom cannot hold in his question. "And that link is . . . ?"

Free Choice

"THE LINK BETWEEN everything and evil," posits Yehudah, "is free choice. Yes, free choice is the name of the game. Once the physical world was created there could be choice. But, as Shimi so eloquently put it a few minutes ago, even with there being the ability to choose, what's the big deal in choosing Hashem? And so Divine Wisdom made it that Creation would not be complete until there was an innovation that made that choice into a very big deal.

"So, ADON OLAM says that 'once **everything** was made according to His Will, only then could we fulfill our purpose of calling or identifying Hashem as the King.' We have the ability to make this identification only when the clouds of physical creation become so thick that they almost completely hide His Essence as the Source and makeup of Creation. Hashem's Spiritual Essence is Truth, while that which hides Him is falsehood, and we were created in order to choose truth over falsehood. The latter choice of falsehood can be defined as 'evil', as related to us by the earlier quote from the prophet Isaiah. The members of the Great Assembly gave evil the name 'All', kol, to show the central purpose that evil plays in Creation. For, if we did not meet the confusions of evil in our every step, then we would never be able to choose truth."

The stream narrows again and the guys are back on dry ground. For the moment Yehudah stops to finish his thought before going on in their adventure.

"There are many different aspects of calling Hashem King from amidst the clouds of the physical world. Each of these aspects has a special message for us. For the rest of the night, we will be delving into these many aspects. Follow me!"

The Burning Bush

INSTEAD OF CROSSING the stream, the group turns onto a path, to their next destination in their new world, My world, the world of ADON OLAM. Let's follow them, Searching Soul, as they, and you along with them, learn how to forge the bridge to find meaning in life. Civilization is left even further away as they walk along.

"Yes," says Yehudah, "our job here is to call Hashem King despite the clouds. As I just told you, there are many aspects of calling Hashem King. We are now going to discover that all of them are based on the fact that the Torah is Hashem's Infinite Will. We, who are finite, are commanded to learn it and observe its commandments. Engaging in Torah study and observance despite the clouds in our way, is calling Him King."

Shimi raises an obvious question: "The stories in the Torah are of people who lived after the Creation of the world. How could the rendition of these post-creation people exist before Creation? And I have more questions: Since the Will of Hashem is synonymous with Hashem Himself, then the Torah, which is His Will, is Infinite. But the Torah that we have in front of us is seemingly very finite, as someone here mentioned already. It begins with the words 'In the beginning' and ends with the words 'In the sight of all Israel.'"

Avi interjects with a knowing smile. He's been here before, and his own question is deliberately provocative: "Moshe Rabbeinu was a finite man. No matter how great he was, he was still just a man. Unlike other religions, we do not deify people. So how could Moshe comprehend the Infinite Will with his finite mind? And how could he then bring it down to us in a finite package?"

Scientific Natan adds his angle: "We already mentioned that a googolplex compared to infinity is nothing. So even if Moshe, who brought down the Torah, understood it better than any man, he was still finite. What percentage of Hashem's Infinite Will was this finite man able to understand? So how can we say that the Torah brought down by Moshe is the same Infinite Torah that created the world?"

"It's time to take off Moshe Rabbeinu's shoes."

"Huh?" This time, it's not only Shimi who's bewildered. They all are. If Yehudah was aiming for the surprise element, he has succeeded. "Avi, please set up the Burning Bush."

Avi grins broadly back. "I'll get going, but walk slowly so I have time to get it ready. You prepare the guys on the way. Get them to understand why Moshe Rabbeinu needed to remove both of his shoes. Then, at the bonfire, we will help them un-

derstand exactly what removing those shoes accomplished.
I'm off."

A Barefooted Pipeline

AND SO, Avi hurries through the valley and up the next
hill. On the way he busily collects dead branches in
order to set up a bonfire. About halfway up the hill he finds the
clearing. It was here at the bonfire, just about two years before,
that for him darkness finally became light. He remembers how
in this spot the fire of the Torah from above lit up his path to the
Torah found below. It was here that he came to understand that
only through Moshe's Torah could we, who are in the physical
world, hope to connect to our spiritual Source. As he sets up
the bonfire, he mulls over the thoughts that ignited his passion
for Torah back then. The conversation from the past still rings
in his ears. Yehudah and Avi, then still called Adolph, had been
standing in front of that earlier bonfire, when Yehudah said,

"Adolph, before you convert you need to accept upon yourself the
whole Torah."

"I'm not a *dummkopf*, I know that, and of course I accept it all."

"Hashem's Torah is likened to fire. How can you hold onto the Torah
without getting burnt? And did you ever wonder how this burning
fire of Infinity is held within the bounds of a single combustible
scroll?"

The heat from the flames of the fire was scorching Adolph's face when
he asked: "We are standing far from this finite fire and are getting
burned. We need to move back. How did Moshe Rabbeinu, who
was a finite man, bring down to the physical world the Infinite
Fire of the Torah of Hashem?"

"He brought down the Torah of Moshe, not the Torah of Hashem,"
Yehudah corrects him.

Adolph's jaw dropped.

"But that sounds like heresy! The 13 Principles of Faith teach us that

Moshe received the whole Torah directly from Hashem. Every letter of the Torah that we have today is exactly what Moshe received from Hashem on Sinai. Moshe did not change a single letter of what he received from Hashem. He was not the author, Hashem was."

"Everything you are saying is true, Adolph, but the Torah could not have come down to the world without first going through the pipeline of Moshe. The physical, finite world could not possibly hold the Infinite Will of Hashem without it first going through Moshe, our Teacher."

"But Moshe was a finite man," Adolph protested again. "He was much smaller than the world. If the entire finite physical world could not receive the Infinite Torah of Hashem, then how was Moshe, who was just an inhabitant of this finite world, able to receive it?"

"By first taking off both of his shoes."

"This I got to hear."

"What you need to hear are the holy words of ADON OLAM. Hidden in those words is the answer to why Moshe Rabbeinu had to remove both of his shoes in order to receive the Torah and to thereby enable us to call Hashem's Name King. ADON OLAM states לעת נעשה בחפצו כל, אזי מלך שמו נקרא ~ L'eis na'asah b'cheftzo kol azai melech Shemo nikra ~ Only when the physicality of Creation was made via His Will could His Name be called King.

"Torah is not merely Hashem's tool for bringing about Creation. It is also our only tool to accomplish our purpose in Creation. But before we try to understand how the Torah enables us to achieve our purpose, we need to clarify exactly what that purpose is. ADON OLAM defines that purpose as using the physical to relate to Hashem as our King."

"How, indeed, are we to fulfill ADON OLAM's words of relating to Hashem as King?"

"We, the finite, can relate to the Infinite only through using a name. A name indicates how we relate to any individual as we know him, what he is for us. When Hashem filtered His Will through Moshe Rabbeinu we were given the only tool/Name through which to relate to Hashem; it is how we know Him, for it was through it that we were derived. Therefore, the Torah of Moshe is Hashem's

Name, and only through it, can we relate to Hashem, and call Him King."

Yehudah paused at this point, and then went on:

"Now we can start to discuss in detail the last words of the first stanza: אזי מלך שמו נקרא ~ Only after everything was created through the Torah, could Hashem's Name be called King. But to understand all that, Moshe needed to remove his shoes."

"I still don't see what the shoes have to do with this . . ."

"You see . . ."

Yehudah explained what he explained, and Adolph-Avi's life was changed forever. Now Avi wants to help the other guys understand what he learned at that fire with Yehudah.

Reigniting the Fire of the Past

AVI COMES BACK to the present, and spots the rest of the group approaching the bottom of the hill. He hurries to have the bonfire ready in time for their arrival.

"So, Yehudah," says Ovadiah, "you mean to say that since Hashem's Will created the world, we need to relate to that Will. But how could it happen? Moshe was flesh-and-blood. How could that body become a vessel for receiving the Infinite? ADON OLAM leaves us hanging. We still have to make a leap of faith."

"The authors of ADON OLAM did not need to relate to us ideas that are clearly expressed in the Torah itself, which describes Moshe receiving the Infinite."

"Where?" Ovadiah queries.

"At the Burning Bush."

"And what is it that you are suggesting happened there at the Burning Bush? What did Moshe do to allow his finite body to become the vessel for the Infinite Torah?"

"He removed his shoes—and his body along with them."

Shimi winces: "That sounds painful." Ovadiah, annoyed, shushes him, "Quiet, Shimi! I want to hear this."

Before answering them, Yehudah shouts up the hill to Avi: "Light her up! We're about to become shoeless."

As Avi lights the bonfire on the hill, Yehudah shines his flashlight at a small broken plank of wood which is hanging from a sagging bough at the base of the hill. Etched on it is an arrow pointing up the hill. Under the arrow the sign reads:

The Shoeless Path

"O.K., GUYS, take your shoes off your feet," Yehudah says authoritatively.

Shimi grumbles: "Who does he think he is, Hashem? Hey, Yehudah, my name is not Moshe. I don't want to walk up this rocky path without my shoes. I'm used to deep shag carpet with a velour finish."

But Natan turns on him: "Just do what he says. How will you ever understand the hidden secrets of the world without a little effort? No pain no gain." Shalom, too, urges Shimi on: "You will understand later. Not all of the world's secrets are written on the wall. Just follow instructions. It's the only way to understand this deep stuff. It's worth it."

Ovadiah, of course, is the first to hurry to follow the instructions. He is thirsty to learn however much he can in whatever way possible. Natan and Shalom are next, and Shimi follows suit reluctantly.

Yehudah notes all this with satisfaction. "Now that everyone's shoes are off, let's start to move up this path in the direction of Avi's bonfire."

As they clamber up the stone path cautiously, 'ouch's' are heard, one after another. Shimi can't help complaining openly: "Hey, Yehudah, stop! I think we all need to put our shoes back on. My feet were meant to wear shoes on them. They are not programmed for walking shoeless on thorns and stones."

"If you think that it's hard to walk on this path with your bare feet," Natan enlightens him, "think of how much more painful it would be to do a handstand and walk up on the palms of your hands. At least the feet were meant for walking. Keep going, Shimi. No stopping."

Shimi sighs resignedly: "I guess you're right. I should be thankful that Yehudah isn't torturing us even more."

"And what if," adds Shalom, "Yehudah told you to walk up this path on your eyelids, what would you say then, Shimi?"

"That would be impossible," Shimi protests. "The skin of the eyelid would be ripped in seconds. It's not made for walking on. What are you guys getting at, anyway? I'm having trouble getting up this hill on foot without my shoes and you are suggesting walking on my eyelids. What a wonderful evening. Yehudah is torturing my feet while you guys are torturing my brain."

Yehudah laughs heartily, and Ovadiah grabs Shimi's hand and, with both of their faces contorted with pain, pulls Shimi up the hill with him.

"O.K., Yehudah," says Ovadiah as they puff up the hill, "we are all following your instructions, but what are you laughing about?"

"I am laughing at Natan and Shalom. A year ago when we journeyed on this path they sounded just like Shimi. Now they are saying to him exactly what I said to them."

Ovadiah frowns. "Would any of you like to enlighten those of us who are tender of foot and tortured of brain as to what is going on?"

"Give it five minutes and you will understand the hidden," Natan replies.

Leave Your Body and Take Your Soul

FINALLY, all the sore-footed climbers arrive at the clearing and the now-roaring bonfire. As the heat of the flames scorches their faces, Avi greets them:

"Just over three thousand and three hundred years ago Moshe, our teacher, stood on Mt. Sinai looking at the bush that burned and was not consumed. Before he approached to view this open miracle he was commanded to remove both of his shoes. This scene is all part of the holy Torah, so it has eternal meaning. Obviously, Hashem was teaching us something much more than just social graces."

Yehudah then picks up the thread: "Remember, Moshe was being chosen to lead Hashem's people out of Egyptian slavery and to eventually bring them back to that same mountain to receive the eternal, Infinite Torah. The *Gemara*[100] tells us that from the moment of Creation the world was waiting to see if Israel would accept the Torah at Sinai. If they would, then the world would continue to exist, if not, then the world would return to chaos."

"The acceptance of the Torah and, as ADON OLAM informs us, using the Torah to call Hashem King, is the purpose of the world," Avi continues. "It was at the Burning Bush that the means to achieve this goal were planted. In order to get the ball rolling Moshe had to first remove both his shoes. Without removing his shoes, the world would never have been able to fulfill its purpose. Clear, right?"

"Seems as clear to me as the mud that I just stepped into with my bare feet." That's Shimi, of course.

So Yehudah explains further: "Many sources[101] inform us that the removal of Moshe Rabbeinu's shoes symbolized the removal of the barriers that stood between the Infinite Torah and its physical creations. Let me explain. Ovadiah asked 'Since the Torah is Infinite, how could it be contained within the finite words of a single scroll? Moshe Rabbeinu was the greatest man, but he was still a finite being. How could it be possible for him to bring down the Infinite Torah?' There had to have been an infinite aspect in Moshe in order for him to be able to receive the Torah."

---

100 Shabbas 88a.

101 The Zohar, *Ha'emek Davar*, the *Malbim*, and *Nefesh HaChaim*, etc.

The Production of the Soul

"**A**N INFINITE ASPECT of man?" Shimi is incredulous. "Even I know that we sound like we are bordering on heresy. Don't some other religions speak about people being gods?"

"Of course Yehudah is not inferring that Moshe was God," says Avi. "Hold on and you will understand." And Yehudah clarifies: "Earlier this evening, we discussed how the physical world came into being, but we never discussed how the soul came into being. We now know that our physical bodies are a product of a chain of thickening worlds, which the Arizal explained to us as being spiritual forces from Hashem that are constantly being filtered down and abstracted ('thickened') into physicality. The same is not true of our souls. The completely spiritual soul comes directly from Hashem. It is an unfiltered version of spiritual forces. This dichotomy between the body and the soul is described best when the Torah tells us: 'And the Lord God formed man of the dust of the ground and breathed into his nostrils the breath of life; and man became a living soul.'[102] When the Torah tells us that Hashem breathed into man's nostrils the breath of life, we learn that it was a direct 'action', with no filters or thickening. Hashem breathed something much higher than filtered, abstracted physicality into our limited bodies. He breathed into us of Himself. This is why the soul is (so often) referred to as a piece of Hashem from Above.[103]

"Just ponder that even a tiny essence of Infinity still has infinite quality."

"Our bodies and our souls are two separate things." Avi goes on. "Our souls existed before our bodies were conceived. When the body dies, the soul separates from the body. The body is here just in order to help the soul perform its tasks in the physical world. In a similar way, the shoe is on the foot just to enable the body to perform its tasks."

---

102 Genesis 2:7.

103 Ramban, Genesis 2:7; *Nefesh HaChaim*, 1, 16, *Eshed HaNechalim* on *Devarim Rabba* 4:4; *Sanhedrin* 91a, *Midrash Shocher Tov*, 2.

"So the infinite soul is contained in the finite body???" Ovadiah is surprised.

"Not quite. Let's look at your bodies. You have a head which contains your mind; this is your body's most important part. This is how you think. It is where your personality is contained. Then you have the main part of your body—the torso and the arms coming out of it. They enable you to receive things from the outside world in order to digest them and use their energy to keep you alive and thinking. Without the torso, the mind would not be able to live. Then there are the legs that move you from one place to the other. They enable the torso to get to the things that it will eventually digest.

"Then there are the feet, which we cover with shoes to be able to withstand the harshness of the paths we walk on. So the lofty mind is dependent upon lowly insensitive shoes, which are not part of the body.

"The body relates to the shoe in a similar way that the soul relates to the body. Even the lowest, most insensitive part of the body, the bottom of the foot, needs to be covered by the inanimate shoe in order to walk the stony paths of life. The lowest, most spiritually insensitive part of the soul needs to be covered by the non-spiritual entity called the body in order to engage with the physical world. The foot, which is in the shoe, does not become one with the shoe; it merely uses the shoe. The lowest part of the soul, which is called the *nefesh* (life force), merely uses the body, but does not become finite and non-spiritual like the body."

Avi pauses for a moment.

Shimi has been thinking: "Now I understand what we said on the way up here. You do not walk on your hands. Nor do you walk on your eyelids. These parts have nothing to do with the coarse activities of walking. So, too, the upper levels of the soul have nothing to do with the body. It is only the lowest, most insensitive part of the soul that is covered by the non-spiritual body."

Avi now turns to Ovadiah: "Now it's your turn to tell us

what it means when it says that Moshe Rabbeinu was told to remove his shoes from his feet."

"To remove the body from the soul?"

"Good," says Yehudah, "but why? What could this have to do with connecting to Infinity?"

Partially Shoeless Prophecy

THE BONFIRE really starts to roar. The boys need to move back. As they regroup a few meters away, Ovadiah holds his head between his hands. Then he looks up and begins to speak:

"You said that the soul was not created from this world. It is, rather, a direct piece of the Infinity of Hashem. It is put into a relationship with the lowest of worlds by way of the physical body. If you remove the shoes from the feet then the still-sensitive foot is exposed for what it is. Similarly, if you remove the body from the soul then all you have is a pure untainted piece of Hashem. This infinite soul without the body could surely conceive of the Infinite Will of Hashem."

Avi is happy: "Great, buddy! You got it! Now, think of this: the leader and prophet Yehoshua[104] was told to remove his shoe, one shoe. Yet the Torah is not called the Torah of Yehoshua. In fact, according to the Principles of Faith, Moshe Rabbeinu is the father of all prophets, and no other prophet could ever or will ever be able to contradict a word of Moshe's Torah. There was something unique about what happened to Moshe at the Burning Bush, different from the experience of any other man who had ever lived or will ever live. So far, we haven't explained what the difference is."

"We've actually mentioned it already," says Yehudah. "Only Moshe was commanded to remove two shoes from two feet. The Zohar[105] relates that never before and never again will there be

104 The Hebrew name for Joshua.

105 Zohar, Parshas Shemos.

such a physical man with the ability to remove both shoes. Other Prophets saw visions, but they were able to understand these visions only by comparing them with what they had known and learned in the physical world. Their ability to translate the lofty concepts that were shown to them was clouded by the definitions learned through the body. Moshe alone was able to remove the 'second shoe'. He was able to completely remove his necessity for the physical world. He could understand spiritual concepts without needing to compare them to that which he learned in the physical world. His completely spiritual soul was able to conceive of spiritual concepts without the barrier of the body as a translator.

"When Moshe Rabbeinu removed both of his shoes, he became a soul without a body. He was that piece of Hashem from above imbibing the Will of Hashem directly. He was able to make direct contact with the Infinite Source of all. As the Zohar tells us, the Burning Bush symbolized the *Shechinah*, the Heavenly Presence. The Presence of Hashem was coming face to face with Its creation."

Manhandling the Non-manmade

FOR A FEW MOMENTS conversation comes to a halt. Everyone is entranced by the roaring fire as it pops and sends its myriad of sparks heavenward. Then Ovadiah looks straight into the fire and starts to speak.

"So let me see if I got this right. Moshe Rabbeinu needed to remove both of his shoes. He needed to remove not only his own barriers, those created by his personality (like all the other prophets), but he also needed to remove all bodily-learned tools. This means that Moshe's prophetic abilities were not influenced by what he had learned in this physical world. His thought patterns were therefore not a barrier to receiving the Infinite Torah. When he described Hashem as big, he was not thinking of the largest mountain that he could imagine. When he described Hashem as mighty, he did not have to picture a warrior. When he got to this level, he was able to converse with the Creator in 'His own language'. The Will of Hashem could be understood on an infinite level only by a soul which was also on an infinite, not physically-imprisoned level of understanding. Yet Moshe was still a man and not God. He became merely a bridge, the only direct bridge, for the Infinite Torah to come down to us in a seemingly finite form, but that form has only a façade of being finite. In truth, the Infinite Will is built into the words of Moshe's Torah."

Avi adds: "Our Principles of Faith go on to tell us that Moshe was the father of all prophets. Never again would there be a prophet who would be able to do what Moshe did. The basis for all other prophecies was the Torah. The Torah of Moshe was complete, infinite. Never can a single letter be added to the Torah of Moshe, because you cannot add to infinity."

"So why did these other prophets prophesize?" Ovadiah wants to know.

"At times our people needed a pep talk about obeying the Torah's commands and warnings of what would happen if they would not follow the words of the Torah. The prophets were sent to bring them back to the Torah of Moshe.

"There are other faiths that claim connection to the original Torah. Their so-called prophets either said that a new and improved version of the Torah was needed, or they simply distorted the information in it. By doing so, they have manhandled that which is not man-made."

"Now, Ovadiah," continues Yehudah, "what does all this have to do with what ADON OLAM describes as calling Hashem's Name King?"

In Search of Meaning

OVADIAH IS AT FIRST startled by the question, but not for long.

"This is amazing. I am starting to really internalize this stuff. Hashem's Name is not His Essence. Rather, it is how we know Him. We can only know the Infinite through the Torah brought down by Moshe, the finite man. So His Name, or the way we know Hashem, is the Torah of Moshe, and the Torah of Moshe is the same Infinite Will of Hashem from above. He and His Will are One. So when we subjugate ourselves to Hashem's Will by learning and living by the words of Moshe's Torah, we are doing as ADON OLAM tells us. We are 'calling His Name King' over us and thus fulfilling the purpose of the world."

Shimi is impressed. "You better watch out, Yehudah. This guy is going to take your place."

"Nothing would make me happier," is Yehudah's sincere answer.

Everyone notices that Ovadiah has suddenly become silent and still. As he sits looking down at the ground, the only sounds heard in the clearing are the pop and crackling of the bonfire. There is real anguish in his face when he speaks up again:

"Just one more piece is still missing. Why would Hashem want to create a world with such a purpose? He is Infinite. Nothing is missing for Him. He does not need us to call Him King. Why so much effort for something that He does not need?"

"What you really mean to ask," replies Yehudah, "is, what difference do we make anyway? Why are we here? Since Hashem is Infinite, consequently there is nothing outside of Him, so what are we really? Is there any significance to our lives? Why do we have to live through so much pain and torture in this lowly world? Is there really any good that could come from us living through all of our trials and tribulations? Hashem has everything, so why does He need me to call Him King? Or does He really need me after all? Maybe life is just purposeless."

Ovadiah turns to look Yehudah in the eye.

"Yes, Yehudah. We've learned a lot tonight, but I still don't get it. My father's last words seemed to be telling me, just like you are, that life has meaning, but I still haven't found it in these deep discussions. What is it all about? Why are we here? Does the Infinite really need little old me to call Him

King? What does Hashem gain from Creation? Everything is His anyway. How can He need or want something from me? Is there really a purpose to living through all of these clouds? Why did Hashem want to create the world of clouds and hiding? Why do I have to attach to the fire of Torah from out of the darkness of this night? What good is it all anyway? Why create me in the first place?"

"There are good answers to your questions, and, God willing, I will give them to you soon, but I think we could all use a little breather. The fire is dying down. It's time to roast the marshmallows before there is nothing left but embers. Hey, Avi, did you bring the bags of marshmallows?"

Avi knows exactly what Yehudah is up to. He is going to use the mundane marshmallow to cushion the next message.

"Yes, Boss. They were on your list so they're here. It's getting late, or maybe you could say it is almost getting early. I think we could all also use the second thermos of coffee."

By now it's 3:00 am, and the boys look for appropriate sticks for their marshmallow roasting. They are fiendishly hungry. Busily, they skewer, sizzle and swallow one marshmallow after another and gulp down the not-so-hot coffee.

So Hashem Wants Marshmallows?

"I THINK MY BRAIN has turned into a marshmallow after all of this depth," says Shimi after a while. "Hey, Avi, do you have any more pink marshmallows? I want some."

Yehudah breaks in: "What does it mean that you want?"

Shimi smacks his forehead with his left hand while being careful not to drop the marshmallows from the stick in his right hand. "I knew it. Even a marshmallow has Kabbalistic significance for Yehudah."

"Hey, Shimi, you may learn something. It couldn't hurt as much as walking up the hill barefoot." Natan is anxious to go ahead on this quest, and so is Shalom, who turns to Shimi and says, "Go ahead and answer Yehudah's question. I think he's just trying to answer Ovadiah's question, and you are just being used as a pawn."

"O.K., Yehudah. I want the marshmallow because I am hungry, and I would like to satisfy that hunger with something that I like."

"Bingo!"

Ovadiah doesn't understand: "Bingo what?"

"You only want that which you lack," answers Yehudah, "and that lack can be filled with something from the outside. So what does the Zohar mean when it teaches that Hashem **wanted** to create the world?"

"As far as Hashem is concerned, there is nothing lacking." Ovadiah states emphatically, "and according to this definition of the word 'want', it does not seem that Hashem could want anything. So how could He want to create the world?"

"You're correct," says Yehudah, "and not only that, but, there can be nothing outside of Hashem, because He is Infinite. Everything comes from and is already contained within Him. As we learned before, Creation itself is happening inside of Hashem. So, in order to understand why Hashem wanted to create the world it seems that we have to come up with a different definition of the word 'want', different from the want Shimi has for the marshmallows."

"The Ramchal in *Derech Hashem* spends many pages clarifying what it means that Hashem 'wants' to create. He concludes that Hashem's desire to create the physical world isn't to fulfill a lack in His Essence, but rather to bestow good upon His creations."

"But some people have painfully miserable lives," Ovadiah is quick to point out. "Many struggle to survive from the moment that they start to live. Others are hit with seemingly insurmountable tidal waves of painful experiences. Is it possible that their struggles and suffering, or senselessly being killed is also considered bestowing good?"

Yehudah is not fazed by the question, as he hasn't been fazed by all those other ones. "Just like we changed our definition of 'want', so, too, we have to now change our definition of 'good.'"

A Purse of Airy Gems

"IF YOU WANT something very good, you may be willing to work very hard for it," Yehudah continues to explain. "*The Hidden Master* tells you to imagine that you wanted an investment that would help you far into the future. So you worked hard for a whole year for a small purse of rare and precious jewels. When you received the purse you were exhilarated, but when you arrived home and opened it, you saw that it was filled with nothing but air. Imagine your disappointment. You are angry and frustrated. All of your efforts were for nothing. You wanted something more, something better. You wanted security. You wanted to build yourself up. At the end it was all a hoax. A year of your life was stolen, never to be returned.

"In order to understand the emptiness of the purse, and our new definition of 'good', we need to remember what we learned before. Any finite number compared to Infinity is zero. Think for a moment of a much more common, but unfortunately more extreme scenario. If instead of a year of work, you had spent your whole life working for goals of emptiness, then the end result would be overwhelmingly devastating. Even if by the end of your life you had succeeded in amassing millions of dollars and were highly respected by thousands of people, this is all still very finite. It is all still equal to zero. When our physical lives end and we stand in front of Hashem, all the money and prestige is worth nothing. We were created for an infinite purpose. If we spend our lives attaching to things or ideas that will not help us to attach to the Infinity of Hashem, then we are striving towards an empty purse filled with morbid frustrations.

So, Searching Soul, as the bonfire ebbs into a pile of crackling embers, you and each of your new friends think of how some of your own wants have just smoldered into insignificance, but listen as Yehudah continues:

"What exactly is true 'good', and where can we find it? And how can it be found amidst even the pains and frustrations of this world? What meaning can we search for to fill our purses with? How do we attach to Hashem's Infinity and consequently have our spiritual purses overflow with an infinity of gems?"

Filling the Void

YEHUDAH PAUSES before getting to the point: "Anything that pulls us away from infinity lures us towards finality, futility, emptiness and oblivion. Consequently, fulfillment, or good, can only be attained by running after attachment to infinity. The *Derech Hashem* tells us that Hashem's purpose in creating the world was to bestow upon us this good, this attachment. He states that:

> True good exists only in God (the Infinite). His wisdom (Torah) therefore decreed that the nature of this true benefaction be His giving created things the opportunity to attach themselves to Him to the greatest degree possible for them . . . they can be considered part of God's perfection as a result of their association with Him.[106]

"This association with Him is what ADON OLAM describes to us as אֲזַי מֶלֶךְ שְׁמוֹ נִקְרָא ~ calling Hashem's Name King. But how do we accomplish this? Avi's Burning Bush is now just a small pile of dwindling embers. What did we learn here about our ability to associate with Hashem?

One by one, the boys have their say. Natan is first:

"I now understand that we, the finite, cannot associate directly with Hashem's Infinite Essence. The greatest degree that it is possible for us to associate with Him is only through the Torah of Moshe."

Shalom is next: "And the Zohar teaches that Hashem and His Torah are actually one. So by busying ourselves with the

Torah and its Commandments we are in essence associating with Hashem."

"So this means that our only hope of not dwindling into oblivion, like these embers, is to attach to the Torah of Moshe and therefore to infinity," is Shimi's response.

Ovadiah sums it up: "This is the 'good' that we need to fill our purses with while in this world."

Yehudah is pleased. "So let's now put the words of ADON OLAM together. The first part of this phrase reads, לעת נעשה בחפצו כל ~ *L'eis na'asah b'cheftzo kol* ~ Hashem made the lowly physical world, and all of its precursors, from His Torah. The purpose in making the physical world was to bestow good. Good is defined as giving us the ability to choose to attach to the Infinite Spiritual Source from which our physical world was derived while still within this finite world of clouds. The next part of this phrase, אזי מלך שמו נקרא ~ *Azai Melech Shemo nikra*, shows that we must choose to follow the Torah properly, and only then are we *calling His Name, the Torah of Moshe, King.*"

Clouds of Light

"BUT WHY DO WE NEED to be in the physical world with all of its clouds? Why do we need barriers to our perception of spiritual concepts? Couldn't we just strive for closeness with Hashem from the spiritual realm? I still don't know why we have to go through all of the pain of this world." The pain is all too evident in Ovadiah's voice.

"It is exactly the clouds that allow you to receive the light. If you do not earn Infinity, it is not yours. There is no way to earn attachment to Hashem as long as there is no free choice. So the greatest good that Hashem could bestow upon us is the ability to earn our own Infinity. The *Derech Hashem* clarifies that:

> The deeper plan of God's wisdom was to arrange things so that even though man must be immersed in the physical, he should be able to

*attain perfection through his worldly activities and the physical world
itself. It is precisely through these that he attains a pure and lofty
state, and it is therefore his very lowliness that elevates him. For when
he transforms darkness into light and deathly shadow into sparkling
brilliance, he is then able to attain unparalleled excellence and glory.*[107]

"If all that you receive is a free gift," Yehudah goes on, "then
you have not been the one to forge attachment to Hashem.
You need to be the one to strive for this attachment. You need
to choose to find the light which chooses to hide behind the
clouds of darkness that make up this physical world. The light
beckons you, yet you must be the one to choose to pull back
the clouds.

"*Derech Hashem* teaches us about this need to forge this attachment:

> *God's wisdom, however, decreed that for such good to be perfect,
> the one enjoying it must be its master. He must be the one who has
> earned it for himself, and not one associated with it accidentally.*[108]

"And also says:

> *He must strive to remove all the obstacles of evil that are attached to
> the physical nature and spiritual darkness of this world. Then he can
> make strong efforts to bring himself near to Him, until he becomes
> attached to Him and becomes perfected by His wholeness.*[109]"

Over the glowing embers Yehudah signals with his eyes
to Avi . . . .

107   Derech Hashem 1,4,4.

108   Derech Hashem 1,2,2.

109   Derech Hashem 4,1,4.

Smack That Cloud Right in the Face

AVI STEPS IN to clarify some more: "We need to strive to perceive Hashem through the clouds of physical existence. It is the entire purpose of His Creation. Hashem wishes to bestow good upon us. That good is Hashem Himself, but as we just heard from the *Derech Hashem*, in order for this good to affect us and raise us up, we need to earn it. There has to be cloudiness to fight against. We must work very hard to remove these clouds in order to see Hashem, Who is hiding behind them. We need to be the masters of the strife."

"What exactly," asks Ovadiah, "does the *Derech Hashem* mean when he tells us that we need to 'strive to remove all the obstacles of evil that are attached to the physical nature?' What are these obstacles of evil? Where do they come from? Is he referring to the Satan?"

"Yes," says Yehudah.

"So he is telling us that the world was created only so that our souls could come down to a physical body and overcome the Satan??? Hashem is the Source of all. Why create the Satan in the first place?"

Yehudah, who has been expecting this question, smiles gently. "Without the Satan, the physical world has no purpose, and we can see this idea hidden in ADON OLAM. The words לעת נעשה בחפצו כל אזי מלך שמו נקרא ~ *L'eis na'asah b'cheftzo kol azai Melech Shemo nikra* teach us that Hashem created the physical world through the Torah, *cheftzo*, only so that we, who are in the clouded world of physicality, could choose to follow the Torah of Moshe. The choice to follow the Torah of Moshe despite the pulls of the physical world is actually a fight with the Satan, and succeeding in this fight is how we call Hashem's Name King."

"But I thought that the Satan is evil. You are now saying that without him there is no purpose to the world. Could you explain this a little more?" Shimi's interest is growing from minute to minute.

Avi gives Yehudah an almost fiendish look and says, "Tonight we are going to let the Satan clarify himself."

"What?! Wait a minute. I don't know about this. This sounds scary. I don't want the Satan coming at us in the forest at night." Shimi's interest is turning into alarm.

"Oh, don't worry," declares Yehudah airily, "I don't mean here."

"So where?"

"It's time to visit the tomb," says Avi.

By now Shimi is losing it. "Are you crazy? You want to meet the Satan by walking into a graveyard at three in the morning?"

"No, we are not going to walk into a graveyard," Yehudah replies. "That would be too boring." Avi laughs while Yehudah finishes his announcement: "We're going to rappel deep down into a crevice in the earth which holds in its depth a two-thousand-year-old crypt. There we will meet the Satan."

Avi sneaks away with the rappelling rope. Yehudah throws his gooey stick onto the remaining embers, says his after-blessing on the marshmallows, and starts the group on its small journey.

Meeting the Satan

IT DOESN'T TAKE LONG for the group to arrive at an enormous rock. Natan notices that there is something very unnatural about its shape: it stands twice the height of a large man. In the moonlight its silhouette appears like a giant, jagged egg. He touches it and feels that the rock has obviously been carved into its shape. Yet the chisel grooves are very weathered. He thinks to himself that this rock must have been here for ages. Its base rests in a carved-out indentation in the bedrock. It fits all too perfectly into this depression in the stone, which seems to cradle it. Obviously, the indentation was also created by man. Shalom asks Yehudah when this stone was placed here, and by whom, and for what reason?

As Ovadiah stands, pondering the strange stone, he gets the feeling that something eerie looms beneath. Meanwhile,

Avi is busily fastening the rappelling rope to a large tree near the "Egg Stone." When Avi finishes tying knots and making footholds, he drops the rope through a narrow elliptical opening at the base of the stone, and calls to the rest of them:

"Leave your backpacks here. I have my backpack. In it is all that we need for down there."

He grasps hold of the rope and swiftly slithers through the opening and slips out of sight. Moments later the sounds of splashing echo out from the depths of the cavern. Shalom then courageously grabs the rope, followed hesitantly by Natan. Splashing sounds seem to thunder out from the narrow opening. Yehudah grabs the rope, and, before disappearing as well, says, "I certainly hope that you guys know how to rappel and swim in the dark!"

Shimi and Ovadiah now stand alone next to the small opening.

"Hey, Ovadiah, what do you say we just head back to civilization and leave these idiots to their own demise?"

"Bye, Shimi. I am going down. I have an appointment. I have to meet the Satan."

The sounds of "Watch out below!!!" followed by splashing and laughter are heard echoing inside the cavern as Ovadiah takes the plunge. Shimi shrugs: "Well if you can't beat them, join them. Or maybe I should say, 'We will all go down together.'" And with this philosophical thought, he leaves his backpack next to the others and musters up the courage to make the plunge.

Many meters below ground, in the musty cavern, the boys are enjoying themselves, swimming and splashing each other in the pitch black. Their frivolous howling seems to echo in a haunting fashion. Avi swims to the 'shore' of the precarious pond.

After a few moments of fumbling around his backpack with his cold and wet fingers, he rips open the watertight seal around the battery-operated camping lantern. Once he lights it, the guys stop splashing around. They all seem in awe of their new but really ancient surroundings. The enormous cave is clearly carved out of the bedrock by hand.

"O.K. guys," says Yehudah, "it's time to go on shore. We have a lot to cover before dawn."

The now-wet and quite chilly group huddles together on the shore of the subterranean pool. While they shiver and share each others' heat, Yehudah's voice is heard echoing through the cavern.

"Take a careful look around you. We are in the antechamber of an ancient tomb. This cavern was chiseled out during the Second Temple period. Its dimensions and structure fit precisely the plans of the crypts described in the Talmud. The deceased was placed here almost two thousand years ago. By now almost nothing remains of the actual body."

"But why did you bring us to this underground tomb at night?" Shimi wonders.

You Have the Right to Bear Arms

AVI IS THE ONE who answers. "We brought you here so that you would be able to get your swords."

A unanimous "Huh?" arises from the group, and Avi hastens to explain.

"We are all born knowing that we will eventually die. It is here, in this crypt of death, that we are about to learn why we are alive in the first place. Here we will come to understand why our souls are put into our bodies. Before you can fully understand this, you need to know the Jewish concept of Satan and evil and with what sharp sword of knowledge you need to arm yourself, in order to fight them."

Yehudah now says,

"*Derech Hashem* explains:

Now, the root purpose of the entire matter of religious service and worship is to have man constantly aware of his Creator. He is to realize that he was created for the sole purpose of being drawn close to the Creator, and hence he was put into this world only to overcome his Evil Inclination and subjugate himself to his Creator through the power of the intellect. He must oppose his physical desire and tendencies, and direct all his activities toward attaining this goal, not deviating from it.[110]"

"That was an echoing mouthful," observes Shimi.

But Natan has understood it: "Let me put that in simpler terms. Tell me if I got it right. His message is that our spiritual souls were put into physical bodies only in order to fight the Satan. Only through this fight are we able to consciously and meaningfully subjugate ourselves to Hashem."

"But, obviously, the nature of this fight is not with fists but rather on an intellectual level," Shalom is quick to point out. "The nature of this intellectual battle is to act against the animalistic nature of the body. We are to use the intellect in order to choose to aspire to a level far above that of the animal."

"By so doing we strive for closeness to our Creator. It is only through our intentionally fighting this Evil Inclination that we gain merit," sums up Avi.

Ovadiah has something to add: "It is obvious now from what we learned up there at the bonfire that the only way to win this intellectual battle and to subsequently attach to Hashem is to choose to follow the Torah of Moshe, which is His Will. As the *Ethics of the Fathers* tells us,[111] we need to make His Will into ours. We do this by fighting against any other will or evil that the physical world presents to our souls. The Torah is the only sword in our hands. Without holding onto it tightly, we will lose the battle."

"I see that my efforts in building the bonfire didn't all go up in smoke." Avi is pleased, and so is Yehudah, who says,

"So far, so good. I told you all that ADON OLAM will enable you to enter a new world. This world of ADON OLAM has its own type of war and enemy. The weapons of the world of

---

110   *Derech Hashem* 1,4,6.

111   Ethics of the Fathers, 2, 4.

ADON OLAM are also different from the world as you knew it before. As Ovadiah surmised, the Torah is your sword, but you are still not ready for battle. You need to know who your enemy is before you can fight him. Let's cross the threshold into the crypt itself and expose the Satan for what he really is. Then we will understand how to stab him with our newfound weapons. Come, follow me."

He then grabs the lantern by the handle and walks ahead into the darkness. The guys follow him through a narrow hallway. As they enter the actual burial chamber Avi shouts:

"BATS!!!"

A swarm of a few hundred bats exit the chamber in a storm of fluttering wings over the boys' heads. They are so numerous that the guys feel the musty air surging through the tunnel. Within a few seconds there isn't a single bat left in the underground tomb. The atmosphere becomes increasingly quiet. In the dull lantern light their eyes start to focus on the damp wall in front of them. They are now standing in front of a very ancient chamber carved into the bedrock.

Yehudah says, "The bats can escape their creepy crevice, but we can never escape our inevitable confrontations with evil. Let's now meet the Satan."

Shimi has been somewhat shaken: "I thought that we just did."

Ovadiah puts it differently: "You guys certainly have a dramatic way about you. I could write a book about adventures with Yehudah and Avi."

A Very Good Enemy

"I BROUGHT YOU HERE," says Yehudah, "in order to conjure up certain emotions. Think about death, darkness, cold, wet and clammy things. Think about fear of the unknown, tumult, chaos, morbid finality, evil, anti-god, the creeps. These are the feelings that are flashing through all of our minds now."

Avi fills in from his store of knowledge: "In many of the other world religions, these are the thoughts that are awakened when their believers think of the Satan or other such anti-gods that they conceive of. But we know that Hashem calls the Satan 'Tov Meod', very good. In the world of ADON OLAM the enemy is considered very good."

"Very good?" Shimi is once again astonished. "I don't get it. What don't I understand?"

The lantern casts an eerie light that seems to make its way into the narrow, carved-out cavity in the wall. Ovadiah looks into it with a blank face.

Ovadiah echoes Shimi: "Very good??? Where do we see that the Torah describes the Satan as very good? What could be good about evil? We all will die one day. We are supposed to spend our terribly short lives fighting our Evil Inclinations. What is very good about this?"

"In the Torah's account of Creation,[112] the only thing that is called 'very good' is the Evil Inclination. The Talmud tells us that the Evil Inclination is synonymous with the Satan who, in turn, is synonymous with the Angel of Death.[113]

"Great!" Shimi groans. "Not only are we going to meet the Satan, but we are going to have a convention with his friends, the Evil Inclination and the Angel of Death. What a party this is going to be! If this is what Yehudah calls very good, I'd hate to see what he calls very bad."

Yehudah places the lantern on the floor. He goes to the end of the burial chamber and comes back with a slightly damp book that Avi had concealed there the day before.

The Prince and the Harlot

"THE SATAN IS CALLED very good," explains Yehudah, "because the Satan allows for the possibility of free choice. As you look into that burial chamber and think about the

112   Ramban, Genesis 1:31.

113   *Bava Basra* 16a.

long-ago decayed remains of that short life that it contains, listen to the words of the Zohar.[114] It brings a parable of a king who wanted to see if his son would listen to him. So the king told his son, the prince, not to have anything to do with bad women. The prince promised to follow the king's will. After some time the king wanted to see if his son considered his father's will to be important enough to follow even when under duress. He wanted to know if the prince viewed his father as his king and ruler, or if the son's own will would win out over that of the king? So the king hired a very bad woman to try to entice the son. If the son would use all the strength of his will to ignore the evil woman, then the king would allow the son to enter the inner chambers of the palace and bestow upon him many valuable gifts. What would be the cause of these gifts?"

"The evil woman, of course!" replies Natan. "You are obviously relating back to what we just learned next to the bonfire. There you told us how ADON OLAM informs us that we are in this world only in order to call Hashem's Name King. We can accomplish this only by living by His Will, which is Moshe's Torah. You seem to be suggesting that the Zohar's story of the evil woman is informing us that in order to gain closeness to Hashem we need to choose to serve. Without the Satan we would be following Hashem without choice."

"The person whose remains were interred here had his or her chance to choose service," says Yehudah. "We also have our chance to choose to serve Hashem. At the end, both those who choose properly and those who choose improperly turn into the same dust. The life of the body is merely our opportunity to use our swords of Torah to attach to Hashem. If our short lives are used properly, then there is nothing to fear in the grave. Instead of death being the end, it becomes a beginning."

Shalom still needs to see the connection between words and concepts: "Fine, Yehudah. I can understand that Hashem sets up the world so that even evil can be used for good, but how does this make the evil into good? That woman that the

114 Zohar, *Parshas Terumah* 4, page 163a.

king sent was still an evil lady. The Satan still seems to me to be evil. So why does the Torah call the Satan and evil very good?"

Here, Avi breaks in mischievously: "Now I am going to turn off the camping light. When I turn it on the Satan will be exposed."

With the light off, they all feel the depth of the darkness. The haunting silence is broken only by the occasional sound of a drop of water landing on the damp floor.

The Jewish Satan Combats Contradictions

AVI SPEAKS in the dark: "All religions have to deal with the existence of evil and the goodness of their so-called god/s. The Greeks were considered amongst the most intelligent of societies in history. When I studied their beliefs on this subject, I thought I was reading a morbid comic strip. Likewise, I was completely unsatisfied by both Western and Eastern religions' incomplete at best and usually contradictory views of this subject. Then I came across a statement of Rabbi Gifter,[115] zt"l,[116] of how differently Torah deals with evil and the Satan. To most of the world's religions the Satan figure is evil, a fallen angel, almost like an anti-god. Even today's prominent religious doctrines are reminiscent of many of the pagan religions, like Zoroastrianism, that believe in a good god and its enemy, a bad god. This is the antithesis of monotheism. For since God is the Infinite and encompasses all, then who is out there to go against Him?

"According to the Torah, though, the Satan is neither an anti-god nor a fallen angel. Actually, just the opposite is true. Rav Gifter tells us that when a Jew listens to the Satan and commits a sin, the Satan actually cries. This shows us that its job is not to move us away from Hashem, or, as others claim,

---

115 A well-known Torah Scholar who recently passed away.

116 Acronym for *Zecher Tzaddik Livrachah*—"The memory of this righteous person is a blessing".

to pull us towards evil and destruction. Rather, its job is to bring us closer to Hashem by way of our choosing to ignore evil's pull. According to the Torah we can define the Satan as Hashem's loyal servant who gives us the ability to serve Hashem through free choice."

"So we stand here blind in the blackness of this underground tomb," Yehudah says. "Why did I bring you here? Why did Avi turn the light off?"

Natan is incisive in his answer: "Without the light of the Torah we are lost in this world. We live with no hope of eternal purpose. We wander around aimlessly until we die. But if we hold onto the light of the Torah in this lowly physical world, then, like the *Derech Hashem* told us:

> It is his very lowliness that elevates him. For when he transforms darkness into light and deathly shadow into sparkling brilliance, he is then able to attain unparalleled excellence and glory."

"So tell me, which world is more important, this one or the World to Come?" Yehudah wants to hear their opinions.

This World is More Important Than the World to Come

"Obviously, the World to Come," answers Shimi immediately.

"Are you sure?" asks Avi.

Yehudah breaks in through the dark: "This burial chamber contains the remains of a body that held a soul. Souls can either be completely blinded by their body, as we can be completely blinded by the thick darkness of this cave, or they can use the body to hold onto the lamp of Torah and fight their way out of the darkness. But in order to use the lamp of the Torah as our own, we must first choose to grasp it."

Avi bends down to grasp the lantern, lights it, and says:

"'One moment of repentance and good deeds in this world is worth more than all of the World to Come.'[117] Now look at this burial chamber. How long did this Jew interred here live? No matter who you are, life is short. There are those who claim that the purpose of this life is to get to the World to Come. This short-lived world seems to therefore take on little importance of its own. They mistakenly depict the World to Come as more important than this lowly world. This too is not true. Judaism teaches us that in this world we have an unbelievable power to get close to Hashem. This power does not exist in the World to Come. Here and now is our only chance to set the stage for our eternity.

"While in this lowly world we are actually the ones in control. We can choose when and to what extent we will or will not set that stage for eternity. As Jews we say one hundred blessings every day. Whenever we choose to say 'Blessed are You Hashem . . .' we are in immediate connection with the Master of Creation. In the World to Come we do not have the ability to connect more than we already had prepared for over here. There we will no longer have the choice and therefore cannot choose to grow. Yes, our bodies, like the one that was interred here, are short-lived. Yet they are the only way the spiritual soul can enter the physical world of choice. This cold, creepy world is our only chance to choose eternal meaning and life."

"It is with this thought that we will leave this crypt," says Yehudah. "Remember that your every step in this world is worth more than eternity. It is only from inside the body that you can be like Avraham our Father and choose to call Hashem the Master of the Hidden World. Be children of Avraham and choose to recognize Hashem in His hiding place.

"It's time to fight the next battle, Avraham's battle. Take your swords with you. This time we are going to continue to fight the same enemy that has been hanging around since the time of Avraham. I know where he is hiding. Let's head out of here."

---

117 Ethics of the Fathers 4, 22.

Longing for Battle

THE GUYS MAKE their way back to the subterranean pool. While standing at the edge of the still, black waters, they all look up at the narrow elliptical opening so far above their heads—about the height of a three-story building. A faint silvery-blue hue of moonlight peeks through, casting almost imperceptible rays onto Avi's rope. Even though he has tied many knots and foot-hold loops along the length of the rope, escape from the cave seems at best precarious. They all know that it will be a hard, arduous climb up, but they have no choice.

"Just a moment," Yehudah stops them. "Before we endeavor to emerge from this dungeon of death we must have a battle plan for when we surface. We came down here to learn how to better battle the world. We acquired our weapon, the Torah.

"ADON OLAM tells us that the nature of the battle is to fight the blindness of this world until Hashem is finally seen as King and called King by His creations, אזי מלך שמו נקרא ~ *Azai Melech Shemo Nikra*. The question now is how much you are yearning to fight, and what the nature of that fight is."

Avi wades through the water, holding the lantern in his left hand. As he reaches the rope, he grabs it with his right hand.

"Does anyone want to stay behind?"

He is answered by a unanimous and adamant "No!"

Yehudah can't help adding, "Maybe we should cut the rope and all stay here forever?"

"What are you guys getting at?" Shimi is annoyed, but Yehudah does not leave him in suspense for long.

"You are all longing to leave. You are in a situation that you are unwilling to stay in. You know of a better way of existence than that of this hidden pit of death. You are all willing to give it your all to get up that rope, no matter how much effort it takes. Your very lives depend upon it. This is the intensity of the fight that Avraham *Avinu* felt against the alien world around him."

Avraham's Fight
Can Become Your Own

"WHERE DO YOU SEE this intensity described in Avraham?" Natan wants to know.

"Remember, he called Hashem *Adon* (Master) instead of *Melech* (King)." Yehudah lets that sink in, and then goes on: "Chacham Ovadiah Yashar explained that there is a great difference between these two descriptions of Hashem as either *Adon* or *Melech*, personal Master or King, which are used in ADON OLAM's first stanza. He tells us that human kingship demands that the servants recognize their human king as their undoubted ruler. If the subjects do not accept the rulership of the king, then they do not consider him to be their king. The ability for the king to rule depends on the servants' acceptance of that rule. Although Hashem's rulership was absolute from before Creation, the recognition of this rulership in this physical world still depends upon His subjects. As long as there remains even one individual who doubts Hashem's complete rulership, there will be a blemish in the recognition of His Kingship.

"Chacham Yashar quotes what we already learned tonight from Rabbeinu Pinchas of Plutzk. He states that the words *Adon Olam* in *gematria* equal the words *Ein Sof*, Infinity. *Olam* refers to the 'Hidden'. He informs us that ADON OLAM's message to us in the first stanza is that Hashem, Who is Infinite, uses His Torah to create this physical world of clouds to hide His Kingship. Although He presently hides His Kingship, we, like our forefather Avraham, know that even before Creation He was always the Infinite King.

"Chacham Yashar continues by saying that it is regrettable that the rest of mankind does not yet recognize Hashem as the all-encompassing and majestic King, and therefore, we, the descendents of Avraham, are presently calling Him our personal Master, *Adon*, instead of the recognized King. Because of our personal relationship, living in this state of Hashem's hiding is intensely painful. This searing pain is awakened whenever we refer to Hashem as *Adon* and not as the King that we know Him to be. When we refer to Hashem as *Adon* of this cloudy world, we immediately feel a fervent impetus to remove the clouds till Hashem is exposed to all as King. When we call Hashem *Adon* we are reminding ourselves not only of our closeness to Hashem, but also of how far we have to go to achieve our goal. We want to do battle until His Name, as ADON OLAM states, will unanimously be called King—אזי מלך שמו נקרא ~ *Azai Melech Shemo nikra.*"

Seeds of Success:
The Necessity to Sprout

*Y*EHUDAH IS ABOUT *to explain to you what the plans are for the battle. Listen well, my Searching Soldier, as he grasps the rope hanging from the entrance far above.*

"It's a long way up isn't it? Are you all wondering if you will ever get to the end of the rope? The situation was the same with Avraham. He viewed his life as an unending battle to expose Hashem's now hidden Kingship to the rest of the world. He didn't know if he would ever get to the end of that battle, but that didn't stop him from fighting intensely.

"In order to help us understand the nature of this battle, Chacham Yashar tells us to think of an apple seed. Infused in each planted apple seed is all of the information needed to sprout into a fruit-bearing tree. If the seed does not succeed in sprouting forth from the ground, it will eventually rot, never to fulfill its life-giving purpose. Avraham was a soul, a holy seed planted in an alien world of idol worship. His life was one of struggle to bear fruit, to have the world recognize Hashem as the undoubted King. Avraham knew that as long as there are still barriers that hide Hashem's Kingship, Hashem could only be called *Adon*. He would only be regarded as Avraham's personal Master, and not recognized by the rest of the world as *Ein Sof, Adon Olam*, the Infinite King.

"So, Avraham spent his life struggling to climb up his own rope. In order to sprout forth from the depths of the world of idolatrous clouds, he needed to remove the barriers to the recognition of Hashem's Kingship. He needed to show the world where the barriers to understanding Hashem as King were. Once their position was pinpointed, he needed to break them down and cast their smashed remains to the winds of oblivion."

Avi picks up the thread: "We are right now buried in a hidden cave. Our desire to get out is intense. As you all struggle with all of your strength to climb this rope for your own personal escape, remember Avraham. Understand that the intensity of your struggle to declare Hashem King needs to be just as intense as your struggle for survival. Remember the burial chamber that we are leaving behind. Life is short, but it has a definite meaningful purpose. Throughout your short lives in this world you need to be constantly aware that you are holy seeds. You were planted in this world only in order to sprout forth the knowledge that Hashem is not only your *Adon*, but is actually the Infinite King of all. Use your newfound swords to break down the barriers and cast their smashed remains to the winds of oblivion. Fight for the day when Hashem will no longer just have you calling Him *Adon*. Like Avraham, you must define your lives as a never-ending struggle to arrive at the day when His Name will be called 'King' by everyone. אזי מלך שמו נקרא ~ *Azai Melech Shemo nikra*."

"Did my grandfather tell us what these barriers are and how to smash them?"

"Yes." Says Yehudah, "but let's first get out of here. I will let the scenery up there adjust your mind to see the world with your grandfather's eyes, the eyes of ADON OLAM. Let's go."

Avi, with his Olympic strength, swiftly pulls himself up the rope. Shalom, Natan and Shimi slowly and painfully struggle their way up as well. Now Ovadiah starts to climb up with great difficulty. About two-thirds of the way up he starts to slip.

"Help! I'm losing my grip!" his cry rings out.

Quickly, Avi pulls the rope up like a fisherman pulling up his line. His long muscular arm reaches out to grab Ovadiah's small bony hand just before it loses its grasp of the rope. In moments he is yanked up and out.

"Are you O.K., buddy?" Avi is concerned.

"Yes, thanks for the help. What would I do without my best friend?"

Yehudah's voice is then heard from down below: "Hey, if all is O.K., would you mind throwing the rope back down? I also don't want to stay here."

"Only if you promise to behave yourself," Shimi yells back. "We've had enough adventures."

Surfacing to Infinite Majesty

COMPARED TO THE CAVERN, the darkness of the night seems as bright as noon. Everyone breathes a sigh of relief to finally be back above-ground. Once they catch their breath, Yehudah takes them a few meters away to the peak of the hill. In the far distance, the Temple Mount can be seen.

"We learn that,

> At the time that Israel enters the synagogues and the study houses and responds 'May His great Name be blessed', the Holy One, blessed be He, nods His head and says, 'Happy is the **King** Whom they praise as such in His house. Woe to the **Father** that banished His sons.'[118]

"This *Gemara* starts with the word 'king' and ends with 'father' to teach us that at the time that the Temple was standing it was suitable to call Hashem with the name, 'King'. But later, at the time of the banishment, it is as if His Name is not complete and His Throne is not complete, and therefore it is only suitable to call him Father. And so, when the *Gemara* states, 'Happy is the King that they praise Him in His House', it is referring to

118 Tractate *Berachos* 3a.

the times of the Temple when He was called **King**. But since the time of the Banishment the *Gemara* does not call Hashem King, but rather states, 'Woe to the **Father** that has banished His sons.'[119]

"Rabbeinu Pinchas states,[120] 'Behold the Holy One, blessed be He, **does not want** to be called now by the name King,' and therefore instead of starting their text by calling Hashem 'King', the authors of ADON OLAM opened with the name '*Adon*'.

"Although we know that Hashem's rule is complete, we live in a world that does not seem consistent with our beliefs. How can we Jews openly state that Hashem is the King Who rules over all of our enemies when we presently see the ruins of Hashem's Holy Temple, which our enemies destroyed? *The Hidden Master* posits that this inconsistency is our biggest barrier to calling Hashem the undoubted King.

"Avraham's life was a constant battle with a similar inconsistency. Throughout the millennia, his children have experienced time and again this very same struggle. And, like Avraham, we have stubbornly and successfully held onto our faith in the face of all that seems to contradict it."

Personally, I am Offended

"HOLD ON just a minute, Yehudah. Obviously, Hashem not only knows about these contradictions, He is the cause of them. Why does Hashem have His servants experience such struggles? What are we supposed to glean from the confusion?" Natan is wondering.

Yehudah answers, "You all just climbed the rope. No one was lazy and tried to get out of the job. You were all keenly focused on one goal and were prepared to do whatever possible to accomplish that goal."

119 Maharasha.
120 *Siddur Shaar HaRachamim.*

"Of course we were," says Shimi. "We were fighting for our lives."

Shalom turns to him: "Don't you get what Yehudah is trying to tell us? When our personal Master (*Adon*) is not recognized by the world as King, it has to feel like a personal affront to us. We have to feel that our very lives depend upon our efforts to right the world's wrongs. The affront should sear through our very beings."

Avi is peering into the distance: "Look at the Temple Mount. Hashem's dwelling on Earth is destroyed, yet the world seems to continue as if nothing has happened."

"It seems that there is an all-night celebration underway somewhere around the Old City," remarks Yehudah, as a faint sound of music starts to waft over the hilltop from a nearby Arab village. "Hashem's blinded creatures celebrate right in the presence of the destruction. How is it possible to still celebrate when our personal Master is not recognized as King? ADON OLAM teaches us how the whole physical world screams to the Jew of Hashem's Will from which it is made. Yet the outside world turns a blind eye to the reality from which it constantly emanates.

"Since many of Hashem's commandments are based on the service in the Holy Temple, therefore it is presently impossible to fulfill all of His Will. These commandments must wait unfulfilled until the time that the Temple is rebuilt. We, the children of Israel, are called children to the Lord our God. As the child of the King, I am personally offended by a world that does not fulfill my Father's Will."

"Whether we were born Jewish or became Jewish later, we are all presently considered the spiritual descendents of Avraham," continues Avi from his own angle. "By calling Hashem *Adon*, Avraham showed us that we should feel offended when we see the world engage in the frivolities of life without first making sure to do the bidding of the Master of All. It should disturb us that the world does not act in a way that is calling Hashem King."

Shimi is indeed disturbed: "Are you suggesting that all Jews should sit on the floor in ashes and never smile? Should our service to Hashem consist of trudging sadly through life, pining after a Kingship that we hope will be recognized in the future?"

When Others Cry, Rabbi Akiva Laughs

AVI IS QUICK to clarify: "Not at all. We are told to serve Hashem with joy[121] and we are warned that evil will come upon us if we will serve Him without joy.[122]"

Yehudah adds: "In order to bring the Torah's definition of joy to life, *The Hidden Master* depicts an event which occurred 2,000 years ago, and which is brought down to us in the Talmud.[123] Take notice that his theatrical rendition of this ancient scene serves both as his conclusion to his comments on ADON OLAM's first stanza, as well as his lead into its second stanza— ואחרי ~ V'Acharei—When all is over and done with."

So Searching Soul, let's take The Hidden Master's lead and imagine ourselves back in the times of that scene. Come with me. It's time for you to meet some of our greatest Sages and learn what true happiness is . . . .

Four men are walking outside of a town:[124] Rabban Gamliel, Rabbi Elazar ben Azariah, Rabbi Yehoshua and Rabbi Akiva. They hear the sounds of masses of people laughing. Three of the great rabbis begin to cry, yet Rabbi Akiva is laughing.

Rabban Gamliel, Rabbi Elazar ben Azariah and Rabbi Yehoshua turn to Rabbi Akiva in astonishment: "Akiva ben Yosef, why are you laughing?"

"And you, my friends," responds Rabbi Akiva, "why are you crying?"

"These horrible Romans who bow down to idols and send up incense

---

121 Psalms 100:2.

122 Deuteronomy 28:47.

123 Tractate *Makkos* 24a–b.

124 Please refer to the Disclaimer.

to false gods are sitting in surety and tranquility, yet the footstool of our God, the Holy Temple, has recently been burned by these evil ones with fire. They sit in comfort and we know no peace. By destroying Hashem's Holy Abode, they have created a great desecration of Hashem's Holy Name. Our nation's whole purpose is to sanctify His Holy Name. With the destruction of the Temple, our greatest tool for bringing this sanctification has been removed. How will we sanctify Hashem's Name in the world when these lowly beasts have destroyed the sacred Temple? How can you suggest that we not cry?!"

Rabbi Akiva is not crushed by their argument: "This, my friends, is exactly why I am laughing! Although you are correct that the desecration is great in the present, I choose instead to look towards the future. For when we now see the peace of those who go against Hashem's Will, we can be sure that in the future the peace and surety of those who do His Will will be infinitely greater. While this great tragedy presently lowers the world's recognition of Hashem as King, we, His children, still know and live by the knowledge that Hashem is the only King. Even through destruction, we Jews live through the clouds of Creation in order to call His Name King: אזי מלך שמו נקרא ~ *Azai Melech Shemo nikra*. Now we experience destruction, but as we hold onto our faith we will eventually merit to bring the redemption and see it.

"The destruction of Hashem's Holy Temple will bring with it atonement for our transgressions. The tragedies that we now experience will eventually lead to the final Redemption. We will then experience the time when all evil will pass away and He alone will be recognized as King: ואחרי ככלות הכל לבדו ימלוך נורא ~ *V'Acharei kichlos hakol levado yimloch nora*."

And, Searching Soul, those are the words of the beginning statement of my next stanza, but let's finish the story first. Rabbi Akiva continues . . . .

We presently experience how the world desecrates Hashem's Name, but ultimately in its wake will come the greatest sanctification of Hashem. And so, my brothers, because you are now crying I am given the encouragement to laugh."

"And so," finishes off Yehudah, "we already have the tools to enable us to laugh at our troubles like Rabbi Akiva did. ADON OLAM can turn our tears into Rabbi Akiva's laughter."

"Yehudah, are you suggesting that ADON OLAM is telling us that Rabban Gamliel, Rabbi Elazar ben Azariah, and Rabbi Yehoshua were wrong to cry?" asks Shalom.

"Heaven forbid. These men were giants beyond our imagination. Their words and actions teach us how much we have to mourn the present lack of recognition of Hashem's Kingship. But Rabbi Akiva and ADON OLAM are bringing up a different point. Rabbi Akiva wanted to emphasize to his holy friends the importance of not only focusing on the present, but rather on the larger picture. Rabbi Akiva wanted to emphasize that which his friends also knew. His outlook highlighted to his friends and to us, the coming generations, that nothing can ever be considered as coming from outside of Hashem. Hashem willed all, and all is just a form of His always intentional Will.

"Rabbi Akiva's friends suffered when they heard the joy of their enemies because they were focused upon the then present desecration of Hashem's Name. But nothing could make Rabbi Akiva suffer. He viewed the never-haphazard present as a mere means towards the future. Such an attitude enabled him to laugh as he saw the present catastrophe as part of a greater non-catastrophic whole. For Rabbi Akiva even the then present destruction was viewed as a mechanism to arrive at a greater recognition of Hashem. This outlook not only nullified his pain and fear but actually caused his laughter."

Deaden Your Pain With Laughing Gas

"I CERTAINLY WOULDN'T have been able to laugh, if I would hear my enemy gloating over my sorrow." Shimi is still puzzled.

"Rabbi Akiva was able to laugh in the face of the enemy," explains Yehudah, "because he understood that their peace was temporary and that their surety was false. He was keenly aware that the only finite efforts worth expending are those used to serve the Infinite. The Romans later punished Rabbi Akiva by flaying his flesh off his dying body with red-hot rakes. His 'crime' was teaching Torah publicly, attaching to the Infinite. As his life was leaving his mangled, bleeding body, he declared Hashem's Oneness: He said 'Shema Yisrael, Hashem Eloheinu, Hashem Echad—Hear, O Israel, Hashem our God, Hashem is One.'[125]

"His actions speak to all future generations. His life is a lesson to every Jew that it is a merit to be serving Hashem even if at times that means enduring terrible hardships which Hashem deems proper to send our way. Rabbi Akiva's words speak to us even now to teach us that 'It must become our will to do Your Will.'[126] With this staunch faith we can face the struggles of this clouded existence with laughter. Through internalizing this great lesson we will have fulfilled ADON OLAM's entreaty to call Hashem King. Our lives will then testify that we, like Rabbi Akiva, are happy that we merited to be commanded to follow Hashem's Will, as we strive to never falter. In this way all of our finite efforts to serve Hashem in this lowly world have real and eternal meaning."

Avi sums up Yehudah's long explanation somewhat differently: "On the other hand, the actions of the heathens are vapid and lead to oblivion. Rabbi Akiva's words and actions shout at us through the barriers of time. They inform us that we can laugh at our difficulties by focusing on the eternal goal of becoming one with Hashem's Will. He instructed us to laugh at the pettiness of the enemy. For, the more they cheer and roar over their meaningless goals and faiths of folly, the more they will fade into eternal oblivion. On the other hand, the more we attach to Hashem's Will, the more we will laugh as we become one with Hashem's Infinity."

---

125 The incident is from *Berachos* 61b, which quotes *Shema* from Deuteronomy 6:4.

126 Based on a similar statement from *Berachos* 17a.

"O.K. guys," Yehudah now snaps out briskly, "grab those swords of yours. It's time to ambush the enemy."

Sneaking Up on Avraham's Worst Enemy

SEARCHING SOUL, my words still hold another important message for you. You now see Yehudah turning right at the bottom of the hill to lead the guys onto a lonely, overgrown, almost imperceptible path that seemingly goes nowhere. Something about this wild trail speaks of ancient times—you wonder whether anyone has been on this path since the days of Avraham Avinu . . . Mist wafts through the trees, while vines hug both sides of the long-forgotten trail. From under their trudging feet you hear the crackle of breaking sticks and the crushing of leaves. To the east the sky is starting to show some orange hues, as sunrise approaches. This enchanted night is coming to an end, but hang around. As they walk, Yehudah is preparing the group to understand yet another treasure buried in my words.

"Tonight you all got a glimpse into the world which Avraham knew to be reality. We now understand that he recognized all of physical existence to be just a different form of Hashem's Will. Now that the night is coming to an end, let's try to use what we learned together. Let's try to understand how Avraham would have viewed this ancient path that we are walking on.

"As Avraham would walk on his path through life, every dry leaf that would crunch under his feet would shout to him of Hashem's Will, from whence it came. He would feel the ground under his feet and reflect upon how the whole world was being recreated each moment anew. For Avraham, Hashem's presence was extraordinarily tangible, yet he knew that he was walking alone on his path."

"How could he have felt alone while at the same time constantly being aware of Hashem's presence?" Shalom brings up the obvious contradiction.

Yehudah stops and turns to the left. He is facing a prickly pile of vines that looks like a bush, but everyone senses that there is something lurking underneath those crawling, prickly vines. Avi starts to gently pull away the vines, and slowly a hideous relic of the past appears.

Shimi cries out, amazed, "It's an ancient idol. What a find. Hey, let's bring it to the museum. We are going to be rich!"

Avi corrects him: "It's not going to any museum. I had my fill of idolatry. I'll destroy it."

"I looked this figurine up in an archeological book," Yehudah says quietly. "It appears to me that it is from the early Canaanite period."

"So it's from the same time as Avraham," Natan points out.

"You got it," smiles Yehudah. "Now we are going to put together all that we have learned so far tonight. Think of what Avraham *Avinu* would have thought while walking his path in life and stumbling upon this false god."

For a few moments no one in the group speaks. Ovadiah is deep in thought. He stares angrily at the ancient form of the idol in front of him. It's about his height, chiseled from limestone that has grayed over the millennia. Ovadiah focuses on the light given off by a glowworm perched on the jagged edge of the idol's shattered nose, and muses, "When we saw the destroyed Temple, we felt pain. Now, here I am in Avraham's world, and I feel Avraham's pain as I stand here in front of this false god. Avraham walked alone with Hashem in a world that did not understand what he understood. On the way to this spot I also started to feel, like Avraham, that every crackling leaf and stone speaks of its Divine Source. After what we have learned together from ADON OLAM tonight, every detail of the finite world reminds me of the Infinite King of all."

Avi rounds out the picture: "But the same sticks and stones that helped Avraham recognize Hashem became the stumbling blocks of the people around him. Those stones which Avraham used in order to smash barriers were misused by his generation to build barriers."

Shimi has a look of wonder on his face: "What happened to me tonight? I am surprising even myself, but I must admit it, I actually feel Avraham's loneliness. For Avraham to look at this idol must have been a searing pain in his soul. He was the lone servant of Hashem who was painfully aware that no one else was willing to take up the battle as a personal challenge."

Avi says, "Avraham needed the world to stop its foolishness. His battle will never end until the whole world becomes constantly aware of the spiritual Source of all."

Ovadiah says feelingly, "Avraham's life was a struggle to bring closer the time when, as ADON OLAM states, 'all will call Him King'. He could not ignore such an affront to his personal Master. He could not rest until the whole world recognized Hashem's Kingship. He would leave no stone unturned until the Source of the stones of this idol was recognized by all as King."

Avi, their expert on world religions, makes a final comment on the subject: "And, guys, idolatry has not stopped, and atheism is at an all-time high. In today's 'Me Generation', worship of the self is the standard. I feel like a lonely servant. Don't you?"

Yehudah adds: "So we now understand why the authors started with *Adon*. We can now only call Hashem our personal Master, *Adon*, and still not the recognized King, *Melech*. Avraham's painful call of *Adon* continues to pierce through the millennia to us, his children. It teaches us to never stop fighting with our swords of Torah until we bring the time when the whole world will call Hashem King. אזי מלך שמו נקרא ~ *Azai Melech Shemo nikra.*"

The Great Switchover

SHIMI IS STILL TRYING to pierce the balloon, more out of habit than for any other reason: "Impressive, I admit it. I am touched, but I still don't understand why this project of getting the world to call Hashem's Name King is the job of only one nation. Why couldn't the understanding of Avraham become accepted by individuals who remained within their own nations? Why is this job only that of Avraham's descendants?"

"Last night," replies Yehudah, "I came out here and etched the answer to just this question on the idol."

Five flashlights immediately start scanning the body of the ancient idol. Ovadiah is the first to find the crude etching on the figurine's foundation, but there is a sense in his words that he is perplexed by the etchings.

"It says here '*Naaseh v'nishma*', We will do all of Hashem's Will and only after we already do it will we strive to understand that Will.[127] This is how the Jews responded to HaShem at Mount Sinai right before they received the Torah. If they had not responded with these words, then they never would have received it. How do these words explain why there has to be one nation serving Hashem, as opposed to simply individuals doing so from among the multitude of nations?"

Avi explains, "Yehudah etched that passage on the foundation for a reason. Avraham was starting the foundation of something new. He was not the continuation of his original nation. He knew that there had to be a new foundation. He was aware that he was making a complete switch. He was not just adding something new to something old, but rather he knew that he needed to remove all of the old."

"Why remove all of the old?" persists Shimi. "Was there nothing of his past culture that was redeeming? Don't other societies also have something to offer?"

"To themselves, maybe," says Yehudah, "but to the new and complete type of service that Avraham was forming, no. Until the Jews agreed to accept the whole Torah at Mount Sinai, anyone who wished to serve Hashem could do so on his or her own impetus. The only obligation G-d had placed upon the descendents of Noach was to stay away from evil. Until Avraham, this minimal level of service was sufficient. "And to this day," Avi continues, "this type of service can still be

127 Exodus 24:7.

done by individuals from among the nations. They can fulfill their obligations and add whatever additional service meets their fancy. They do not need to completely abandon their past. Removal of a few evil practices is all that is required. They can do this type of basic service while still being part of their own nations.

"But Avraham was planting a seed that would bloom only when his children unequivocally accepted the entire Torah on Mount Sinai by responding *naaseh v'nishma*. There, at Sinai, the Jews made the Great Switchover. It was there that they, as a nation, started to call Hashem their King."

The Ultimate Navigator

"SO AVI, what you're saying is that *naaseh v'nishma* actually means that we have chosen to trust Hashem completely and allow only Him to make the decisions regarding how we should serve Him. From that moment on, our ancestors recognized that a servant neither dictates nor decides how to serve the King. At Sinai, Avraham's children came to the realization that in order to call Hashem King one first needs to trust Hashem and accept His entire Will, whether one understands it all or not."

"Right on, Natan," says Avi. "Let me tell you all something that happened to me. The day I finished my conversion I had a very special meeting with the *Rosh HaYeshivah*, in which he officially accepted me as a new student in the *yeshivah*. Before I left his office he taught me something that I will carry with me for the rest of my life."

Back to the yeshivah administration office two years before.

The Rosh HaYeshivah is pleasant and inviting: "Avraham Ben Avraham. I like the name. Well, young man, you have made quite a major stride today. Welcome to the team. I gladly accept you to our *yeshivah*."

"I won't let the *Rosh HaYeshivah* down. I intend to use this opportunity to its fullest."

"I have a message for you that I think will help you to never stop striving for the heights. Never forget that from Sinai and beyond the Jew constantly needs to answer one question: 'So what are you doing now?' You just finished the previous commandment: *Mazel Tov.*[128] But what are you doing now to serve Hashem? Even the sleep or rest that we take must be with the consideration of regaining strength to be able to continue to serve Hashem, and you must serve Him according to His rules, not yours."

"The *Rosh HaYeshivah* taught me in a few sentences what Judaism's attitude towards proper service is. It's not enough to do only what you feel is right, what you sense is right and what you think is proper. The servant neither dictates nor decides what service to perform and how to do it. What I learned that day, as I entered the *yeshivah,* was that Judaism is never-ending service based upon handing over the reins of service completely to the Boss."

Neither Day nor Night

OVADIAH TURNS OVER the message of Avi's story in his mind, and then notices that it is becoming light. This reminds him of something . . . .

"I have a similar story. Nearly a year ago, not long after my father's murder, I arrived at the *yeshivah.* As I was trying to put myself back together and find myself, I was also struggling with the magnitude of new responsibilities that Jewish Law seemed to cast upon me. During that period, Rabbi Perlman pulled me aside for a conversation. He explained to me that for the Jew there really are no voluntary activities. Everything in

128 Congratulations.

life is either obligatory, or not allowed. He quoted our Sages, saying: 'For the words of the Torah are our lives and the length of our days, and in them we will concentrate and be busied day and night.'[129] He told me that if you find a time that is neither day nor night, then you are free of your obligation to busy yourself with the Torah. Since there is no such time, we come to understand that our very lives depend upon the Torah every single moment. Just like you have no choice about breathing, so too, you lead your life knowing that you have no choice but to constantly learn and follow Hashem's Will."

"It seems to me that Avi and I got the same message. In order to be a good Jew you have to hand over the paths of your life to the Ultimate Navigator. That's how we call Hashem King."

Understanding That You Don't Need to Understand

"So, GUYS," says Yehudah, "Shimi asked, 'Why only one nation? Why couldn't the mentality of Avraham be that of individuals while they remained within their own nations?' Now that we heard these two stories does anyone have any answers?"

Natan speaks up first: "Hashem first told Avraham that he needed to leave his land, his nation and his father's home.[130] Only then did Hashem tell him that He would make him into a great nation.[131] What he was starting was new. It was the basis of a new nation, not the outcropping of a previous nation. If Avraham were to start a nation that would just be the continuation of a different value system, then the old system might taint the new nation's soul. This nation's basis was what you etched on this idol's base. To the Jew there can be nothing less than complete subservience to Hashem's Will. Other, contradicting

---

129   From the blessings before Kri'as Shema in the evening prayers.

130   Genesis 12:1.

131   Genesis 12:2.

world outlooks need to be viewed as improper foreign deities, just like that idol in front of us."

"In short," Shalom gives his own analysis, "a proper Jew views anything short of total service as verging upon idolatrous behavior."

"And so *naaseh v'nishma*—Se will do and then we will understand—means that we chose to not scrutinize Hashem's Will because we learned to trust Him no matter what. We became willing to subject our own will to His. We chose to busy ourselves with this Will all the days and nights of our lives. This is what it means to be a descendent of Avraham; this is the nature of the new nation," Yehudah says triumphantly.

Avi wants to make sure that an important point is absolutely clear: "But, guys, you should keep in mind that although Avraham was starting a new separate nation, he did not start a new race. His nation was and still is open for all who wish to enter. Anyone who desires can still make the decision to do just as I and others have done and become part of the Holy Nation. All one has to do is to join those who live by the words '**we will do, then we will hear**'."

Yehudah says, "We're done here. It's time to get back to civilization. Maybe someday I will need to bring some other guys out here. In the meantime let's cover up this disgraceful thing."

The members of the group carefully conceal the disfigured idol. Vines are pulled from all ends to cover it up so no one will notice it. Avi, who towers over the repulsive figurine, gently drapes the longest vines over its broken face.

Exit, but Don't Leave Anything Behind

AS YEHUDAH LEADS, Avi and Ovadiah walk side by side behind the rest.

"You really seem to have understood a lot from tonight," says Avi.

"Don't think that I don't still have more questions."

"And don't think that Yehudah is done with you just yet, Ovadiah. There are many more stanzas to go. ADON OLAM has a lot more to offer you. We're just beginning."

"It is amazing what our Sages put into a few short words."

The rest of the group seems to be deep in thought as well. There is not much talking as they retrace their steps over the various terrains. They pass the secret sepulcher. The cinders from the bonfire still waft their burnt scent through the early-morning air. Finally they spot the Stark launching pad.

Upon arriving at the edge of the pine forest, just before the bank of the river and the makeshift rope bridge, Yehudah stops and says to them,

"Please, everyone, before we leave, put a hand on the forest floor and grab a handful of the pine needles and broken twigs. Feel them in your palm and then let them fall through your fingers to the forest floor. These pine needles and sticks lived and died. Nothing was created without a reason. Everything has a purpose. Now they are dead and nothing is left but their shells which just slipped through your fingers. You may still be wondering about yourselves. What significance will you have when you are no longer alive? Will your significance slip through the fingers of time and out of existence? The answer starts in the next stanza of ADON OLAM:

ואחרי ככלות הכל, לבדו ימלוך נורא,
והוא היה והוא הווה והוא יהיה בתפארה

~

V'Acharei kichlos hakol, levado yimloch nora,
V'Hu hayah v'Hu hoveh v'Hu yiheyeh b'tifarah

~

And afterwards when everything will cease to be,
only then will He reign alone in awe,
and He was and He is and He will be in splendor (tifarah).

"With that ethereal thought, let's cross the stream."

When all are safely across, Ovadiah turns around and stops

for a last long glimpse of the small stream. Yehudah approaches him.

"We've got to go, buddy."

"I know, Yehudah. I was just thinking about streams, and rivers. So much water just passes through rivers and is carried away as if it had never been. I don't want to be like that. I want my life to have meant something. I don't want to leave this forest and forget what I learned. Now that you have brought me to this new world I don't feel that I can leave. I want it to affect me for the rest of my life. Help me take this world of ADON OLAM with me and not leave anything behind."

"Don't worry, Ovadiah. The rest of ADON OLAM is all about making the words of the first stanza real in your own personal life. Our Sages handed over to us messages that remain alive and won't die for you when you leave this forest. They were meant to be a guide for all those who search for meaning. Hold on tightly to what you have learned so far. We still have a lot to learn together before you can really internalize these concepts. Come on. Let's go. We have to get to Shul[132] for morning prayers.

So far, Searching Soul, we have used my words to start you on your search to unearth the depths of meaning in your life, but my holy authors knew that the messages which they infused in my first words were far too compact for you to fully appreciate on their own. Being bombarded with such an array of thoughts and ideas can sometimes thicken the clouds. They therefore chose to expand my text to enable searching souls like yours to grasp the seemingly unfathomable. To reword what Yehudah just said to Ovadiah, the rest of my words were composed to take some of these esoteric concepts that you have just encountered and make them applicable, thus helping you see through those obscuring clouds.

Let's continue your search . . . .

---

132   Another term for synagogue.

SECTION TWO

V'ACHAREI:
When All Is Over And Done With

*Y*ES SEARCHING SOUL, *it's me again,* ADON OLAM. *I've been waiting to see if you would turn that page. Seeing that you did, I know now that you are serious about your search for meaning. I'm glad to have you back and won't let you down. Before we move forward, let's recap what we already know and then, together, we will go yet further in your search for meaning.*

My first words gave you the beginnings of understanding why Hashem created the physical world. Remember, Hashem's 'desire' for Creation was not like any desires of your own. Obviously it was not a craving to fill any void in the Infinite, but rather was and is the completely benevolent wish to bestow good upon His creations. So Hashem created and formed His completely spiritual will into a seemingly finite physical package, which is your cloudy world of physical existence.

Do you remember why it is only through the clouds of this finite world that you can achieve closeness to the Infinite?

I see that you are learning well, Searching Soul. You are correct. If you were given closeness to your Creator as a free gift, you would not have earned it and therefore it would not really be yours.

We also learned that the clouds of confusion of this physical world can only be pierced by using Hashem's Infinite Wisdom, from which they were created in the first place.

So when we learn that "Hashem looked into His Torah (His Infinite Wisdom) and through it created the world",[133] *we conclude that not only is it through the Torah that Hashem creates these clouds of physicality, but also that the Torah is the only tool to help you peel these clouds away.*

Not satisfied? Still feeling lost in the clouds of seemingly senseless suffering? I know exactly what you mean. My next words are the embodiment of the answer to that hollow meaninglessness that has plagued the human soul throughout history.

Do you really think that the Members of the Great Assembly were going to forget about man's trials and travails and leave questions unanswered? Do you think they would have left the future generations of Hashem's people to become a mob of aimlessly wandering orphans without writing the messages that would bring order to the bewilderment produced by the sagas of time? You know better than that! And so my authors composed my second stanza in order to clarify just how and why these blemishes of both history and the present fit into Hashem's greater scheme.

---

133   Zohar, *Parshas Bereishis.*

I was written by those who knew that you, along with the rest, would eventually get fed up with the array of empty answers that the non-Torah World handed down to you as to why bad things happen to good people and peoples. I see written on your soul that you have had it with the vapid clichés of these so called "religious" groups. So here I am. My words will guide you away from the clichés and towards the Torah's truthful and meaningful answers.

Empty answers bring with them a feeling of gloom, yet Hashem commands us to serve Him with joy.[134] So come with me, my friend, and learn how to expel your feelings of gloom. I have many more adventures in store for you.

It Takes Guts

*B*UT, SEARCHING SOUL, *I am warning you, it takes a lot of guts to swallow the real answers. In order to digest the answers, you must first learn to let go of some of the standardly-held definitions of freedom. Once you have discarded these errant thoughts, their place will be taken by a type of servitude that you may have never before understood. You will soon discover that it is precisely through proper servitude that you can find real freedom from the emptiness that you are presently experiencing. As you come to understand my next words, you will gain clarity of how all tragedies and difficulties fit precisely and splendidly into the most perfectly planned puzzle. Together we will go to both exciting and terrifying places to obtain this clarity. I hope you do not have a weak stomach. So if you*

---

134   Psalms 100:2.

dare to know the real answers, let's start to look into
my next words . . . .

וְאַחֲרֵי כִּכְלוֹת הַכֹּל, לְבַדּוֹ יִמְלֹךְ נוֹרָא
וְהוּא הָיָה וְהוּא הֹוֶה, וְהוּא יִהְיֶה בְּתִפְאָרָה

~

V'Acharei kichlos hakol, levado yimloch nora
V'hu haya vehu hoveh vehu yihyeh b'tifarah.

~

And when all evil will have completed its purpose,
then He will reign alone, an unchallenged Kingship,
He was, is, and will always be in the perfect
combination of splendor.[135]

Off to the Desert

IT'S BEEN TWO WEEKS since the nighttime walk
in the forest. Yehudah has spent much of that
time in Rabbeinu Reuven's study going over the words
ואחרי ככלות הכל לבדו ימלוך נורא ~ *V'Acharei kichlos hakol, levado*
yimloch nora ~ And when all evil will be over and done with,
then He will reign alone, an unchallenged Kingship. After
each meeting, Yehudah sits to recap the main points with Avi.
Together they have been planning how to give over these messages to the others. Yehudah approaches the *Yeshivah* dining
hall, where Natan, Shalom, Shimi and Ovadiah are just sitting
down for their Thursday morning breakfast. As they are pouring
themselves milk for their cereal, Yehudah walks in.

Natan greets him with a hearty, "*Baruch mechayeh hameisim!*[136]
We were giving up hope on ever seeing you again. Where have
you been?"

"Oh, I've just been wasting time as usual," Yehudah responds

---

135 In order to understand why the Hebrew was translated in this manner, please refer to the
Disclaimer.

136 Literal translation: Blessed is He Who revives the dead. This statement is made whenever
someone hasn't seen an acquaintance for a long time.

flippantly. But the boys don't fall for that. By now, they know better.

"Well, actually," Yehudah continues after their laughter has subsided, "I have been preparing the second stanza of ADON OLAM."

Shimi groans, despite the spark of a new adventure alight in his eyes. "Oh no, another walk in the woods."

"No, we are not going to the woods. We are going on a journey to understand what redemption means. The best way to do that is to really understand what it means to leave bondage and to enter into a state of freedom. So instead of going to the woods we are going to the desert."

"The desert!!!???" Images of vast stretches of barren land, accompanied by parched throats, go through the minds of some of the young men, those who have never experienced the desert firsthand.

"Yes, the desert, and there we will meet our ancestors as they are leaving Egyptian bondage and entering the desert just over 3,300 years ago. We will learn about the Mouth of Freedom."

"The Mouth of Freedom?" Shalom is puzzled. "I never heard of freedom being referred to as having a mouth."

"Yes you have!" says Yehudah. "But before I show you where, let's first try to understand what it was that the members of the Great Assembly intended when they wrote the second stanza of ADON OLAM.

"Imagine that we're back on the ancient Temple Mount. Think for a moment of the thoughts and words that might have gone through the minds of our ancient Sages that could have prompted them to write the words of the first half of the second stanza. ואחרי ככלות הכל לבדו ימלוך נורא ~ *V'Acharei kichlos hakol levado yimloch nora.* We'll see deeper meanings in this pretty soon, but for now we'll translate that as 'After all will have completed its purpose, only then will Hashem be able to reign alone, an unchallenged Kingship.'

When It's All Over

YEHUDAH GETS his own breakfast, and then continues: "So what seems to have prompted ADON OLAM's illustrious authors to write this second stanza? Together we already learned that their words in the first stanza were written to teach us how the world came into being through and because of the Torah. There they successfully expressed the central role of the Torah-observant Jew in this Torah-created world, but as we know, they did not finish their composition there. To understand what prompted them to write their next words, we must keep in mind that these Sages stood on the brink of a major turning point in history. They knew that Hashem's Chosen People would soon embark upon a journey through a strange world that they had never before experienced, and that there they would experience Hashem concealing Himself, and there would be no prophecy.

"Their next words gave us messages that have successfully enabled our ancestors to endure thousands of years of longing for Hashem's returned Presence without losing hope of the final reckoning and redemption. ADON OLAM's second stanza conveys to the Jews of all generations that their painful longing will eventually come to an end by using the Torah to reveal Hashem from His state of hiding. These are the messages hidden in the words, 'After all (הכל ~ hakol) will have completed its purpose, only then will Hashem be able to reign alone, an unchallenged Kingship.'"

"But what is it that will have completed its purpose? What is hakol?" Shalom asks.

"Think hard for a moment. Haven't we already learned together other texts by these same authors, in which they use the word hakol (all)?"

Natan speaks up. "We learned during our nighttime walk in the woods that in the blessings before the recital of Shema Yisrael, the members of the Great Assembly composed the words, "Blessed are you, Hashem, King of the universe Who forms light and creates darkness, makes peace and creates **everything** (*hakol*)."

"Excellent!" Yehudah responds. "And you remember there that we showed how the word 'all' is a signal word for evil."

Avi, who has just come into the dining room, sits down with the rest of the guys and takes the hint:

"You showed that evil is not some force outside of Hashem, but rather it is the ability for us to make free will decisions. Without this ability there is no purpose for Creation."

Yehudah welcomes him with a nod. "Exactly! Now, let's understand this a little further by delving into the words of King Solomon in his book of Ecclesiastes. There he uses the same term *hakol*: 'The last word, when all (*hakol*) has been considered: Fear God and keep His commandments, for that is the whole of man.'

"King Solomon was the wisest, richest, and most powerful man of his time. He had investigated everything from gluttony to self sacrifice, from prowess to meekness, from battle to peace-seeking, and he wrote Ecclesiastes to inform all generations of the futility of **all** human desires.

"When human desires differ from those of Hashem, when we choose our will over His, then, King Solomon tells us, our will is *hevel havalim* **hakol** *havel*. 'Futility of futilities, **everything** is futile.' The 'everything' that is being described is our misguided whims and desires. **All** misconceptions which lead us to choose something over Hashem's Will are what is called **evil**."

When White Becomes Black

"BUT I DON'T GET why the members of the Great Assembly, instead of just writing 'evil' like it appears in the verse, used the word 'all'. Shalom wants to know.

"I think I got the answer," says Ovadiah. "Since we are so misguided, we may consider some of our deviant thoughts not to be evil. ADON OLAM is telling us through the words of King

Solomon that absolutely everything that we conceive of, if it is not conducive to fear of Hashem or doing His commandments, is absolutely evil. All of it, even that which you now perceive as white, is actually black if it goes against the Torah."

Avi, as usual, is pleased with Ovadiah, and adds his own summary: "So we see that ADON OLAM seems to just be mirroring King Solomon's message. From him we learned that after all of man's futile, misguided and evil whims have been considered, we will come to the final conclusion that we must 'fear God and keep His commandments, for that is the whole of man.'"

Yehudah continues the thought. "On the same note, ADON OLAM states, then, that *After all—that is, evil—will have completed its purpose*, or once all of our whims have been proven to us to be nothing other than futile evil schemes, then we will recognize that only His Torah and its commandments will reign eternally. And it is precisely this recognition that King Solomon states is the whole purpose of man being put into this world."

Shalom goes back to the Hebrew version of the line in question. "So what exactly did the members of the Great Assembly mean when they wrote in ADON OLAM that after we have recognized evil for what it really is, then לבדו ימלוך נורא ~ *levado yimloch nora* ~ He will reign alone in trepidation?'"

The bell rings to send the hundreds of young men to their Torah classes. All, that is, except for the group sitting around Yehudah . . . .

The Mouth of Freedom

SUDDENLY A DEEP HONK is heard from the street just outside the dining hall window. Yehudah opens the curtain and motions with his hand to the army mountain-terrain jeep waiting outside. It is really out of place, dusty and weather-beaten. This does not look like a *Yeshivah*-mobile.

"It's time to go," Yehudah says, "but not to the classrooms upstairs. We have a different classroom to go to. We're off to the Judean Desert."

"Hey, I've got to go to class," protests Shimi.

Avi slaps him on the back: "No you don't. If Yehudah says that you are going to the desert, then the administration lets us, and if not, Yehudah will make them let us."

All laugh, and get ready to go, saying their after-blessings and making their way out to the vehicle, reassured by Yehudah's explanations:

"Don't worry, I packed water, and my wife made and packed food. Hop on. I would have taken my dilapidated van but I thought that that way we would never make it home. Meet our driver, Boaz. He is an old friend of mine who works for the Border Patrol. I arranged with his commander to give him the day free. You see, his commander, whom we all lovingly call Pharaoh, owes me a big favor."

"How did you arrange this? We can't just take an army jeep!" Shimi wonders aloud.

For this he gets another slap on the back from Avi: "You're new to this. Stick around and you will see that Yehudah can do just about anything, and knows just about everybody. Not only that, but the Holy Land is his classroom, and He knows every inch of it like the back of his hand."

The jeep leaves Jerusalem, and goes down the Maaleh Adumim[137] road, behind Mishor Adumim,[138] to the base of a Tank Corps unit. It then turns right and slithers down what is meant to be a path, and heads up and down rocky mountains that become increasingly more smooth and desert-like.

Yehudah stops the driver: "Boaz, stop here, please. You can have the next three hours off. We will meet you at the hideaway that you and I have for years called the Hanging Mountain."

Boaz pulls away, leaving the guys with nothing in sight except for dirt and rocks.

Shimi looks around: "It looks a lot like the moon out here."

137   A city in the Judean Desert.

138   An industrial area, also in the Judean Desert.

Shalom agrees with him. "Sure does. I wonder what Yehudah has up his sleeve now."

Ovadiah is also staring: "What a complete wilderness. I can imagine Moses coming over a hill like that one over there."

Yehudah breaks into their observations:

"*The Hidden Master* starts its section on the second stanza by bringing a *kina* from the end of the *Kinos of Tisha B'Av*:[139] 'The Torah, the Testimony and the Order of the Temple Service were taught to me when I departed from Egypt. May I obtain gladness and joy, and let sorrow and sighing flee away when I return to Jerusalem.' There Chacham Yashar tells us that when we come to understand what our ancestors learned and did in order to enable the final Exodus from Egypt, we will have hope of understanding how we can bring the final redemption. This, he tells us, is the message of the first half of the second stanza of ADON OLAM."

As the young men walk along, through the dry soil and pebbles of the Judean Desert, with their backpacks heavily laden with water, they get increasingly hot, even though it's early spring. But this is a study tour, and Yehudah doesn't forget this.

"We think that we understand what it was that our ancestors, the slaves of Egypt, got rid of when they embarked on their journey through the desert. Can anyone tell me what was the evil that they left behind?" He asks.

"The Egyptians, of course," says Ovadiah.

"So you think that when they entered the desert what they got rid of was the Egyptians?! What is it that we presently have to get rid of in order to bring the final redemption?"

"Beats me," Shimi huffs. "Maybe this heat."

Shalom, with the sweat pouring down from his carrot-top brow to his pale, freckled face, looks quite out of place here. "Instead of trying to have us decipher hidden messages, maybe you could enlighten us as to what you are referring to?"

"If we look closely at the text of the Torah," says Yehudah, "we will find that there is a hidden prerequisite to the Egyptians being destroyed and then being left behind at the shores

---

139 A *kina* is a lamentation. Many lamentations were written for Tishah B'Av, and collected in a book, for use on that sad day which commemorates the date of the destruction of both the First and the Second Temples.

of the sea. In order for us to better understand ADON OLAM, we need to understand what our ancestors really left on the shores of that sea. From the sea they went to Sinai to receive instruction on what is expected of those released from slavery, and the same is true for us. Only once we understand what we need to leave behind, can we start to understand how to achieve the final redemption."

Suddenly a small dust devil, which is like a mini-tornado—only a few meters high, and, like its name, carries nothing more than dust and small bits of debris—goes right through the group. When it passes, they wipe off their now-muddy brows. Then Yehudah continues:

"Before our ancestors could embark upon freedom at the Sea of Reeds, something very basic had to change in their world outlook. Once that would change, then, just like a cloud passes and dissipates, the Egyptians would fizzle away to nothingness as if they had never been."

Ovadiah continues to look at the disappearing dust devil as he continues to walk. Avi notices this.

"Hey, Ovadiah, stop looking off into space and pay attention. You need to look where you put your feet in the desert. There are sudden cliffs and ravines, like the one you almost fell into right now."

And indeed, in front of them is an opening in the earth that looks like a giant mouth whose length spans more than a kilometer, and whose depth seems the same.

Ovadiah is rueful: "Oh, thanks." He peers down into the abyss. "Wow. Look at this."

"I jokingly call this place Pi HaChiros, 'the Mouth of Freedom'," says Yehudah. "That's the name of the location that our ancestors reached, after turning around at Eitam upon leaving Egypt. Through perceiving what our ancestors accomplished at that impasse in Eitam, Chacham Ovadiah Yashar enables us to begin to understand what the members of the Great Assembly meant in ADON OLAM's words נורא ימלוך לבדו הכל ככלות ואחרי ~ *V'Acharei kichlos hakol levado yimloch nora* ~ After the finishing of all evil, only then will Hashem reign in a way where His awe will be recognized. Or, as we mentioned already, after all (*hakol*) will have completed its purpose, only then will Hashem be able to reign alone, in an unchallenged Kingship. Before crossing the Sea of Reeds, they needed to cross an impasse like this one, which we will soon cross as well. But for them, ropes, hooks and clips were not enough. They needed to leave something behind them. What was it that they needed to leave, and why?"

Leaving Egypt and Going to Tahiti [140]

BEFORE PREPARING TO RAPPEL into the ravine, they lie down to catch their breath, drink, and eat. The scene looks like that of a bunch of young men tanning at a beach, but there is no body of water in sight. However, resting their bodies does not necessarily mean resting their minds as far as Yehudah is concerned:

"All of the miracles that led to the children of Israel leaving Egypt," he tells them, "were not performed just in order to release them from slavery to Pharaoh and then let them take a vacation in Tahiti. The Torah states that when Moshe was instructed by Hashem to demand that Pharaoh release the Children of Israel, he was instructed to say as the messenger of Hashem 'Let My son go, that he may serve Me . . .' [141] What was that service?

"The acceptance of the Torah as Hashem previously said to Moshe, [142] 'When you have brought the people out of Egypt, you shall serve God upon this mountain.'" Natan snaps out an answer.

But Yehudah surprises them all: "Close, but no cigar. Not only were Pharaoh's slaves leaving Egypt in order to serve Hashem on Mount Sinai, but, more precisely, these slaves

---

140 The next few pages are based upon a lecture heard from Rabbi Zeev Leff. The lecture was eventually written up in his book, *Outlooks and Insights on the Weekly Torah Portion*, published by Artscroll Mesorah, wherein it can be found on page 95, entitled "A Three Days' Journey in the Desert".

141 Exodus 4:23.

142 Exodus 3:12.

needed to get to a mentality where they would be able to accept the Torah on that mountain, as sons of Hashem."

"What's the difference?" asks Shalom.

Yehudah answers, "In order to understand, let's look closer at the demand to leave Egypt. In Exodus (5:1–3) it says, 'Afterwards Moshe and Aharon went in, and told Pharaoh, Thus says the Lord God of Israel, Let my people go, that they may hold a feast to Me in the wilderness. And Pharaoh said, Who is the Lord, that I should obey His voice to let Israel go? I know not the Lord, nor will I let Israel go. And they said, The God of the Hebrews has met with us: let us go, we pray thee, **three days journey** into the desert, and sacrifice to the Lord our God.'"

"Pharaoh's answer does not quite respond to the demand." Natan is being incisive, as usual. "He was told to let Hashem's people go, and he responded 'nor will I let Israel go.' No mention was made of them being specifically Hashem's people."

"That's all that bothers you?" asks Shimi. "Let's face it. Moshe had no intention of being a conduit for a year of miraculous plagues on Egypt, which were to debilitate the largest superpower the world had seen, for the purpose of having a three-day picnic in the desert. Hashem said that they would serve Him on the mountain and, also, they were told[143] that they would be brought to Canaan, the land that their forefathers were promised, which was to be a lasting homeland. So what's this business with the three-day hike? My rabbis taught me when I was a kid that Moshe and his Torah are true, so now we need to understand how it could be that Moshe was not lying when he requested three days. Hey, Avi, please send over another cold Coke. I think I am about to faint."

Yehudah smiles happily. "Both of you have very good questions, but the questions do not stop there. Why were we taken out of Egypt in the first place, and what was going on in the minds of our ancestors when they were leaving Egypt? All of these questions can be answered by closely studying what really happened on the third day of the slaves' escape from Egyptian bondage. From there we can understand the depth of ADON OLAM. *The Hidden Master* describes it like this:

143 Exodus 3:17.

Free at Last [144]

THERE THEY ARE. Millions of our ancestors are free at last. It was a brutal bondage unlike any the world had ever experienced. As they flee through the sand, you can see that what they endured would forever be etched on the souls of their new nation. They are filled with hope as they leave the never-before breached borders of ancient Egypt. Three days have passed since Hashem came down and slaughtered the firstborn of Egypt, and the Hebrews are now at Eitam.[145] They leave their slavery behind as a terrible memory. Their hope is to build the nation of the Master of All, but have they really left Pharaoh behind? Hashem has one more test in store for these tired, tattered slaves, the sons of slaves, before they are allowed to continue upon their journey to receive His Torah.

You see that Moshe our Teacher is now standing facing the people. He has been instructed by the Master of All to tell the people to turn back in the direction of Egypt. What an unbearable letdown. What do you imagine you would have done in such a situation? Remember that they have endured hundreds of years of slavery under a cruel dictatorship. Finally, as the hot sand pushes between their toes, they can taste freedom. Would you have listened to Hashem's decree and turned back?

But look, my friend, they don't even question. They are turning back. Let's see what they are thinking and saying about this torturous decision:

FIRST SLAVE:

> Now I understand that Moshe was not lying. A year ago, when he first came to demand our freedom, he asked Pharaoh to let us go for a three-day journey. I thought that he was trying to trick Pharaoh into letting us go without stating his true intentions of us running away for good. Three days have passed, and now we are turning back. Now I see that his request was not a lie.

SECOND SLAVE:

> After the plague of darkness, Pharaoh told Moshe that all Israel could

---

finally go, but that we would not be allowed to take our cattle with us. Moshe responded, " . . . and we do not know with what we must serve the Lord our God until we come there."[146] Now we are finally being told what that service is.

FIRST SLAVE:

Yes! We must serve Him through relinquishing our freedom.

But don't despair. Just because they are turning back towards the house of bondage doesn't mean that they are returning to the slavery of Pharaoh. Quite the opposite! By listening to Hashem and turning back to Egypt they are not giving up their freedom from Pharaoh, they are becoming free from him. They are able to throw off the shackles of Pharaoh only by first becoming full servants of Hashem alone.

Let's jump ahead a few more days. Now, after backtracking, the slaves are standing in a place called Pi HaChiros (the Mouth or Opening of Freedom), which is at the edge of the Sea of Reeds. We now revisit those two slaves.

FIRST SLAVE:

Look there, my brother, at that cloud of dust.

SECOND SLAVE:

Our worst fears are coming true in front of our eyes. That cloud is hundreds of Pharaoh's chariots charging towards us to either kill us or take us back to bondage.

FIRST SLAVE:

Don't despair. Just run with me into the split waters of the sea in front of us. Moshe just informed us that we should remain silent, for Hashem will fight our battles. Right now we are standing at the Mouth of Freedom. When we chose a few days ago to listen to Hashem's Will instead of to our own wills, we chose correctly. We chose to turn back towards Egypt because we knew that no one is our master other than Hashem, not even our own wills. Remember that when Moshe first appeared before Pharaoh he exclaimed in the Name of Hashem, "Send out My People so that they can serve Me."

For a year we have been witness to Hashem bombarding the world's

146 Exodus 10:26.

largest superpower with plague after plague. We were not freed in order to become a nation like other nations. Egypt did not tumble to destruction so that we could go on vacation. My brother, we are able to stand here at the Mouth of Freedom and in between these walls of water only because we chose to cancel our will in the face of Hashem's. Now we have fulfilled what Moshe first exclaimed. On the third day we chose to serve Hashem instead of ourselves. We chose to become not just the children of Israel, but rather the people of Hashem, Hashem's only son. That was the service that was demanded of us.

SECOND SLAVE:

And when we became the servants of Hashem we ceased being the servants of Pharaoh.

FIRST SLAVE:

Right. So don't worry about the approaching Egyptian chariots. See! They are stuck in the mud while we walk on the dry sea bed. We have erased Pharaoh as our master and made room for Hashem to take his place. As Moshe said, 'Be silent, Hashem, our newly recognized Adon, Master, will fight our battles.'

And then the Sea of Reeds crashes down upon the Egyptian oppressors. With Pharaoh's army dead on the shores of the sea, our ancestors now start their journey towards understanding how they must achieve proper servitude towards Hashem. They are on their way to Mount Sinai.

"So now," says Yehudah, "can anyone answer my question? What is the difference between Pharaoh calling our ancestors Israel and Moshe stating in Hashem's Name that they were His people?"

"To Pharaoh, Israel was a group of slaves, who happened to be the descendents of Israel,[147] and who belonged to him," says Avi. "Hashem, though, was referring to His nation as a group of people that chose to recognize that they were the servants of Hashem first and foremost. They became Hashem's servants when they set aside their own wills and replaced them with the desire to serve only Hashem."

Shimi has more than a glimmer of understanding in his

---

147 Israel was another name given to the patriarch Jacob (Yaakov).

eyes, as he says, "So Moshe was not lying and neither were my rabbis. Moshe Rabbeinu was asking for a three-day journey to be undertaken by the slaves of Pharaoh. By the end of the third day they were no longer Pharaoh's slaves, nor were they slaves to their own desires; rather, they were subjects of the Master of All."

Yehudah gives him a thumbs-up and a grin, and then says, "As for why we were being taken out of Egypt in the first place, you will all have to wait until we describe the Revelation at Sinai. This will happen when we get to that huge cave down there in the valley. Let's start our descent."

So now you understand, Searching Soul, that by turning around at Eitam those slaves were showing that there was no doubt in their minds as to Who was the real King. They knew that there was an eventual end to the Egyptians and their evil. They realized that they were inconsequential compared to Hashem, Whose rule would never end. They were expressing in the most extreme way that all evil, including mighty Pharaoh, has an end and that only Hashem will rule in awe, unchallenged, forever. I think that you are starting to understand the first words of my second stanza. ואחרי ככלות הכל, לבדו ימלוך נורא ~ V'Acharei kichlos hakol, levado yimloch nora ~ After all evil will have completed its purpose, only then will Hashem be able to reign alone, an unchallenged Kingship. Let's continue; there's a lot more . . . .

Born to a Slave
in Order to Become a Slave

AS THE SMALL GROUP cautiously climbs down the cliff like the bunch of city boys they are, they spot in front of them a band of Bedouins[148] who seem to traverse the rocky terrain even more sure-footedly than the goats that they lead.

148   A nomadic tribe that still roams through and around the Land of Israel to this day.

Shalom gestures towards them and asks, "Why did Hashem have us become slaves to flesh and blood before we would become servants to Him? Why couldn't we just skip Egyptian servitude altogether? Why did we have to go through such difficulties? Couldn't Hashem have taken a band of free men like these Bedouins and have them led by a wise man like Moshe to become Hashem's special people? What strengths did we need to acquire before becoming Hashem's servants that those people in front of us don't have?"

"Hashem's people are more than once referred to as His flock," replies Yehudah, as he skips down the rocks. "We are more likened to the goats you see than to their masters. Avraham *Avinu* was informed at the *Bris bein Habesarim*, the Covenant between the Parts,[149] that his seed would be slaves for hundreds of years and only then would they go out to freedom. Imbedded into their slave-mentality was the fact that they were the children of maidservants, just like those goats are the offspring of goats. Going from slavery to slavery was the only way for them to become the ultimate and eternal servants, Hashem's flock. And so, at the *Bris bein Habesarim*, Hashem informed Avraham *Avinu* that his children would be formed into a people specifically when they emerged from the bondage of slavery."

"Now I understand what we say in Hallel,"[150] says Avi. "King David states there, 'Answer me, Hashem, because I am Your servant. I am your servant, the son of your maidservant.' When King David wrote this he was the strongest monarch of his time, but that did not stop him from understanding what it meant to be a lowly servant. He was expressing that he was not only a servant but the servant who knows nothing other than to serve, because he was raised as a servant by a servant. He was stating that only because he was the son of a maidservant of Hashem, was he enabled to become a complete servant of Hashem."

They can no longer make their way down the side of the ravine, as the incline has become a sheer cliff. Yehudah pulls out some rappelling rope and hooks from his backpack. After

149 This is the covenant where Hashem promised Avraham that his descendants would be beyond counting, like the stars, and would inherit the Land of Israel.

150 A set of specific Psalms, recited on many of the Jewish holidays.

receiving a few quick safety rules, the boys rappel down a sheer cliff. When all are down and unclipping themselves, Ovadiah states:

"I think that now I understand that there seems to be more in his words than I previously understood." King David goes on in the same sentence to state, 'You have opened up my shackles'. And what is it that he will do once these shackles are opened? He says that he will not run to seek his own fulfillment by striving for false freedoms, nor go on a frenzy of searching for pleasures to serve himself. Rather, 'To You I will offer up a thanksgiving offering'. His job as a servant can never end. When He releases him from servitude it is only so that he'll be able to serve Him better. And so the verse ends, 'And in the Name of Hashem I will [continually] call.'"

Duck! There is a Mountain Flying Over Your Head

THEY DASH THROUGH the tiny stream which splashes through Wadi Kelt[151] in the winter and early spring months. Now they stand at the entrance of a mammoth cavelike formation. But this 'cave' has no walls. It is formed by the walls of the ravine jutting out over the ground beneath. The massive bedrock seems to hover over them. Now that they have entered, they look high above themselves at this most magnificent natural, and weird, phenomenon.

Shimi is awed: "It kind of feels like the mountain has been uprooted and is hovering over our heads, ready to drop any second."

"*Wunderbar.* That's why Yehudah brought you out here," responds Avi.

"So Chacham Yashar tells us," says Yehudah, "that our ancestors were camping next to Mount Sinai. The Torah then states:[152]

151 A valley in the Judean Desert.

152 Exodus 19:17.

'And Moshe brought the people out of the camp to meet with God, and they stood at the foot of the mountain.' Chacham Yashar then quotes Rashi,[153] who explains: 'According to the simple meaning it would mean at the base of the mountain, but according to the Gemara the mountain was uprooted from its place and was hanging over them like a roof.'[154] Rabbi Avdimi Bar Chama Bar Chasa states that the verse is informing us that the Holy One blessed be He hung the mountain over them like a roof and told them that if they accepted the Torah, great, and if not, that place would be their burial spot. The Gemara is informing us that the Jews accepted the Torah under duress."

Shalom wonders: "How could that be? We already learned that the Jews accepted all that Hashem would instruct them when they said 'na'aseh v'nishma' (we will first do without questioning and then we will hear what it is that Hashem will tell us)."[155]

Natan seconds him: "I'm with Shalom. The Gemara here seems contradictory to what we have learned so far. We know that when the Jews turned around at Eitam on their own volition, they were giving up their freedom in order to become servants of Hashem. Why would such heroes need to be forced to accept the Torah, which is the Will of their Master? Didn't their choosing to go from Eitam to 'the Mouth of Freedom' (Pi HaChiros) prove that they had already replaced their own will with that of Hashem's?"

"Your question is the same as that of the Sifsei Chachamim[156] who reminds us that the incident of the mountain hanging over their heads occurred after they had already said na'aseh v'nishma. This means that as a prerequisite to standing at the foot of Mount Sinai they had already accepted Hashem's Will as their own before they were even told what that Will would be. They did this like true servants, who were the sons of servants."

---

153   This is an acronym for Rabbi Shlomo Yitschaki, 1040–1105, the major medieval commentator.

154   Tractate Shabbos 88.

155   Exodus 24:7.

156   Rabbi Shabtai ben Yosef Bass (Meshorer), 1641–1718. He wrote a commentary on Rashi.

"So why did the Torah need to be forced upon such perfect servants? It seems that they did accept whatever God would say willingly," Natan persists.

Shimi is confused and says so. Ovadiah turns to him, and says in an understanding tone:

"You are not alone in your confusion. Not even a single soul objected to returning to the slavery of Pharaoh, for they knew it was Hashem's Will. The idea of accepting the Torah theoretically received a unanimous statement of 'we will do whatever You say.' But to stand there and actually receive the Torah directly from Hashem—for this they had to be forced?"

Shimi is already desperate: "So what does all this mean?"

Avi leans back comfortably on the only wall of the cave. "The answer to your questions lies on the floor and walls of this cave. First look outside at the barren desert from which we came. Now look around you."

Shalom examines their surroundings: "The wall is green with thick moss, similar to the picture my parents brought back from their trip to Ireland. Under our feet is lush, soft undergrowth. Only here, only under this freakish mountain hanging over us, is anything alive."

"It's because the mountain is hanging over this spot that life is able to survive," explains Avi.

And Yehudah picks up the thread: "Here is the key to your answers. Chacham Yashar brings us the Kli Yakar[157] on the verse, which states, 'See and understand that so long as you do not accept the Torah, behold you are considered like the dead, for both in your lives and in your deaths nothing will remain of you. Rather this will be your burial place . . . but by means of the Torah your lives will be considered life in this world and in the future life.' The Kli Yakar is teaching us what we have already learned in the first verse of ADON OLAM, that the whole of Creation took place only so that the creations would call out to Hashem via accepting to do His Will, His Torah."

Shalom is fingering the moss. "And how does all this relate to the second stanza of ADON OLAM?"

157 Shlomo Efraim Miloshits, 1540–1619, a commentator on the Torah.

Metamorphosis Beneath the Mountain

YEHUDAH EXPLAINS, "In the first part of the second stanza, ואחרי ככלות הכל ~ *V'Acharei kichlos hakol*, the authors are enlightening us on two points. First, they are instructing us that the confusions or evil don't only need to be removed, but they also need to be removed specifically by us. This can only be done when we are not looking for our own pleasure or 'freedom', but rather for servitude to Hashem. Our focal point must change. Like our ancestors at Eitam we must become God-centered.

"Their second point, לבדו ימלוך נורא ~ *Levado yimloch nora*, that [only] then will Hashem be able to rule alone, reigning over an unchallenged Kingship, can be understood best when considering our ancestors' metamorphosis under the mountain. There they visualized that being God-centered was only the beginning. They arrived at the realization about which the *Kli Yakar* enlightens us. They finally understood that in order to become the most proper servants, they needed the whole of their existence to become the Torah. Under that mountain they understood that the whole of this world is only the Torah.

"By viewing the mountain of Sinai hanging over their heads, they were internalizing the idea that without the Torah received on that mountain, there is no 'me'. Their new clarity seared through their minds till they felt forced by it to accept the Torah. Yes, the mountain was hanging over their heads. They were forced into it, but only by having first merited through Eitam to come to this realization, and ADON OLAM's words enable us to feel that Mount Sinai is still hanging over our heads to this day."

"I don't understand where you see all of that in the words of ADON OLAM," says Shimi petulantly.

"You see . . ."

But Ovadiah breaks into Yehudah's words. "I want to answer this. ADON OLAM seems to be grabbing our hands and pulling us into a world where we will understand that, after **we** have caused all of the apparent evil to finish, we will arrive at an existence like our ancestors had at Sinai, where we will merit seeing the world as being nothing other than Hashem's Kingship.

"The second stanza starts with the words '*After all will have completed its purpose*', meaning, when there will be an end to evil. At Eitam the Jewish slaves realized that there was an end to the evil that they had experienced. They divested themselves of the shackles that tied them to false powers by dismissing the world's definition of freedom, and willingly became subservient only to Hashem's Will. They understood that the goal is not emancipation, enlightenment, or independent national goals. That would be looking for the trip to Tahiti. ADON OLAM is showing us that we need to make the same choices as our enslaved ancestors. These choices will lead to the false powers of each generation being left behind us, dead, on the shores of our souls.

"The mentality that this choice will create needs to be so real to us that it will seem that the mountain is actually constantly hanging over our heads like the ceiling of this cave. As the *Kli Yakar* said, in order to become one with Hashem's Torah, we needed to internalize that the only definition of life is the complete service demanded by the Torah. This seems to be the message of the authors of ADON OLAM. From Sinai each Jew should know that there is no reality, no life, no choice, outside of the parameters of the eternal, never-changing Torah that we received at Sinai, and Hashem will be recognized by Creation as **reigning alone unchallenged**—לבדו ימלוך נורא—only when we, His servants, envision the mountain as constantly hanging over our heads."

"You're getting there, Ovadiah," says Yehudah enthusiastically, "and *The Hidden Master* states here that,

> For thousands of years ADON OLAM has been taking the hand of each Jew and leading him to understand the words of the verse: 'For it (the Torah) is your life and the length of your days.'[158] Rabbi Yonasan ben

---

158 Deuteronomy 30:20.

Uziel[159] comments on this verse: '. . . for behold the Torah which you are toiling in, it is your life in this world and the length of your days in the World to Come . . .' Only when we completely accept Hashem's Kingship will we merit life here and in eternity.

Loud beeping noises sound out in the desert.

"It's Boaz. Just on time," says Yehudah cheerfully.

"Where is the jeep? I hear it but don't see it. Besides, there's no road here. How did it get here?" Shalom is puzzled.

Natan looks around. "The jeep's camouflaged. If you look at that wall carefully, you'll see it. The only giveaway is the two words, 'Border Patrol' on its side."

Yehudah motions them on. "All aboard, unless you would like to spend the night in the desert."

The Invitation

WHILE BEING JOSTLED around the jeep that is rushing to get back to civilization before the early spring day ends and darkness sets in, Yehudah is still talking:

"We have so much more to do. My wife said that she is inviting you all for the Sabbath. As Pharaoh said, Mi va'mi haholchim, Who will be coming?"

Needless to say, the invitation is accepted unanimously.

"O.K., I'll see you all tomorrow afternoon, then, about an hour before the Sabbath, at my home. For those of you who have not been there before, Avi knows where I live."

The next day passes quickly with all of the preparations for the Sabbath. The boys arrive together with Avi at the Stark apartment. There they meet Yehudah's children: Kayla, a pensive and artistic young girl, and her younger sister, Hadassah, a pleasant ball of smiles. For a girl so young, she has a surprising memory. Menachem is a skinny, active lad, a very studious boy who always has the answers. Chananiah, his twin, is an impish

---

159   Also called "Targum Yonasan". He translated and wrote commentary on the Torah in Aramaic.

boy with something always hidden behind his saucy smile. He is always getting into trouble or getting someone else into trouble. Then there is the three-year-old, Rafi, whose sun-yellow side-locks catch everyone's attention. He talks a mile a minute and is quite precocious. Finally there is a newborn baby, Akiva.

In the Stark household there is room in the heart for all, but there isn't an extra meter of sleeping place, so the guys are ushered by a veritable flock of children to a basement apartment a few streets away, where they will all be sleeping. The tenants are away for Sabbath and have kindly handed over their modest home to the Starks' guests. They go down the stairs and are confronted with children's bicycles, discarded appliances and baby strollers strewn all over the hallway. Who would have ever guessed that tucked away behind all of that debris there was a family's tiny, but warm and cozy home?

After settling in their rooms, the young men regroup at the Stark home and all go to synagogue together. Later, there's Kiddush,[160] HaMotzi,[161] a wonderful meal, songs, and . . . .

"O.K.," says Yehudah, when everyone has eaten their fill, "what is the name of the weekly Torah portion?"

"Trumah!" All the children, except for the baby, know that.

"Chananiah, what is a trumah?"

"A gift. So this is the Torah portion where you are told to give me a gift?"

And indeed, Yehudah pulls a candy from his pocket and gives it to Chananiah.

"Now, Chananiah, give me back the gift."

"But I want it. It's mine."

Hadassah whispers into Chananiah's ear that he'll get it back, but first he has to give it to Daddy. She remembers the little play from the year before. She remembers everything. Chananiah then goes over to Big Avi, as he calls him, and says in his ear,

"If my daddy doesn't give me the candy back, you grab it back for me. You're bigger than him."

160 The sanctification of the Sabbath recited over wine.

161 The blessing over the bread.

"Of course!" Avi is obliging, and Chananiah hands back the candy.

"Menachem, is there anything in the weekly Torah portion that would explain why I just asked for the gift back?"

"The trumah was not given to us. We gave it to Hashem, and yet we understand that all that we have is from Him. So really we are not giving, but rather just returning to Hashem what He gave us."

"What was the nature of this gift?"

Kayla chimes in with bits of information: "They gave finely spun wools of many colors, precious stones, huge amounts of gold, silver and copper, oils, and fragrant spices. Their gifts were transformed into everything that was needed to build the Tabernacle in the desert. That is where the people worshipped. The purpose of building the Tabernacle was to create a home for the Presence of Hashem, so that it could rest upon the Jewish People."

"Very good, Kayla. Does anyone know if we were happy to give the gifts? Chananiah, were you happy to give me your candy?"

"No. And if you don't give it back, boy oh boy." He smiles an impish smile and jumps into Avi's lap. Rafi giggles and shakes his finger at his daddy.

But Menachem knows: "You want us to say that they were happy to give the gifts because it is a great opportunity to give something to Hashem, but I don't see why they would be happy. I agree with Chananiah."

"Chananiah, you gave me your candy. Great! You deserve a big hug." While giving the hug he slips the candy back into Chananiah's pocket.

Hadassah speaks up. "I know what you're talking about, Dad. Our people were being punished for the sin of the Golden Calf. The punishment was that they would no longer have the Presence of Hashem resting upon them. They were given a way out, though, where through their own efforts they could bring Hashem's Presence back. This required them giving their most precious things to make a physical dwelling for the spiritual presence of Hashem. They were very happy to do this in order to get that Presence back; just like little Chananiah is now getting your hug. And you slipped the candy into his pocket, not to avoid being hit by Avi, but rather to show Chananiah that we do not lose by giving."

"What a bunch of smart children. Mommy do we have dessert for them?" Yehudah is pleased.

Luscious chocolate cake appears and is divided up among everyone.

"While these intelligent kids are enjoying their well-deserved cake," the host says, "I have a question for the guests. Yesterday we went to the desert and understood servitude to Hashem's Will to be life itself. When we look at what the children just taught us about this week's Torah portion, and with what we learned about the second stanza of ADON OLAM, could you define the nature of this servitude?"

"ואחרי ככלות הכל ~ *V'Acharei kichlos hakol*—instructs us that Hashem's Kingship will finally be realized by everyone when all the barriers to our service will have been removed. From what your kids just taught us we understand that not only does our service have to be complete, but it also needs to be performed with joy. Our ancestors never would have merited the building of the Tabernacle and having Hashem's Presence if they had not willingly and joyfully donated towards that realization."

"Right, Avi. We'll talk about it some more as I walk you guys back to your apartment, but for the moment, chew over this question with your cake: Can we serve in joy while living in the midst of anguish?"

Thirsty Souls

THE SABBATH MEAL is over and the children are on their way to sleep. As Yehudah walks the guys back to the apartment where they are to be sleeping, he continues with this thought.

"Questions often rise in our minds, such as what if it could have, should have, or would have been different. So much anguish comes from doubts. Our Sages tell us that there is no joy like the alleviation of doubts.[162] I must tell you a true story of someone I became close to, who successfully removed the stain of doubts while enduring one of the darkest clouds the world has ever seen. He lived through experiences that would have pulled the strongest of us down, yet I always think of him as a man of joy, may he rest in peace.

"Thirteen years ago I was working for a Chassidic lady, Mrs. Migdal, a caterer in Monsey, New York. After a while she invited me, the new baal teshuvah,[163] to her home for Sabbath. Soon after arriving at my boss's home that night, something very unusual happened. As Mrs. Migdal's father-in-law gave his grandchildren the traditional blessings to become great servants of Hashem, he . . ."

Searching Soul, let's go back 13 years, to the Sabbath table that Yehudah experienced, and hear the old man's blessing . . . .

"May you become like the great righteous people of our past. May Hashem bless and keep you. May He shine His countenance upon you and be gracious to you. May Hashem lift His countenance to you and give you peace."[164]

Yehudah notices that the old man begins to cry. He turns to Mrs. Migdal: "What is going on?" And Mrs. Migdal explains: "You see, my father-in-law is a Holocaust survivor. He lost five of his children to the Nazis, and giving the blessings to my children reminds him of my deceased brothers and sisters-in-law. So let's go on to more pleasant things. After all, it's the Sabbath. The children just asked me if you know any new melodies to the Sabbath songs, as they always like to hear new ones."

Yehudah momentarily sets aside his sympathy for the old man and

---

162   Metzudas David on Proverbs 15:30.

163   This term literally means master of repentance. It refers to Jews who were not born into a lifestyle of observing the laws of the Torah, but who later chose to become observant Jews.

164   Adapted from Numbers 6:24.

sings a very peppy version of Tzama Nafshi, the Sabbath song that speaks of the soul thirsting for the living God. Upon finishing, the children seem puzzled, while Mrs. Migdal responds by turning to one of her sons, Yoely, and requesting: "Please sing the holy song, Tzama Nafshi, with the burning desire it deserves."

When 15-year-old Yoely finishes the song, young Yehudah is pale as a ghost. After years of singing empty words, the song has become alive to him. He thinks to himself of how, in the intonations of this boy's rendition, is hidden a truth, a thirst for God as the song's words express, that he does not yet know, but wants so much for it to become his own.

Mrs. Migdal hands Yehudah a plate of sugary gefilte fish and says: "Eat this. You look like you could use it."

"While you're eating, let me tell you something, young man. Service to Hashem is not in peppy tunes to holy words. You need to thirst for Hashem's kingship. You need to know what you're striving for, and you need to know how to live your life accordingly. You need to do all this with purity. Nothing else should hinder or stop you, for nothing else has any meaning. It's only to test you. We are in this world to prove to Hashem, and, more so, to prove to ourselves, that our souls thirst for the living God like the song says. Only through serving Him do we really have life."

The old man then speaks to Yehudah for the first time . . . .

An Ember Saved From the Fire

"THE NAZIS, may the name of the wicked rot, gassed and burned my pure little servants of Hashem. They thought that they could stop us, but they were wrong. My children's souls were not destroyed. No step taken to strive towards service to Hashem in this world is ever wasted. They lived their short lives and brought us all closer to the time of the final Redemption. Remember what I'm telling you, young man, and teach it to all you come across in life even after I am gone. A Jew needs to always be aware that there is no such thing as giving up in his service to Hashem. And so, after the war I decided to start again, and bring more righteous people into the world who would continue on in this world with joy, the joy of service to Hashem no matter what."

"My father-in-law taught my husband and me," Mrs. Migdal fills in, "to teach our children to fear Hashem joyfully and to follow His commandments with a thirst."

Yoely, with his black velvet hat and curly, two-foot-long sidelocks, then turns to Yehudah, who is sitting next to him:

"We are a lone people, serving the lone singular King. My parents and grandfather raised me to realize that we Jews need to know only Hashem and serve Him. I sing that song with all of my heart, and my mama cries with tears of pride. Why does she cry? She is proud to have successfully raised her family to follow the commandments and fear Hashem even though the world out there is not like us.

"I am yearning for the day when the whole world will recognize Hashem with no doubts, like I have no doubts. The thirst that you felt in the tune that I sang is the yearning of the Jew of the Diaspora to have wickedness removed so we can serve Hashem in peace. Just like my grandfather ended the blessings to me with peace, he ended his blessings to my late uncles and aunts, May Hashem avenge their blood. Peace, the peace of solitary undoubted Kingship of Hashem."

After the Sabbath meal the old man and the young boy walk Yehudah home to his *yeshivah* dorm. As they approach the dormitory, Yehudah finally gets up the guts to ask the old man something that is on his mind:

"I understand why you cried when you blessed your grandchildren. Yet there is an obligation to serve Hashem in joy. I saw tonight that you do serve Hashem with joy. Could you explain to me how you successfully serve Hashem in joy while simultaneously living with such sadness?"

Then Our Mouths Will
Be Filled With Laughter

*THE OLD MAN TURNS to face Yehudah and with his
wrinkled, weak hands grasps Yehudah's young strong
hands and looks him hauntingly in the eye. Listen carefully, Searching Soul, to the words of wisdom of a true
servant of Hashem, who learned from my words . . . .*

"Young man, I know that Hashem is correct in all that He does,
but we live in a broken world where it is hard to understand
His actions. It is hard to see the hand of Hashem in the events
around us. I long for the time that ADON OLAM tells us will be—
ואחרי ככלות הכל ~ after the disappearance of all evil—a time
when the whole world will recognize His hand in everything.
In the meanwhile, just like the words of the song that we sang
expressed, my pain is an impetus which causes me to thirst for
Hashem's recognized singular, undoubted Kingship."

Yoely then adds, "King David tells us[165] that at the time of that final
revelation 'our mouths will be filled with laughter and our tongues
with singing'. My grandfather lived through one of the Earth's
darkest moments, yet he lives every moment with such a joy in
knowing that with all the stones on the road, he still has a map and
knows that he is bringing the Redemption closer with every step."

And his grandfather says, "As for my beloved deceased children, may
Hashem avenge their blood, when all evil passes away, and it will,
through my continued service and yours, too, my young friend.
Then you and I and they will be together in a world, like ADON
OLAM tells us of—לבדו ימלוך נורא ~ *levado yimloch nora*—where
all will finally recognize His unchallenged Kingship. My joy is to
know that while I am still alive I will use my strength to make
every one of my steps a step toward that goal, toward Hashem's
goal. Whether alive or dead, all who served Hashem here in this
world will eventually merit living in the times of redemption,
which they helped to bring about."

165 Psalms 126:2.

"So, as King David tells us, 'then our mouths will be filled with laughter and our tongues with singing'. Not now but then," Yoely clarifies. "For now, no matter how much we may realize that Hashem is the Boss and runs everything, this is not what we experience. We are very far from it."

"Right, Yoely. We, like Avraham Avinu, experience the world of Adon, the world of the personal but not yet universally recognized Master of All. And with the world's lack of recognition of Hashem's kingship, we experience pain and it is real. We experience incongruence, yet we believe in His Oneness. Although we know that ADON OLAM tells us that the clouds will dissipate, right now we are engulfed by a storm. Now is not the time for laughter but rather the time for *zecher la'churban*,[166] to sit on the floor, to cry and pray for the ultimate revealing of Hashem's Glory. It is the time for us to thirst to bring out the hidden and make it revealed. It's the time for us to actively pull back the clouds that hide Hashem's reign. We must serve through the difficulties, and Hashem commands us to serve only with joy. Remember, the Torah says that we will actually be taken to task for not serving Hashem in joyfulness and gladness of heart.[167]

"My new young friend, my joy is in knowing that even though our lives are lived in a storm, we are still on the correct path. The clouds are only dispelled when we have no doubts that what we are doing is 100% correct. Being on the path that the Master of the Universe has set for us makes every step a step without doubt. The rest of the world does not yet recognize His reign, but I do, and there is no greater joy than living with this knowledge, the knowledge that the day will come that 'our mouths will be filled with laughter and our tongues with song'."

---

166 Literally, 'remembering the destruction'. The term refers to the two destroyed Holy Temples and also all of the customs that serve to remind the Jewish People of the destruction of the Temple in their daily lives.

167 Deuteronomy 28:47.

ADON OLAM is Pointing Its Finger at You

*N*OW LET'S GO BACK *to Yehudah and his students, 13 years later. I'm counting on him to bring my words to life for them and you, Searching Soul. They have arrived at the entrance to the building where they will be sleeping. He has just finished telling them about his experience with the Migdal family. Listen, as Yehudah uses the messages of that night to shed light on my messages.*

"So my friends, ADON OLAM tells us that once evil has been discarded, Hashem will reign as an undoubted awesome King. By deciding to discard the doubts brought about by the Pharaohs and Nazis, we are preparing our minds and souls to accept this absolute monarchy. ADON OLAM is right now pointing its finger at us. Its holy words demand that we actively work to achieve this most lofty goal of recognizing Hashem's undoubted Kingship, even in the face of the multitude of false kingships which endeavor to pollute our faith with doubts."

"But these 'false kingships' or harsh situations seem very real," Ovadiah points out. "Wishing them away doesn't make them go poof, gone. Pharaoh didn't just melt away because we wished him away, and the various 'Hitlers' of later times still continue to plague us. How can we bring about Hashem's undoubted kingship in the middle of all of this evil?"

"By knowing that all that Hashem does is for our good, even that which we do not yet understand," answers Yehudah. "Learn from Mr. Migdal that your struggles shouldn't lead to doubts, but rather towards service with joy. That joy comes from recognizing that לבדו ימלוך נורא ~ *Levado yimloch nora*— nothing is haphazard, but rather, all is undoubtedly planned by the King for a reason."

Neither Ovadiah nor you can honestly leave the doubts

behind. Admit it. You still have doubts about Hashem's total Kingship. You are still wondering why the Nazis were allowed to take those little children, and Ovadiah wonders about the 'meaning' of his father's 'meaning-less' murder. Although both of you are encouraged by the old man's strength of character, your souls pang over why Hashem sometimes seems to turn a blind eye to evil and seemingly desert the world.

Know, my friend, that my words ואחרי ככלות הכל לבדו *ימלוך נורא ~ V'Acharei kichlos hakol levado yimloch nora, are not a mere speculation of how in the future, after the passage of the mirage of evil, Hashem's King-ship will be beyond doubt. Rather, they are an impetus which can lead you to presently push away all of your doubts. Ovadiah and his friends used me to work their way through their doubts. Through watching them get through the next minefield, I hope to show you how to do the same with your own doubts . . . .*

Uprooting a Haphazard Minefield?

OVADIAH IS STILL SKEPTICAL: "I admire that old man's positive attitude and tenancity—he has real 'stick-to-it-iveness', but I think of him as more than just a tough act to follow. How or why should there be joy in the face of injustice? Surely Hashem could have thought of a better way to bring us close to Him other than tragedy. Maybe Hashem is just not looking? Perhaps we were left alone in the world?"

"Your words remind me of those of the prophet Ezekiel,[168] who expressed the people's erroneous perception that 'Hashem does not see us, Hashem has deserted the world'," remarks Avi.

But Ovadiah persists: "Don't you sometimes experience the world that way? Why does Hashem hand us such devastating

168 Ezekiel 8:12.

tests? Life sometimes seems like walking through a haphazard minefield of meaningless tragic events."

Yehudah breaks in: "Would you like to uproot the minefield?"

"Wouldn't we all? But how?"

"The time has come for you to discover that the donkey has horns."

Once again, everyone is stumped by this non-sequitur.

"It is a little cold out here for a donkey ride," admits Yehudah. "Let's go inside. We'll climb aboard while sitting on the couch there."

The group never really seems to get used to Yehudah's eyebrow-raising statements. Whatever it is, they know that they are in for yet another adventure with Yehudah, and so are you.

Obstacle Course

THE BOYS ENTER the building and go down the stairwell, which descends to the basement level. The hall light was mistakenly left off, and, since it is the Sabbath, they may not turn it on. So they have to fumble their way through the obstacle course they encountered earlier that day. Shimi steps on a toy car. He skids and lands on a tossed out, threadbare mattress. Eventually, they all manage to maneuver their way through the scattered debris to the door of the little basement apartment.

Avi gropes around in the dark for a moment and his large fingers finally detect the hidden key that he was foraging for. He feels the wall until he finds the door and unlocks it. The house is warm, but quite dark. The flickering candles that the guys lit a few hours before, just before Sabbath began, are the only light there. Avi closes the door and all head towards the L-shaped, beaten-up old couch that seems to take up the entire living room. Yehudah sits down in the corner and Ovadiah settles next to him. As the candles flicker in the small room, shadows jostle haphazardly all around.

Shimi looks around. "I don't think that even Yehudah could hide a donkey in here. This place is really tiny and no donkey could have gotten through that obstacle course."

But Avi sets him straight: "Yehudah promised a donkey and a donkey I am sure we'll get."

"Indeed you will," says Yehudah. "But in order to find this donkey, we'll let *The Hidden Master* take us all back to ancient Athens.

Shimi groans. "Of course! Where else would a donkey with a horn hide?"

"Silly us," remarks Shalom from his end of the couch. "We thought that we were going to sleep and now Yehudah has us traveling to Athens."

"Hey, we're not supposed to travel on Sabbath!" says Natan from the shadows.

"No, Natan, we won't be traveling on Sabbath. Once again, Chacham Yashar has us travel through time. This time he uses the *Gemara*, which brings us through a deadly obstacle course that leads to the hideaway of the so-called Wise Men of Athens, and so he tells his readers . . ."

Matching the Caesar's Bet [169]

WE'RE OFF TO ANCIENT Athens, Searching Soul, but first we need to stop in Rome and visit the Caesar . . . .

CAESAR:

Rabbi Yehoshua ben Chananiah, how dare you claim that the Torah's wisdom is superior to that of the philosophy of the Greeks?

RABBI YEHOSHUA:

Your Majesty, the Torah's wisdom is superior to all wisdom.

---

169 The following story, found in the Gemara *Bechoros* 8b, is presented here in a somewhat embellished and adapted form. Please refer to the Disclaimer at the beginning of this book.

CAESAR:

    We'll have to see about that. I order you to travel to Athens and see if you can bring all the Wise Men of Athens to me here in Rome. You will need to outsmart those that no one has yet succeeded in outsmarting. I think that we will not be meeting again, for you will surely meet your doom, you and your kind.

RABBI YEHOSHUA:

    Hashem alone reigns over every detail of the world. לבדו ימלוך נורא ~ Levado yimloch nora. His truth will win against their lies. We will see who will meet their doom. I will return with all sixty philosophers promptly.

CAESAR:

    I am not holding my breath. Off with you. Go to your doom, Jew.

The Donkey's Horn Plows Down the Swords

RABBI YEHOSHUA ARRIVES in Athens. Using the wisdom given to him by the Torah, he stealthily sneaks through a maze of hidden passageways. At each turn another ambush lurks, anxious to eradicate him. Finally, he crawls through the last hidden passageway, leaving a few guards and thugs dead behind him. He now walks right up to the sixty shocked Wise Men of Athens.

FIRST PHILOSOPHER:

    Who are you and how did you get past our traps? No one who is not of superior intelligence could have outwitted our snares.

RABBI YEHOSHUA:

    I am one of the great Rabbis of the Jews.

SECOND PHILOSOPHER:

    And why have you come to us?

RABBI YEHOSHUA:

    I wish to learn wisdom from you.

THIRD PHILOSOPHER:

    Let's see just how wise you are. Before we let you ask us, we will see if

you can answer some of our questions on your faith. I am sure we will
be able to stump you with questions beyond normal human wisdom.
Then we will bring you and your people to doom.

HEAD PHILOSOPHER:

Most wise of the Jews, how do you remove furrows of haphazard
swords?

ALL THE PHILOSOPHERS:

That's a good one. There is no answer to that. You have surely stumped
him and shown the falseness of his errant faith.

Rabbi Yehoshua doesn't even flinch. His response is sure and fast.

RABBI YEHOSHUA:

With the horn of a donkey.

ALL OF THE PHILOSOPHERS:

Wow! He understood the question. But what do we do with such an
answer?

Much discussion is heard between the philosophers and then the
tumult subsides and the Head Philosopher questions again:

HEAD PHILOSOPHER:

And does a donkey have a horn?

Laughter of victory is heard from the group. Rabbi Yehoshua smiles
with knowledge of his coming success.

RABBI YEHOSHUA:

And does a furrow sprout swords haphazardly?

The philosophers seem immensely disturbed. They have no response.
Rabbi Yehoshua has shaken their belief system at its very core
with an answer which reaches far beyond what they now realize
themselves to be. All of Greek philosophy has gone up in smoke
in front of their eyes with the few carefully chosen words of the
great Rabbi.

Triumph! Now Rabbi Yehoshua lures them all into his own trap back to Rome, where they meet their final end.

Puzzled? Just read on, Searching Soul as Yehudah Stark now begins to explain Rabbi Yehoshua's earthshaking message to the guys . . . .

Create a Fate

"THE MAHARAL[170] explains that the Greeks, like you, Ovadiah, saw a world with unexplained, illogical tragedies. Their philosophers chose not to believe, as ADON OLAM posits, that there is an all-powerful and all-knowing Being that constantly reigns over the world and controls its every event. Rather, they reasoned that tragedies crop up like swords in a field, for no particular purpose. Happenstance became one of their central convictions."

"You are referring to the Fates, aren't you?" asks Avi.

"The who?" This comes from Shimi.

But Yehudah is plowing on. "Avi's right on target. What more can you tell us about the Fates?"

"The Fates were a concept of godlike beings that haphazardly played around with people's lives and world events. Whenever something happened that could not be explained logically, the Fates became the chaotic wildcard to answer injustice. The Fates were the Greeks' simple and terribly empty answer as to why bad things happen to good people, why tragedies crop up like swords in the middle of the fields of life."

Natan nods. "Now I understand why some of the highest Greek philosophers were of the lowest moral stature. No wonder the Epicureans believed that they should eat, drink and be merry, 'for tomorrow they shall die'. With such a theology of deities whose moral character is flippant, there could not be moral demands upon lowly creatures."

---

170   Maharal of Prague—Rabbi Yehuda Loeve ben Betzalel, 1513–1609, a well-known commentator, known best for his explanations of Aggadic, or story-like accounts, like this one.

"Correct," says Avi. "They did not believe that there were just reasons for what was happening to them, nor did they believe that there was any comeuppance to their own behavior."

"So belief in the Fates meant a disbelief in Divine justice, reward and punishment," Natan analyzes the situation.

Avi goes on. "Belief in the Fates creates a worldview where there can be no right or wrong but just chance and injustice. Belief in the Fates is in direct opposition to ADON OLAM's claim that לבדו ימלוך נורא ~ *Levado yimloch nora*, which teaches us that since Hashem's reign is complete, nothing ever happens by chance."

"And so, the Maharal tells us that the philosophers asked Rabbi Yehoshua, 'How do you remove furrows of swords?' How dare you claim that Hashem reigns when we all see a world of willy-nilly events that have nothing to do with Divine justice? The Greek philosophers held that 'Hashem does not see us. Hashem has deserted the world.'"

Yehudah's voice rings out in the darkened room, as he continues:

"The question of the philosophers to Rabbi Yehoshua was 'Do the Jews have anything to say to demolish our conclusion? Why do you Jews hold tightly onto your Torah with all of its rules and regulations? Because of the Fates there is really no difference in the end, and therefore there is no consequence to your actions. Why burden yourselves and the world with the Torah, when both the good and the evil trip on the same happenstance swords? We Greeks see the Jews holding onto the Torah as destructive foolishness. There is no need to subjugate your will to that of a Higher Being Who will not intervene on your behalf. And when the Fates do get you, then you have something to worry about, for there is no way out of your bad luck.'

"Guys, as you search the innards of your souls, can you honestly assert that you do not believe like the Greek philosophers do? If you see the difficulties that come upon man as coming arbitrarily, then how can you believe in ADON OLAM's words that Hashem alone reigns, in an undoubted and complete Kingship, and that there is no happenstance?

"Now, let's climb up on the donkey and see how its horn points you towards understanding how Hashem rules even over your seemingly haphazard tragedies, and why."

But Donkeys Have No Horns

YEHUDAH IS IN a playful mood. He lifts his hands up to the candles and contorts his fingers till on the opposing wall the image of a donkey head with a horn appears.

"Rabbi Yehoshua said that these swords could be plowed down with the horn of a donkey."

"Hey, that's cute, but what is the horn of a donkey? Donkeys have no horns. How will nonexistent animal parts get rid of the seemingly haphazard tragedies that come upon man?" Shalom asks.

But Yehudah seems to ignore him. "Natan, what is the root of the word 'donkey' in the Holy Tongue?"

"*Chamor* translates as donkey. The root is *Chamar*."

"And are there any other words with that root?"

"*Chomer* is similar, and it means physicality."

"And does anyone here know what the word horn, *keren*, means, if not referring to something that appears on top of an animal's head?"

"Well, we have the verse, 'And He will raise the *keren* (horn) of His Anointed (the Messiah)'[171]," Ovadiah says.

"Obviously," says Shimi, "the word *keren* there does not mean that the Messiah will have a horn in the middle of his forehead—or does it, Yehudah?"

"Of course not. The word *keren* refers to greatness or elevation. Rabbi Yehoshua was prompting the philosophers to ask yet another question that would then enable him to lead into his final answer, which would undermine their belief in the Fates.

"And they fell into his trap. They asked, 'Does a donkey have horns?', meaning, does physicality have horns? Does the physical have the ability to be different or even elevated from what it is? The Maharal explains that their question is that since matter, as opposed to the intellect, is thick and physical and will decompose over time, how can you relate greatness or elevation to that which is lowly and decomposing? They believed that people, being physical, are completely bound by their physical world. Therefore they held that we are all trapped in the surrounding field of swords and are waiting to become helpless innocent victims of the Fates."

The Ripple on the Rope

YEHUDAH COMPLETES his explanation of that mystifying discussion of long-ago to the entranced group around him: "So the Maharal explains that Rabbi Yehoshua's response is that the world does not sprout haphazard furrows of swords. Tragedies do not come upon the world by happenstance; there are no Fates. The Holy One, blessed be He, created the physical World in a way that it should have sprouted only good, but we were given the ability to change that.

"We learn[172] that there is no suffering without sin. When we transgress—go against Hashem's Will—we have planted seeds that will eventually sprout as swords in the physical world. From the time of Creation, improper actions continually twist the channels of good and reform them into channels of suffering. The *Nefesh HaChaim* explains how each infraction against the Torah affects many worlds and eventually leads to the 'injustice' that we experience.

The Hidden Master takes us now to Volozhin, where Rav Chaim of Volozhin is composing his historic masterpiece, *Nefesh HaChaim*. As Chacham Yashar has us fly through the open attic window to his study, we notice that a small candle is casting its yellow light on the many sheets of heavily-scrawled paper that lie in neat piles all over the desk in his study. He depicts Rav Chaim of Volozhin as pacing back and forth thinking out loud to himself . . ."[173]

172 Tractate *Shabbos* 55a.

173 Please refer to the Disclaimer.

"A rope. It's like a rope suspended from a high ceiling. If I grasp the bottom of the rope and twitch it even slightly, then this movement is felt even at the top of the rope. This is how our actions, both good and bad, influence the higher worlds."

He continues to pace back and forth while simultaneously stroking his long white beard furiously. He strolls over to the open attic window. He leans out and looks up at the stars. After a few minutes, deep in thought, he continues to speak his thoughts out loud . . . .

"Every action that we do down here in the lowest physical world makes its way up through each of the spiritual worlds that caused our existence. Eventually every action makes its way up to the Creator. Not only do our actions travel through these worlds, but they actually affect these worlds.

"How frightening a thought. Each of our actions here has the ability to affect many worlds. The Torah tells us that our Father Jacob dreamed that there was a ladder, and upon it there were angels going up and down. Our actions create spiritual existences that travel through the rungs of the ladder of successive spiritual worlds until they arrive at the Creator. While moving on the rungs, they affect them. When they eventually descend, they themselves are affected by the worlds that they had previously altered and in turn affect our world upon which they land. Our deeds can either support us or haunt us. The choice is ours."

You're Putting a Hole in our Boat

"SO, GUYS, what Chacham Yashar is telling us is that actually the world was originally set up without swords," explains Yehudah. "The *Nefesh HaChaim* informs us, like Rabbi Yehoshua informed the wise men of Athens, that the swords in our field are the product of man, and they did not sprout up haphazardly."

"I am also an inhabitant of this world," says Ovadiah. "What if I am innocent of any wrongdoing? What about Mr. Midgal's innocent children? Why should I—or they—have been punished with a world of swords when we were not the ones to cause the swords to sprout?"

"Two thousand years ago, Rabbi Shimon Bar Yochai came to answer your question.[174] He likened the relationship between any random group of Jews in our long history to that of a group of friends on a raft in very deep waters with no land in sight. Clearly, he informs us, if one person from the group were to bore a hole under his seat through the bottom of the raft then it is understood why the whole group would be in trouble."

"All Jews are responsible for each other,"[175] quotes Natan automatically.

"In other words, we are all in this together," says Avi. "This physical world is not just a game of a collection of individuals; we are collectively responsible for the success of our common mission."

"And so Rabbi Yehoshua affirmed to the Wise Men of Athens that no matter how righteous anyone may be, he or she may suffer. There are no haphazard swords. Even if a certain individual is not the direct cause of the events in front of him, he is still a member of a greater whole, and we as a people have a collective responsibility to fix the world."

"But how do we fix that which has already become crooked?" Ovadiah wonders.

My Horn is on Fire

YEHUDAH SMILES. "Rabbi Yehoshua already told us. With the donkey's horn."

Pointing to the flickering candles, he continues: "Notice how that flame over there uses the physical fuel of the candle to reach for the sky. So too, the Maharal informs us that 'as opposed to the lowly physical body, the elevated human soul, the *keren*, can enable man to use the physical world to escape

---

174 *Vayikra Rabbah* 4:6.

175 *Shevuos* 39a.

from the lowliness of the physicality of his body (*chomer, chamor* {donkey}), and then to rise above the incidents that he has to battle.'

"Rabbi Yehoshua informed the philosophers and us that we were not put into this lowly physical world in order to be pulled down by haphazard events, but rather our souls enable us to use what is purposely sent our way to raise ourselves above the physical."

The last candle suddenly dims and goes out, leaving the room pitch black.

"Our world may seem dark but all is not lost. We can use the horn of the donkey, the soul, to plow down the swords. What we learn from Rabbi Yehoshua is that not only is the trap of swords not haphazard, but it is not a trap at all. Just as the individual—and mankind as a whole—has caused the difficult tests that we meet, so too does the individual and mankind as a whole have the ability to plow down the swords that were purposely placed in front of us.

"Chacham Yashar informs us that Rabbi Yehoshua ben Chananiah, Rav Chaim of Volozhin, and Rabbi Shimon Bar Yochai, really have just one message. Through time, we as a people have caused our own predicaments. Each individual is part of a greater whole. If your foot encounters a toy car and stumbles, does not the whole body fall?"

Shimi grimaces in the dark.

"And so we have learned that there are no haphazard swords sprouting up. If those who caused them have not dealt with the consequences, or cannot deal with them, then the rest of the holy nation has to straighten that which was previously bent. And since you are part of a greater whole, when you succeed in overcoming the stumbling blocks which Hashem now places in front of you, you will be fixing a much greater picture than you presently realize.

"Judaism shows the world that there are no Fates. Rabbi Yehoshua not only won the argument in ancient times, he gave us a message for all eternity, but he was not the first to bring this message. ADON OLAM's words existed generations before he was born, and they are the seed which sprouted into his message. It was written in order to melt feelings of senselessness and hopelessness. Everything that you could ever experience is part of a bigger picture, but never is it too big to overcome. You can plow down all of the manmade swords."

"But how, Yehudah?" The quiver in Ovadiah's voice is telling; it reveals how much he is yearning for an answer.

Summing up from Eitam to Volozhin

YEHUDAH'S VOICE RINGS out in the dark room.

"In order to answer you, Ovadiah, let's first see what you guys learned over the past two days. When our ancestors went willingly from Eitam to Pi HaChiros, Pharaoh and his 'strength' faded away. Likewise, ADON OLAM informs us that all evil will eventually end by us understanding that evil never existed independently in the first place. We must strive to reach that understanding in the here and now.

"We have now come to the realization that there are no Fates, nor is there such a thing as meaningless chance. There is only the undoubted complete Kingship of the Master of All. And it is precisely this recognition that ADON OLAM and Rabbi Yehoshua tell us that we can use to flip the world of supposedly haphazard tragedies upside down."

Yehudah leans backwards and flips himself with a summersault into a standing position. Then he says,

"ADON OLAM says that the world will recognize this when all evil eventually dissipates. Its message to us is that we don't have to wait until the whole world recognizes this. We are our only barriers to understanding that Hashem reigns now. Like Mr. Migdal told me, right now we need to joyfully strive towards the time when that Kingship will be undoubted by all.

"You guys look tired. I have to go. My wife gives me the night shift with the sleepless children. I'll see you tomorrow bright and early at synagogue."

Avi's Darkest Secret

THE HAVDALAH[176] candle has been extinguished in the wine. Yehudah's sons sing 'Eliyahu HaNavi[177] with their father and their new friends. A wonderful Sabbath is over. It was a Sabbath in which the young men became attached to each other and to Yehudah's kids, but it is not yet time to go.

"O.K., kids, quickly get into your pajamas, and then we will have a Melaveh Malkah.[178] As I promised, our guests brought their guitars."

With lightning speed the kids race to change their clothes. Minutes later there is a knock at the door. The guests have returned with three guitars. For about an hour, lots of singing is heard in the Stark living room. While everyone eats treats that Mrs. Stark has prepared, each of Yehudah's sons has gotten warm and cozy in a lap of one of the boys, as the girls sit smiling on the couch. After all of the guys have played their best renditions of the many songs sung at a *Melaveh Malkah*, Avi, a superior guitar player, soothes to sleep the remaining children with a slow, heart-warming rendition of ADON OLAM.

"It worked," notes Mrs. Stark with satisfaction. "They are all asleep. You're hired—come every night!"

Ovadiah turns to Avi: "That was really moving. You put a depth of feeling into those words that hit me straight in the gut."

Ovadiah is mustering up the courage to ask the question that has been on his mind since he was first introduced to Avi. He admires his huge, Viking-like friend—and not for his physical strength alone; there is more to it than that. Ovadiah longs to not only have knowledge like Avi's, but also acquire his strength of belief. Avi never seems to have any doubts. Maybe now is the time to ask? Yes. He turns to Avi hesitantly:

"Avi, I have a question. I . . . I hope you don't mind if I ask."

176 *Havdalah* literally translates as separation or distinction. Here it is referring to the religious ceremony at the end of the Sabbath, performed with a braided candle, which marks the distinction between the holy Sabbath and the rest of the week.

177 A song which speaks about Elijah the Prophet coming to announce the coming of the Messiah soon in our days.

178 This is a festive meal held after the conclusion of the Sabbath, which many times is accompanied with music and songs.

Avi's warm look dispels Ovadiah's fears. "After a Sabbath of bonding together like this you can no longer be nervous to ask anything. Ask away."

"You have a depth to your approach to Judaism that inspires us all. You live with a strength of belief that is reminiscent of a large Mack truck. Nothing budges you. I long for that. You have helped me bring so many parts of the Torah into my life, and that in a more meaningful way than anyone else has been able to do before. I would like to know where all of this strength comes from. Where does this fire in you come from? You come from a non-Jewish world. What was it that sparked you to leave where you were and to search for Judaism?

"Even after Yehudah's story of Mr. Migdal, and even after the donkey ride we had last night, I still feel that I live a life of doubts, but I know that you don't. How did you do it? How did you become the Avi that we all know? What pushed you out of your non-Jewish world to become one of the most 'sure of himself' Jews I have ever met?"

Ovadiah is startled to see the change that comes over Avi's usually cheerful face; darkness descends upon it, as Avi remembers his previous life. Since he has left it, he has spent his time running away from that despicable heritage. As he is about to divulge the secrets of his past, he cannot bear to look at his friends. He casts a lonely look towards Rafi, the chubby toddler with long blond side-locks, who is now sleeping on his lap. After putting down his guitar, he gives the sleeping child a gentle, almost needy, hug before exposing his secret to the world. He knows that his message will affect their lives—and yours too, Searching Soul. The time for hiding has ended for Avraham ben Avraham, or, should I say, Adolph Reich.

Nazi Roots

Avi's voice is quiet as he starts to speak.

"I grew up not as Avraham ben Avraham, but rather as Adolph Reich, knowing that my grandfather was once an 'honored' soldier in the Nazi Army. I heard from him many repugnant and gruesome stories of the torture that he personally administered to Hashem's beloved people. I despised him since my early youth. Every gift he gave me as a child I threw into the garbage pail. When he hugged me, I recoiled in disgust. I didn't want to touch him."

The silence in the room is intense. Even Mrs. Stark stops washing dishes in the kitchen to listen surreptitiously to the rest of Avi's saga.

"When I was seventeen, I went to a place of worship for a holiday with the whole family. My mother sat me next to her father, against my will."

Come, Searching Soul; let's go to Düsseldorf, Germany:

There's 17 year old Avraham—I mean, Adolph—8 years younger, somewhat skinnier and shorter than the present Avi. He is in the back row of pews. Sitting next to him is an old man with a harsh and sinister wrinkled face. The grandfather sits reading the book of prayers and droning words of acceptance of the kingship of the 'Lord'. Adolph is noticeably uncomfortable. As he focuses on his grandfather's ancient, gnarled face he thinks of the horrid history lying behind each of those wrinkles. He starts to burn inside. Finally he gets up the courage and says:

"Grandfather, if you accept the Master of the Universe's Kingship then why did you lust to kill His servants?"

The old man glares at his grandson, but not for long . . . Recovering from his initial surprise at the question, the old but still strong fiend slams his fist harshly and coldly into Adolph's face. Blood quickly starts to stream out of Adolph's nose and mouth. Adolph's mother doesn't dare say anything. She knows what it is to live under the control of her father's hatred-infected mind. With tears in his eyes, Adolph turns to his mother:

"I am not going to live this way anymore. I am not going to continue with the nightmare of a life that this family has been forced into by this dog."

He stands up and looks the old animal directly in the face, and with perfect aim spits a bloody glob in his direction—bull's-eye right between his eyes. He then runs out of the building yelling:

"Goodbye, Grandfather. Goodbye, seething misplaced hatred. Goodbye, Germany."

Adolph's Path to Avraham Begins

LET'S GO BACK to the Stark's living room. Avi has paused, and is looking down, away from his friends. He is stroking Rafi's blond side locks.

"That evening, after I got out of the hospital, having had my nose set, I decided that I needed to finally get away from my besmirched past. Soon after, I left Germany and settled in Antwerp. I wanted no part of this hatred. When some time later I heard of my grandfather's demise, the only thought that came to my mind was 'If only it had occurred 70 years earlier . . . I hope his bones rot.' I was and am still tortured by the knowledge of where I came from."

Many an emotional glance passes between the friends. Avi just continues to look down at the sleeping child in his lap, making sure to avoid eye contact with them. He doesn't want to know what his friends are thinking. He has become a deeply religious Jew. He is everyone's friend and mentor, yet he is the grandson of a sadistic Jew-hating murderer. Sitting hunched over, closed in on himself, it is quite clear that he does not want to discuss his feelings. Part of him will always feel like a stranger in the world he has done so much to become part of. But he knows that now is not the time to emote. He has an important message to give over which will help his buddy Ovadiah, and with him, you also, Searching Soul, realize how to view difficulties in a way that will make them into merits.

Ovadiah's jaw has dropped. Avi puts his large pointer finger under Ovadiah's frail and delicate chin and lifts it so as to close his mouth.

"Don't be sorry about asking, buddy. Actually, I am glad that you did. What I have to tell you now will put together many of the details of ADON OLAM that we have learned up to this point."

Thank You for the Merit . . . .

"COMING FROM A HISTORY of falsehood, I decided that it was time to look for truth. My search was long and involved. It seemed clear to me that there must be a God, yet the inhabitants of this world have many varied ideas as to who He is. Judaism was by no means my first stop. I decided to take up the study of world religions in Antwerp. I flipped through many of the world's 'main' religions and looked into some of the not-so-mainstream ones also. Truth seemed pretty hard to find. Consistency was uncommon. One day it happened. I somehow found myself wandering into a small, ancient-looking, Jewish study hall in Antwerp, on Jacob Jacobsstraat. When I was about to exit I noticed that there was a young rabbinical student reading a handwritten sign in Hebrew posted next to the exit. I asked him to please translate what he had just read. I then heard for the first time the now-familiar words that we say when we leave the study hall:

I thank You, O Hashem, my God. that you have established my portion with those who dwell in the study hall, and You have not established my portion with idlers; for I arise early and they arise early; I arise early for words of Torah, and they arise early for idle words; I toil and they toil; I toil and receive reward, and they toil and do not receive reward; I run and they run; I run to the life of the World to Come and they run to the pit of destitution. As it is written: And You, O God, will lower them into the well of destruction, men of bloodshed and deceit shall not live out half their days, but as for me, I will trust in You.

"The young man left, and I continued to stand there, deeply moved. My ancestors hungered to kill this holy people. Until that moment I imagined that the poor Jews were trapped in a position that they could not get out of. I felt sorry for this poor outcast destitute nation that the world tried time and again to annihilate. Now, for the first time, I realized that they did not feel sorry for themselves—just the opposite! They gave thanks for the merit of being good Jews. How could that be? Later in life I would discover the depths of the meaning of that merit."

"What do you mean?" Ovadiah is listening intently, but Avi seemingly ignores the question.

I Am Not Worthy to Merit Their Troubles

"A NUMBER OF YEARS PASSED, and I became disgruntled with yet another religion that I was checking out. As usual, all I found was yet another list of contradictions with no answers. I was beginning to wonder if there were any consistent and non-hypocritical religions. Then I remembered that study hall. My search for truth eventually found me making my way to Jerusalem. I arrived at the Ohr Somayach Yeshivah.[179] Soon enough, I realized that this was it. I had finally found truth. These people were not afraid of questions, but rather thrived

179 Name of a yeshivah in Jerusalem.

upon then. Their answers were consistent, non-hypocritical and screamed of truth.

"Soon after that, I started to learn towards becoming a convert. The administration then set me up with Yehudah. One day he taught me the text of the *Shulchan Aruch*[180] on the laws of conversion. It states there that when someone wants to convert to Judaism, he needs to meet the *beis din* (rabbinical court). At this meeting the rabbis who make up the court should ask the conversion candidate what it was that he saw that brought him to convert, even though he knows that the Jewish People are persecuted. The potential convert should answer that 'Yes, I know that they are persecuted and rejected by the world, and what's more—I am not worthy of joining such a people.' I was dumbfounded. What could that mean?"

Everyone is silent. You can hear the bubbles from the Stark family's fish tank; the hum of the pump seems to fill in the silence.

"I yelled at Yehudah: 'Why should I be unworthy? I don't want to be pompous, but I feel I am worthy.'"

"You seem to be more worthy than any of us, Avi," Ovadiah says warmly, and is seconded by everyone else.

"Thanks for the compliment. Yehudah said the same, but then he added: 'Allow me to add to your confusion. The Commentators[181] state that 'I am not worthy' means 'I am not worthy to take part in their troubles, and oh, who will allow me to merit this.' So I wondered, why should anyone want troubles?"

"And what could it mean to merit troubles?" adds Natan. "Troubles are something you have to endure. They are not something that you long to merit."

And Shalom says simply, "I fail to understand that explanation." To which Ovadiah adds, "I've had a lot of troubles, and, believe me, it's no merit."

Shimi puts it more simply: "Seems crazy to me to think that troubles are a merit."

"Well," says Avi after they've all had their say, "It was then

---

180   Code of Jewish law written by Rabbi Yosef Karo, first printed in 1565.

181   Rashi on Tractate *Yevamos* 47a, which is the original source of this quote from the *Shulchan Aruch*.

that I again thought back to that handwritten sign in the study hall. 'Thank You for putting my portion with those who study Your Torah.' Remember what we learned together back in the woods. All that our souls know and experience in this world is from the Torah. Those, like my ancestors, who busy themselves with the emptiness of the cloud, use their experiences to blind themselves and therefore enter the well of destruction. Those who busy themselves with the Torah and know that all else is futility of futilities[182] pull away the cloud and aid in the bringing of the final redemption. Yes—it is the biggest merit in the world to be able to be part of this people and to attach to Hashem."

The Father's Punishment Can Fix the Sword

"BUT THAT DOESN'T EXPLAIN how troubles can be a merit."

"Yaah, I was waiting for someone to ask that," says Avi. "The Torah tells us, Ovadiah, that when the Jewish nation as a whole will fulfill the commandments of the Torah and scrupulously live by Hashem's Words, all will go well with them, and there will be no need for troubles. On the other hand, if we as a people do not follow His Will, then tragedies will confront us until, through the troubles, we learn to find our way back to the proper relationship with our Master.

"This was the message that Yehudah gave us last night with the Donkey's Horn. Everything that Hashem does is planned, intentional, and for the good. Even our confrontations with calamity are meant for our betterment."

"How can confrontations with negativity serve a purpose?" asks Shimi.

"We all understand," answers Avi, "that when a small child runs into the street after his ball, he does not realize why his loving father pulls him back. He sees that his ball just got run over by a car and does not understand that the same might

---

182 This is a reference to a quote which appears in King Solomon's book of Ecclesiastes twice: 1:2, 12:8.

have happened to him, if his father hadn't pulled him out just in time. While being pulled back, the son does not understand the love of his father. He can't understand yet why it is bad to run into the street. He thinks that his father is just being cruel. Why did Dad let my ball get ruined? But one day he will realize that what happened was the completely proper thing. He will come to appreciate that if not for the pain of being pulled back and the lesson of the possible slap, he would not have survived to eventually attain the understanding of the father's concern and love.

"A proper father may administer a punishment for the good of his child. This punishment helps to steer his child back on to the straight and narrow. We as a nation also need to look at our tragedies introspectively."

Natan tries to reword the answer: "So what you are saying, Avi, is that each trial that we confront as a people has its own message that we need to decode. And if we understand and implement these messages we will fix that which created the swords and we will thereby merit closeness to Hashem."

"*Yaah*. This is exactly my point, or should I say, exactly the point of the *Shulchan Aruch*. You see, my friends, troubles can actually be a merit, because they can sometimes be the only thing that will lead us back into the open arms of the Torah."

Soon after, the Melaveh Malkah concludes, and the boys go back to their dormitory. Yehudah spends much of the next two days with Rabbeinu Reuven, learning my next phrase:

וְהוּא הָיָה וְהוּא הוֶֹה וְהוּא יִהְיֶה בְּתִפְאָרָה

~

V'hu haya vehu hoveh vehu yihyeh b'tifarah.

~

And He was and He is and He will be in splendor.

The messages captivate him, but on his way home after completing the section, he is wondering how to give these concepts over to Ovadiah, when . . . .

The World Will Never be the Same

*F*IRE FALLS FROM THE SKY, *and debris comes smashing to the ground. The air is filled with a torrent of death. And then—the second of the Twin Towers collapses as well. Minutes earlier, both towers were hit by passenger airplanes. Now it's clear to the whole world that this is not an accident . . . A storm of hatred has just hit the world. The realization that none of us are ever safe again against the evil schemes of terrorism has come to stay—with an immense bang. Peace and stability are lost forever. Thousands lie dead. But they are not the only casualties from today. Billions—in fact, every single human being—has lost trust in mankind forever. Many a mind thinks the thought "Where was God?" The world will never be the same again.*[183]

A few hours after the attack Yehudah is on the phone, trying to calm down Ovadiah.

"Even the dismal and difficult have a place in the greater picture of history. There's just so much we don't understand, but that does not mean that Hashem is unjust or absent. Eventually we will see how this tragedy fits into the puzzle of our world."

Suddenly a spray of bullets is heard from outside Yehudah's apartment. Two of those bullets enter the Stark home. The sliding glass door to the front yard shatters and the kids scream. Rafi runs towards his mother with his teddy bear, whose head has just been blown off. Ovadiah hears the commotion in the background as Yehudah lets the phone fall to the floor.

Mrs. Stark is in a flurry to grab the children.

As Yehudah runs out the door with his gun, Mrs. Stark says, "I think the bullets came from behind the kindergarten across the street." By the time she finishes that sentence Yehudah is well on his way to just that place.

Whoomp. Yehudah is on the ground with his pistol pointing, as he scans through the bushes and around the small

---

183   For the sake of the story-line, the attack happens in the spring, instead of in the fall.

kindergarten. For the next few minutes he crawls and peers wherever he can. The streets are unusually silent. Yehudah has missed the terrorist this time. He is nowhere to be found. He must have escaped down into the valley. Three ambulances and five police cars come scurrying into the neighborhood. Yehudah briefs the sergeant and returns home.

"Better luck next time," he says as he comes in. A glance at his wife shows him that she is somewhat shaken. "How are you? How are the kids?"

"A little shell-shocked, and by the way, we have to buy a new teddy bear for Rafi."

They chuckle and then from the corner Yehudah hears Ovadiah's voice coming from the cordless phone. He runs to pick it up:

"We're fine. All is well," he reassures him.

Ovadiah is beside himself. He just cries and says goodbye. As Yehudah starts to sweep up the shattered glass, he recalls what he learned with Rabbeinu Reuven just hours before.

Power and Awe's Splendorous Return—*B'tifarah*

"SO FAR," says Rabbi Reuven to Yehudah, as they sit in his book-lined study, "*The Hidden Master* has taught us how Hashem's plans created the world and are leading that world to a focused goal. Now, with the word B'tifarah (in splendor), we are going to receive the key to understanding global difficulties and their function in the greater picture. In order to understand why the illustrious authors wrote this word, I need to give you a little historical background.

"While still in the Babylonian exile, Daniel the prophet, who later was to become one of the first members of the Great Assembly, removed the mention of Hashem's power (*HaGibor*) from his prayers. Just a few years earlier, at the beginning of the exile, Jeremiah the Prophet had removed mention of

Hashem's awesomeness (*HaNora*) from his prayers for similar reasons. Both were living in times of turmoil when Hashem's power and awesomeness were hidden from view. We are taught that they removed these words because they could not bring themselves to mention in their prayers that which they could not outwardly perceive. Both were expressing that neither Hashem's awesomeness nor His power were recognizable while His holy people were in exile and His Temple had been reduced to rubble.

"But when the Great Assembly later came to write the words of ADON OLAM, they chose to create a world outlook where Hashem's infinite power and awesomeness will never be doubted again. They chose to show recognition even while Hashem was hiding. In this chapter, my father will show us how the line והוא היה והוא הווה והוא יהיה בתפארה ~ V'Hu haya v'Hu hoveh v'Hu yihyeh b'tifarah ~ And He was and He is and He will be in splendor—teaches us that our downtrodden state as a people does not need to appear to us as if there is a lack of Hashem's power (*gevurah*).

"He reminds us that the prophets, Daniel and Jeremiah, were certainly not suggesting that Hashem lacks either power or awe. They only wanted to express that Hashem's power and awe, while constantly existent, were there hiding behind the horrifying events of their times.

"In my father's chapter on *b'tifarah* he speaks of a clear pane of glass that is broken into shards by the winds of a storm. He tells us that from the times of the Great Assembly until the times of the Messiah our people will endure one storm after another. The winds of terror, persecution and destruction will jostle our people to the point where, as a community, our faith, like the clear pane of glass, will be in danger of being broken to shards. Unlike those who came before the authors of ADON OLAM, the new generations would no longer have any prophets to guide them through the upcoming storms and to put the shards back together for them. So it was time for those last prophets and sages to write into ADON OLAM the specific messages that would guide them to unbroken clarity and stability of faith. "He tells us that the word *b'tifarah* was written to immunize our people against even the strongest attacks to our nation and show them that it is Hashem Who—powerfully and awesomely—not only creates, but also purposefully controls the entire storm. B'tifarah's message will enable our nation's faith to stay whole, and not shatter.

"And so they told us in ADON OLAM that there will come a time when Hashem alone will again be recognized as the awesome undoubted King, as we learned in the previous sentence לבדו ימלוך נורא ~ *Levado yimloch nora*. Its authors knew that that wouldn't be enough for our people. And so they continued their composition of ADON OLAM with these words . . . .

"והוא היה והוא הווה והוא יהיה בתפארה ~ And He was and He is and He will be in splendor. This is what can lead us to the conclusion that even worldwide terror, chaos and destruction are in the most perfect and splendorous balance called *tifarah*—that all that was, is, and will ever be, is never haphazard, chaotic or by chance. Everything has a perfectly planned purpose in the bigger picture of time. This is the meaning of *b'tifarah*, in perfect splendor.

"Let me show you how . . ."

Back in his living room, Yehudah finishes sweeping up the pieces of the glass window shattered by the bullets, and wonders how to help Ovadiah. As he dumps the last dustpan of shards into the pail, he says, "B'tifarah."

Helicopter?

T HE NEXT MORNING, bright and early, Yehudah knocks at Ovadiah and Shimi's door. Ovadiah answers—because, as usual, nothing short of an atomic bomb would wake up Shimi.

"Yehudah, what are you doing here so early? It isn't even time for morning prayers!"

Yehudah hands Ovadiah a sealed envelope, and says, "I'm

sorry I won't be able to help you through this right now. I won't be around for the next few days. I have some other responsibilities out of town. After I got the kids to sleep last night I received a call from the Army Intelligence Service. Since I won't be here for you I wrote you some food for thought. Please read and think about what I wrote. We'll discuss it when I return."

"Where are you going?"

But all Yehudah says is, "Read what I wrote you. I have to go. In ten minutes a helicopter is picking me up at the pad near Hadassah Hospital on Mount Scopus. It'll take me five minutes to get there. Bye."

"Helicopter?"

But Yehudah has already disappeared down the stairs of the *yeshivah* dormitory and the exit door is heard clicking shut. Ovadiah is left in the quiet hallway, much puzzled. He looks at the envelope as he returns to his room and takes a seat on his bed. Shimi is snoring really loudly now. There are still a few minutes before the alarm should ring. He opens the seal and reads . . . .

With the fall of the Twin Towers we have all just experienced what could only be described as having the rug pulled out from under us, but the rug is still there. You just have to know how to find it. The Torah clarifies the confusion and havoc that the world is experiencing. Our Sages lead us to stability even through the earthquakes of time and help us to find the rug. Ovadiah, here are some Torah sources to think about. I will be home, God-willing, in a few days. Then we will go over b'tifarah, which will enable you to stand unjostled amidst all these tremors. Sorry to go now, but I am needed somewhere else.

*Our Rabbis state,[184] "We are obligated to bless Hashem for the bad in the same way that we bless Him for the good. For it states in the Torah[185] that 'You shall love the Lord your God with all of your heart'— written as **levavcha**—as opposed to **libcha** . . ." This change of spelling is meant to teach us that we need to serve Hashem with both of our inclinations, the Good Inclination, and the Evil Inclination. The verse continues by saying that we need to love Hashem "with all of our life*

184 Mishnah, Berachos 9:1, Gemara Berachos 54a.

185 Deuteronomy 6:5.

force," which means "even if your life is being taken away . . ." Then the verse finishes by saying we have to love Hashem "with every measurement that He deals out to us."

On this, rabbis of later generations[186] relate that:

A person is obligated to make the blessing on the bad with complete and full knowledge and with burning desire in the same way that he makes the blessing in joy on the good. For the bad is to the servants of Hashem their own good and joy. This is so because they accept with love what Hashem set forth for them. This means that in the acceptance of this bad, one is serving Hashem. This service of acceptance is what becomes one's joy.

On this point a later commentator[187] emphasizes that:

He (The Tur) was very specific in his words, and stated, "with complete knowledge and with burning desire in the same way that one makes the blessing with joy on the good . . . This is because it is impossible for man to be happy with the bad, and therefore he needed to explain that this is the meaning, that just as one makes a blessing on the good with joy and complete knowledge and burning desire, therefore the blessing on the bad is also with joy. This is because in the acceptance of the bad, one is serving Hashem, and it is this service that is that person's joy."

Ovadiah, these sources teach us to accept worldwide tragedy knowing that both the good and the bad come from Hashem. When we are completely sure of our loving Father's hand purposely painting the whole picture we have a certain aspect of joy. It is the joy of knowing that nothing is haphazard.

The Torah[188] tells us that all of the curses that will ever come upon our people come only because we did not serve Hashem joyfully. King David[189] told us that we need to serve Hashem joyfully and that we are to come before His presence with singing. A commentator on this psalm[190] states that:

186 Tur and Shulchan Aruch, Orach Chaim, 222:3.

187 Bach on Tur, ibid.

188 Deuteronomy 28:47.

189 Psalms 100:2.

190 Tefillos David.

There is a great difference between serving people and serving Hashem. Serving people is filled with sadness, because one is not certain that one will receive payment. And even if one will get paid, it is only after the work is done. The work itself is only a means. Not so when serving Hashem. For the service itself is the reward. The goal of this service is to be in a state of joy during the service. The joy is in knowing that even what you now see as confusion will one day become clear.

Think about it. I hope to speak to you more when I return.
You can do it. Hashem does not send us any test that we cannot pass.

YEHUDAH STARK

As Ovadiah folds the letter back up and returns it to the envelope, his alarm goes off. It's time to start his day. He has to get to morning prayers, breakfast, classes. But even after the letter, he just doesn't have the heart for it all anymore. He is overwhelmed both by the immense tragedy of the numerous dead and by the future repercussions of what happened the day before. Where was Hashem? Why this way? Are You out there?

Hiding While Guiding

SEARCHING SOUL, you and Ovadiah are about to find out that, of course, Hashem is 'out there' but not always does He choose to be seen openly. Hashem can simultaneously be hiding while still guiding. I will show you in the next few pages how this is exactly the message expressed in my word, b'tifarah.

B'tifarah is not the only place where the Members of the Great Assembly convey this message of Hashem's guiding while hiding. For example, Mordechai was amongst the first members of the Great Assembly. We are most familiar with him from the Megillah or Scroll of Esther.

*You may have thought that Esther was the only name of the heroine of the Megillah. But actually Esther's name was also Hadassah. When she and Mordechai wrote the Megillah, they called her and the scroll by the name Esther and were also meticulous to never mention Hashem's Name even once in the Megillah. They did both of these things in order to inform the world that for Hashem there is never any absence there is only hiding, **hester**, for our People's benefit. Their message in that holy Scroll is that we should see Hashem's hidden hand splendorously (בתפארה ~ b'tifarah) guiding history even while it is hidden in the midst of the darkness of the evil regime of Achashverosh.*

Why do I choose the word 'splendorously'? Come, let's see together.

The Splendorous Vase

YEHUDAH IS BACK and has taken Ovadiah for a nighttime walk in the rain. Destination—unknown to all except Yehudah. On the way they speak about the sources in his letter. Now, while they are both under Yehudah's enormous umbrella, Yehudah tries to explain what he learned from Rabbeinu Reuven just a week earlier. Let's go back together to that meeting . . . .

"Yehudah," Rabbeinu Reuven says, "it's time to discuss how Hashem was, is and always will be in *tifarah*. Hummm. This is a hard one. I will follow my father's lead and I hope you will understand its deep implications. Have you ever studied the implications of the way the items of the Passover *Seder* plate are positioned?"

"Not really. I mean, I know how to set up the plate but I do not know any of the deeper meanings as to why the varied items are placed in that particular arrangement."

"Each of the items on the plate needs to be positioned precisely. The design of the *Seder* plate[191] was set up in accordance to the diagrams of the *Sefiros*.[192] You have heard of the *Sefiros*?"

"Of course, they are complicated kabbalistic concepts of how Hashem enables us, in a small way, to understand His actions in the world."

"In a very simplified sense, Yehudah, you are correct. In most books dealing with Kabbalah, you will see really bizarre diagrams depicting very specific positions of the *Sefiros*. Here, let me show you one of these diagrams. Which *Sefirah*, or channel to understanding Hashem, is in the center of this diagram?"

"*Tiferes*."

"The Sephardic rendition of ADON OLAM articulates that גָּדוֹל כֹּחַ וּגְבוּרָה ~ *Gadol Koach U'gevura* ~ Great is the recognizable power and the power of pulling back (restraining) through hiding. And all of the traditions teach that **He was, is and will be in splendor, tifarah**. These statements, Yehudah, are both speaking about the same thing."

"Recognizable power and the power of hiding are seeming opposites," notes Yehudah.

"Exactly. And it is precisely this perfect constant combination of these two concepts that is described by the word *tifarah*. Which as you just saw in the diagram, is placed in between the *sefiros* of recognizable power and restrained power."

"What exactly is splendorous about this combination? And what does this have to do with the *Seder* plate?"

Rabbeinu Reuven reaches behind his chair and takes a multicolored vase from the window ledge.

"The word *tiferes* comes from the same root as *mefoar*. This root describes how it is that many aspects can come together to form a single unit. If a vase was painted one pretty color, then it would be called *yafeh*, beautiful. On the other hand, a

---

191 *Seder* translates as 'order'. It is the ceremony performed on the first night(s) of Passover. During the ceremony we teach of the miraculous exodus from Egypt. The '*Seder* plate' is a plate with designated sections in which the items necessary for use during the *seder* are placed.

192 This is according to the Arizal, but there are also other customs regarding the *Seder* plate setup.

vase like this one, which has many colors in its design, including dreary black, unifies the multifaceted, and is called *mefoar*, splendorous. In kabbalistic thought, *tiferes* is the mixture of the two seemingly opposite traits of loving-kindness and strict justice, mixed in perfect proportion and always given out at precisely the proper time. These traits can also be described as Hashem's recognizable power which He sometimes chooses to pull back and hide."

"The world does not always understand the black dots on the vase of history; we don't always understand every piece of the global picture. We might mistake Hashem's *gevurah*, hiding or pulling back, for absence. But just because you don't understand the whole picture doesn't mean that you can't comprehend that there is a bigger picture and that there is a Master Painter painting that picture and giving it its splendorous form.[193]

"Now that you understand the vase, could you please stand on the chair and pull down the copper Passover *Seder* plate from the top shelf over there?"

Yehudah is quick to do so, taking down the *Seder* plate carefully.

"Yes that's it. What item does the engraving show is to be placed in the middle of the plate?"

"*Maror*, the bitter herbs."

"*Tifarah* is placed in the center of the *Sefirah* diagram, and *Maror*—in the middle of the *Seder* plate. They are the same, Yehudah. What is the *Seder* plate teaching you?"

"Splendor and bitterness. Why are both of these central?"

Bittersweet Design

A S YEHUDAH AND OVADIAH enter the Beis Yisrael
neighborhood,[194] Ovadiah stops and looks at Yehudah quizzically through the pelting rain.

---

193 HaRav Shimshon Pincus, zt"l, Pesach, p. 22.

194 A neighborhood in Jerusalem.

"*Seder* plate, bitter herbs, diagrams, *tiferes*, splendor, what does this have to do with the towers going down?"

"The most conspicuous and disturbing placement on the *Seder* plate is that of the bitter herbs. It's your grandfather's book which informs us that this placement tells us that sometimes the bitter is the most central. *Maror*, the bitter herbs, are put in the center to represent splendor, *tiferes*."[195]

"*Maror* expresses splendor? I don't see anything so splendorous about horseradish. When I eat it on Passover, it makes my eyes water and I start to cough."

"The bitter herbs remind us of our embittered slavery to that bloodthirsty king, Pharaoh. But there was a silver lining to the cloud of Egyptian slavery. '. . . Egypt was evil to us and our forefathers. And we called to Hashem and He heard our pleas . . . and He took us out of Egypt.'[196] If not for the bitterness, we would never have called out for Hashem's help, and consequently we would never have merited to receive the Torah and to become Hashem's holy people.

"Sometimes the most caring of gifts that the Holy One blessed be He gives us is the bitter, almost inedible, *Maror*. *Maror* embodies the concepts which describe *tiferes*, splendor. Many times it is the bitterness of life—the difficult tests that we constantly meet up with—that, if passed, actually enable us to attach most strongly to Hashem."[197]

"Is bitterness the best method of bringing Hashem's people closer to Him? Couldn't it be done a little more pleasantly?" Ovadiah is still not convinced.

So Yehudah tells him of something that happened to him many years before . . . .

---

195 HaRav Shimshon Pincus, ibid.

196 Numbers 20:15–16.

197 HaRav Shimshon Pincus, ibid.

Air-Raid

PANIC SEIZES THE INHABITANTS of the Holy Land as the air raid sirens pierce through every heart and home on this, the first evening of the Gulf War. The streets of this coastal region city are empty, except for the figure of one frantic 23-year-old young man carrying two gas masks.

"Little Srulik, where are you? Come on, little boy, come to Uncle Yehudah, it's very dangerous out here."

At that instant Yehudah sees the Scud missile, which he fears might be filled with poison gas, arching through the sky, and then there is a terrible explosion. The earth shudders; some windows break.

"Srulik, come to me now. I'll buy you a big chocolate bar, just come now."

Only then does Srulik appear from his hiding place behind some bushes with a big smile: "Chocolate! You promise?"

Swiftly, Yehudah whisks the small boy off of his feet and puts on his gas mask and then the boy's. He dashes for shelter, entering the first building they get to and hides with Srulik in the stairwell. More Scuds land, not where they are, but close enough to shatter windows in nearby buildings. Yehudah holds onto the little boy. With tears in his eyes, he wonders how many of his fellow Jews may have been hurt or worse by each of these deadly missiles. "Hashem, why do our people have to again and again endure such world hatred? Where are You when we need You the most?" he wonders—

Back to the present.

"That bitter moment," says Yehudah, "and many others are now in the past. I was not married then, but both my wife and I say the same thing about that war: 'That was a great war.'"

"What was great about it?"

"Our dire situation forced our whole nation to focus. As the expression goes, there are no atheists in foxholes, and our people were all together in one big foxhole. Overnight, the mighty Israel became vulnerable in a way it had never before experienced. Nothing could save us. We all felt the dire need for Hashem. And the more we opened our hearts in prayer, the more we saw the open miracles.

"As the war progressed, so did the reports of miracle after miracle. Thirty-nine scuds fell on our tiny country. We all saw the unbelievable pictures of the missile that fell and exploded right between two buildings. Nothing happened to their inhabitants. Then there was the one that fell in Tel Aviv and blew up right near a main gas line. Nothing happened to that line. Had it fallen a few feet closer, hundreds would have died. There was the building that was destroyed—but all its inhabitants were out for the evening, etc. Hashem was right there and with us all the time. We simply needed to find Him.

"But not every ending has the characters living happily ever after. Four days ago wasn't a happy ending for the thousands that died in the Towers attack."

Just then they turn the corner and find themselves standing in front of the Mir Yeshivah.[198]

"Ovadiah let me tell you just how this *yeshivah* got here."

A Funny Thing Happened on the Way to Shanghai

*T*HE WHOLE YESHIVAH *has fled the town of Mir. Their destination at this point—Vilna. They have arrived at a certain hiding place along their long journey, which will actually culminate in their going to Shanghai and thus being saved. Still in occupied Nazi territory, they are in no way out of danger. While hiding in an unoccupied building, the sounds of the Nazi soldiers searching for them are heard outside the door of the large room where they are all concealed. While his students and friends pray silently and tearfully, Rabbi Shmuelevitch starts to quietly whisper to himself over and over again "Ein od milvado, there is nothing other than Hashem."*

198 Name of the largest *yeshivah* in Jerusalem.

*Doom could be imminent. If they are found, there will be no escape. The Nazi soldiers' boots thunder on the wooden floor just outside the door. The Rabbi is saying over and over again that there is nothing other than Hashem. Searching Soul, while you are busy looking at the frightening scene in front of you, I will help you to use what you already learned from the Members of the Great Assembly, and from Yehudah, to imagine what may have been going through the Rav's mind between his fervent whispers of "**Ein od milvado**—There is nothing other than Hashem."[199]*

Ein od milvado: There is nothing other than Hashem. All that might happen to us is from You, Almighty, and all of the tests that You will send upon the Jewish nation we have the ability to pass. Some erroneously think that in this particular circumstance You do not have the power to intervene. But, dear Almighty Master of All, I am saying now that—

Ein od milvado: There is nothing other than Hashem, for I know that there is nothing outside of You. Even these Nazis are from You. There is nothing happening by chance. Divine Providence means that everything that is happening is for a reason, an ultimate reason coming from a much larger whole, a larger complete picture. So I say again—

Ein od milvado: There is nothing other than Hashem. As the Nazis get closer to our door we know of no reality outside of You. If the holy *yeshivah* of Mir will be slaughtered, Heaven forbid, it is not because of some outside force. So many of our brethren and holy rabbis have already been slaughtered like sheep, yet we are a nation of believers, unlike those who come to slaughter us. You bring the Nazi and the bullet and you will bring the Messiah and the final Salvation of Your people.

Ein od milvado: There is nothing other than Hashem. We know that we have not fallen haphazardly into a wicked trap. All is planned by the all-knowing Master. Everything has a greater purpose, even if we are so small that we do not presently understand what that greater purpose is.

Ein od milvado: There is nothing other than Hashem. We must never forget, not even in the middle of the most frightening moments, that there is nothing to be frightened of. All is coming from Hashem. Even the evil that is presently hunting us for our blood does not exist independently.

Ein od milvado: There is nothing other than Hashem. ADON OLAM teaches that all evil will one day disappear. Hashem was, is and will be recognized in splendor. So we Jews know at all times that everything has a purpose.

Ein od milvado: There is nothing other than Hashem. When all evil is finished, *V'Acharei kichlos hakol,* we will understand and recognize that You alone reign, *levado yimloch nora.* Our enemies are nothing. Maybe not now, but someday, the world will understand that You run world history *b'tifarah,* with splendor. There is a hidden reason why our people have to go through this test, whatever its outcome will be. Our faith will never be swayed, for we know that the outcome is only from You and not from them. You are always acting בתפארה ~ *b'tifarah, b'tifarah . . . Ein od milvado: There is nothing other than Hashem.*

The Nazi soldiers start to leave the hallway. Thank God, the yeshivah has been saved.

Quickly, come with me now. It's time to catch the present while we can. Back to the corner outside of the Mir Yeshivah in Jerusalem, where the sound of Torah study wafts out of the study hall, into the street.

"Listen through the rain: You can hear the Mir Yeshivah; the voice of Torah still rings out from it. But our enemies were not always so unsuccessful. From Rabbi Shmuelevitch we can learn that there is never any extraneous power, because everything is within the dominion of Hashem. Even the fall of the Twin Towers."

Ovadiah thinks a moment. "So in the stanza of *V'Acharei,* ADON OLAM informs us that there is an end to all of the seemingly-evil clouds. And we know that at that time Hashem's Kingship will be undoubted. In the meantime, the only way to live through our own present hell is by knowing that even the black will eventually be shown to have always been an integral part of the whole splendorous picture."

Yehudah nods. "So now you understand why Egyptian slavery, which is represented by the *Maror*, is in the center of the plate. The destruction that we have just experienced is also somehow part of the bigger picture. There is no other place to put the *Maror* except in the center. There are no mistakes. Hashem has not left us and never will leave us; rather— והוא היה והוא הווה והוא יהיה והוא בתפארה ~ V'Hu haya v'Hu hoveh v'Hu yihyeh b'tifarah ~ And He was, and He is, and He will be in splendor. But that's not all. Let's keep walking. There's something else I want you to see."

The Tests *Are* Hashem

THE RAIN COMES to an abrupt stop, just as it began. It's 10:45 pm. Yehudah stops at the entrance to the courtyard of an old Iraqi synagogue. There is an eerie mist rising from the Jerusalem streets. It feels like walking through a cloud.

"Even if I know that Hashem sends the storm, it is still very dark and ugly," remarks Ovadiah. "Why did the Great Assembly choose to describe Hashem's workings in the world as always being splendorous?"

"It's only dark and ugly if you think that Hashem haphazardly threw at you something other than Himself."

"What did you say?"

"I'll show you what I mean."

The two climb the narrow slippery stone stairs and, through a catwalk, enter this modest relic of the past, built long before the State of Israel was even a dream in anyone's mind. The small Eternal Light[200] above the Holy Ark casts its flickering beams through the darkness across the ancient room. The intricate

---

200 In every synagogue, above the Holy Ark, in which are placed the Torah scroll(s), is an 'eternal light' to remind us that the Torah is the only true light.

plaster bas-relief work that can be detected on the walls of this holy room, even in the dark, dazzles the eyes.

Ovadiah is impressed. "Royalty. Elegance from a different era. The variety and detail are amazing."

"Look above the Eternal Light. Can you make out the words emblazoned over there?"

As Ovadiah squints to make out the colorful letter-ing, he recognizes my words as brought down by the Sephardim.

בְּלִי עֵרֶךְ בְּלִי דִּמְיוֹן, בְּלִי שִׁנּוּי וּתְמוּרָה,
בְּלִי חִבּוּר בְּלִי פֵּרוּד, גְּדוֹל כֹּחַ וּגְבוּרָה

~

**Beli Erech Beli Dimion, Beli Shinui U'temura,
Beli Chibur Beli Perud, Gadol Koach U'gevura**

~

*"[Hashem is] without the ability to be valued,
without comparison,
He is not able to be changed or switched.
He can neither connect nor separate.
Great is the recognizable power
and the power of pulling back through hiding."*

Now listen as Yehudah will teach Ovadiah, and you as well, what he learned from Rabbeinu Reuven during the conclusion of his latest session with him.

"The only way out of the clouds of life is to know, like Rabbi Shmuelevitch said, that there is absolutely nothing other than Hashem. These words above the Holy Ark were put up in so prominent a place, where anyone lifting up his eyes in the midst of prayer would see them. Certainly many a person read these words as our nation experienced so many upheavals. And as they prayed, the words of ADON OLAM shouted to them that **'He is without the ability to be valued, without comparison,'** for there is nothing outside of Him by which to appraise Him.

'**He is not able to be changed or switched**,' for He is all reality and there is nothing that He is not, which He could change into or switch to. "**He can neither connect nor separate**", for there is no way for Him to separate from His inseparable singular unity. '**Great is the recognizable power and the power of pulling back through hiding.**' We must understand that He is controlling our world even when we do not yet discern His hidden actions.

"*The Hidden Master* teaches us that these words are meant to comfort Hashem's broken people by informing them that all that they experience is really just Hashem calling out to them."

"So when ADON OLAM tells us that Hashem has always and will always be in tifarah, it means that even the difficulties sent our way are not only purposeful, coming from Hashem, but they are Him," Ovadiah concludes.

"Right. And when we recognize Him because of the dark clouds, then, as we already learned in the woods from *Derech Hashem*, we transform darkness into light and deathly shadow into sparkling brilliance.[201] That's why this congregation placed these words above the Eternal Light. By doing this, they were teaching us that we have to see that the darkness is Hashem Himself in splendor."

Ovadiah is working on applying all this: "So neither the destruction of the Twin Towers, nor the Holocaust, nor the Scud missiles are haphazard. Evil has no existence on its own. And like you told us last Sabbath, there are no Fates. Hashem not only runs it all, but **is** all. Although I don't presently understand what just happened to the world or what it means for the future of mankind, I now know that Hashem sent it, or, should I say, Hashem sent Himself."

"And one more thing," adds Yehudah. "The destruction was sent to us to create a new test for our generation. It would be foolish to assume that it was sent so that we could fail. We are meant to pass the tests sent our way."

Silently, the two leave the beautiful synagogue and turn to go home.

201 *Derech Hashem* 1:4:4.

Open the Curtain

THE NEXT DAY, when the Morning Service is over in yeshivah, Ovadiah walks over to Yehudah, who is rolling up his tefillin.

"It was a good talk we had last night," he tells him. "I turned it all over in my mind as I lay in bed. But, if you have a moment, I still have a major question that just did not let me sleep: ADON OLAM's second stanza starts by telling us that in the future all of this horrid evil will eventually be finished. Will we forget it, or will its memory forever haunt us? Will our people ever be able to say a final goodbye to all of these memories, i.e., good riddance, or is even the World to Come going to be plagued by the memories of our past?"

"That's an excellent question!"

"And do you have an excellent answer for me? I need one."

"Me? No. But your grandfather did. Come with me for just a minute and I'll show you, or maybe you will show me."

"Huh?"

With their tefillin bags under their arms, the two walk to the back of the study hall. There Yehudah pulls out his large set of keys and opens the door of the Rosh Yeshivah's private study. There seems to be no place that is off-limits to Yehudah. He shuts the door without turning on the light.

"If you don't like the electric light, do you mind if I open the curtain?" asks Ovadiah.

It's good he can't see Yehudah's gentle smile as he replies: "Go right ahead."

The bright sunlight streams into the small room. Off to the side, the curtain still sways slightly.

"You just answered the question, Ovadiah."

"How? What?"

"Your grandfather quotes Sefer Yetzirah[202] to teach us that evil will never be forgotten. He states that there is no light if there is no darkness. But when the time of the Revelation arrives, it is not that you are removed from the area of the darkness, and go to the area of the light; no, not at all. You just pushed the

---

202 This is an ancient, esoteric kabbalistic work. Its authorship is attributed to Avraham Avinu.

curtains back, allowing you to see what is behind them and enabling the light to stream in. You did not go to the place of the light, but, rather, the darkness has been transformed into light.

Yehudah now grasps the orange curtains. "The curtains are still here. So too in the future, the darkness or curtains of evil will not be removed but just peeled back, allowing you to see Hashem's hand in everything that ever occurred. And then you will realize that it was only because you toiled to push the evil aside that you were able to arrive at this final realization of Hashem."

"So what you are trying to say is that when ADON OLAM states that 'all evil will have completed its purpose . . .' it means that instead of being a barrier between us and Hashem, evil will be seen as what pushed us to reveal Him."

"Exactly. This is *tiferes*. Splendor, the black spots will still be there, but they will not detract from the beauty. Rather, they will add to the splendor.

"I got it. Yehudah, I got it! This is why ADON OLAM tells us that not only was and is Hashem in *tifarah* but also that He **will be** in *tifarah*. The tests that our people went through will still be there, but they will not haunt us. Rather, they **will be recognized** as part of a whole that brought us to where we needed to arrive."

Splendorous, isn't it? Oh, sorry, I didn't mean to startle you, Searching Soul. It's just me again, ADON OLAM. Before we move on to my third stanza, let's get our bearings as to where we are. As I have told you before, even though all of my depth is hinted at in my first stanza, the subsequent stanzas are needed in order to really understand some of the most mystifying points in the first one. Let's now try to discover what it was about my first stanza that V'Acharei, the second stanza, came to clarify for you.

Remember that V'Acharei starts by speaking of how only when all of the confusions of this physical world eventually disappear, Hashem will be recognized by all as the undoubted King. Then my text calls upon every Jew, you included, to view all present world events and tests as being constant testimony to just how complete Hashem's rule was, is, and always will be. The theme is clear: the global recognition of the rule of Hashem.

As you keep that theme in your mind, peruse my first stanza again and you will see what points needed more explanation and why, therefore, the words of V'Acharei needed to be composed.

*My first stanza opens with the words, **Adon Olam reigned before all forms were created**. This originally left you wondering: Over what was Hashem reigning? Then, just a few words later, you came upon the words, **only after the creation of the physical world is His Name called King**. You came to understand from the combination of these two statements that the purpose of Creation is that those created and dwelling in the clouds of physicality will pull back the clouds to enable them to recognize and subsequently call Hashem their King.*

But you, who search for truth, perceive that the inhabitants of the physical world rarely choose to search beyond the clouds of their physical existence. The clouds seem to stand staunchly intact, hiding Hashem's Kingship from his creations.

And so the words of my second stanza, V'Acharei, have come to inform you that even though the world at large does not yet recognize Hashem's Kingship, the duty of every Jew is to recognize Hashem's hand ruling over every event. We are Hashem's Chosen People. We have been chosen to be held responsible to peel back those clouds in order to presently and continually recognize the singular Ruler behind the clouds.

But do you really understand Who is ruling from behind the clouds? I am not so sure that you fully appreciate the implications of belief in One God, namely, what is known in Western culture as monotheism. And so, together we will now go on to that point in my next stanza . . . .

SECTION THREE

V'HU ECHAD:
Monotheism

I KNOW YOU CALL yourself a monotheist or you wouldn't be reading this book. Don't be offended, but I have a question for you. How do you know that you are a monotheist? Really, it's a serious question. Like I said to you at the end of the previous section, I am not so sure that you understand the depths and implications of what monotheism really is.

As you are already aware, some of the members of the Great Assembly were prophets. Clearly, these prophets and their successors knew that in the future there would be misunderstandings and subsequent bewilderment that would sprout from claims of so-called monotheistic beliefs. Although my first stanza is unmistakably monotheistic, not all of the implications of that belief are stated clearly in that stanza, nor are they understood by the world at large. So the authors continued in their composition and came up with my words:

וְהוּא אֶחָד וְאֵין שֵׁנִי, לְהַמְשִׁיל לוֹ לְהַחְבִּירָה
בְּלִי רֵאשִׁית בְּלִי תַכְלִית, וְלוֹ הָעֹז וְהַמִּשְׂרָה

~

V'Hu Echad v'ein sheni, Lehamshil Lo lehachbirah,
Bli reishis, bli sachlis, v'Lo Ha'oz vehamisrah.

~

And He is One and there is no other
Which can compare to Him or be His comrade.
He is without beginning and without end.
His is the power that is Torah and the dominion.[203]

Come with me, as Yehudah and his disciples delve into just what these words mean in your search for meaning. It's time to find the One God.

Yehudah is driving them in his van to the north. As this foggy day darkens to dusk, conversation in the van starts to get to our subject.

"O.K., guys, we're now onto the third stanza of ADON OLAM, so we need to discuss the Oneness of Hashem."

"What is there to discuss? He's One and not two or three," says Shimi lightly.

Shalom turns on him immediately: "Not so simple. We went on this trip with Yehudah last year discussing just this point, and, wow, were we surprised, weren't we, Natan?"

"It was a real intellectual brain warp, I mean revelation. I never understood the depth of the implications of One until then. Monotheism took on new dimensions. I learned then that faith in one God entails belief that there is absolutely no type of bifurcation, unlike what many of the other main 'monotheistic' religions of the world believe. After all, ADON OLAM says, 'He is One and there is no other.'"

"There is more to what Natan just said than you imagine. Did you ever consider the ramifications of Hashem having no parts?" Shalom is continuing to work on Shimi, when Avi speaks up:

203 In order to understand why the Hebrew was translated in this manner, please refer to the Disclaimer.

"And do any of you fully understand why the monotheism of Judaism is the only real monotheism in the world? I too went on the same trip that Shalom and Natan did with Yehudah, about a year before them. But lately Yehudah and I have been . . ."

"Ehmmm . . . going a little bit deeper than before, should we say." Yehudah is quick to intervene.

"That's an understatement, Yehudah."

"You see, now that we have *The Hidden Master*, everything is so much more than I had imagined before," Yehudah concludes, and then, in a more business-like tone says,

"So this is how the night is going to go. Once we arrive at out destination, Avi is going to take everyone to our secluded beach while Ovadiah and I are going it alone on to the Sea of Galilee. We will all meet in the morning. Then Ovadiah will teach you guys some concepts that even Avi and I have not seen together. But first, let me just give you all a little food for thought about the section in *The Hidden Master* that discusses the third stanza.

"In this chapter, Chacham Yashar was trying to lead a wayward generation back to its source. He was trying to show Hashem's confused children how to get back home. And for those who were holding on and didn't know why, he was trying to give them strength to continue. In this chapter there are the answers to mistaken ideologies and paths that the Jew is bombarded with by the outside world. It directs us to hold onto everything that is in ADON OLAM without getting confused by the multitude of lies that our surrounding societies feed us.

"Anyway, in the meantime, start blowing up the rafts, please."

The guys start to blow up the rafts in the back of the van, and soon there is less and less space to move. Night falls, and the van enters an unfriendly Arab area. Yehudah turns the internal lights of the car off, rolls up the windows, and speeds up. He seems to know exactly where he is going. It is almost as if he lived here once.

"Guys, please be quiet and stop carrying on like a bunch of American *yeshivah* boys. I was once almost killed here in the

Aqabat Jaber refugee camp. I need to concentrate to get us out of this horrible place."

Sudden silence descends on the van. Something in Yehudah's tone makes them understand that he means business.

Once they are beyond the village, Ovadiah says, "You are going to tell us what happened to you there, aren't you?"

"God-willing, one day. But not now."

"Maybe on the way home?" asks Shimi.

"We're not coming back this way, but someday I hope to tell you. For now, just keep blowing up the rafts."

"Where are you and I going in the pitch-black on rafts?"

"To another world, Ovadiah," answers Avi. "To another world."

"You got it," says Yehudah. "Keep blowing."

Time passes and it is now quite dark outside. The van turns sharply to the right as they leave the Jordan River Valley road and arrive at Lake Kinneret (the Sea of Galilee). Five minutes later the van squeals to a halt on a dirt path in the middle of high reeds.

"We're here," announces Yehudah.

"We're where?" asks Shimi, in his usual, down-to-earth manner.

"He means get out," translates Natan.

The boys squirm out like a foot being removed from a tight shoe. Then, they extract the larger of the two rafts, which now appears larger than the entire van.

Yehudah pulls Avi aside to go over the list of up-and-coming events.

". . . O.K., that's it. I am counting on you, Avi. You're in charge of making sure that this night all happens like German clockwork. We will see you in the morning."

"We will see you at precisely 5:25."

"Hey, guys," Yehudah calls to the rest of them, "please help push us off so we won't be wet the whole night. Through the reeds. That way."

"What a fog!" notes Shimi.

Shalom is also awed by it. "You would think we were in the

clouds. Yehudah, are you going to be able to navigate?"

They reach the edge of Lake Kinneret, and Yehudah and Ovadiah climb into the raft, which has already been placed in the water.

"O.K., One big push, Heeeeeeve!" Avi calls out, in good mariner's fashion.

"Here is your oar, Ovadiah. Keep rowing until I tell you to stop," says Yehudah.

Within seconds the shore has disappeared from sight in the fog.

Foggy Barbeque

BACK ON SHORE, Avi drives the van down the bumpy road hugging the eastern bank of Lake Kinneret. Because of the fog they all have their eyes almost touching the glass. It is very hard to find this secluded beach tucked away behind the reeds even on a normal, bright day. They have unknowingly passed it a few times and are now backtracking for the third time. Suddenly—

"Stop!!!!!!!!" Natan calls out.

The van screeches to a halt.

"There, I am sure of it."

Shalom looks around. "See, he is right. Now turn to the right. Now to the left. Watch out for that boulder. Now straight and there it is, that beautiful beach."

They unload the barbeque equipment and set up camp. Within a few minutes the hot dogs and potatoes are on the fire, and Avi, Natan, Shalom and Shimi are sitting and looking out in the direction of the lake. It is only a few meters a way, and you can hear the small waves hitting the rocks, but you cannot see the water.

"Shimi," says Natan, "when Yehudah brought us here it was also in the fog. There is a reason for this. In order to understand what One really means, first you need to understand that

Hashem is not inhabiting the world, rather He is the whole world and beyond, as Yehudah already pointed out to us."

"So when ADON OLAM states that there is nothing other than Him, it does not just mean that there is no other god, it means that there is nothing at all other than Him," explains Shalom further.

"So we brought you to this place in the fog to have you focus on the one thing that you think you can still perceive . . ." says Natan.

"Yourself." Avi completes the thought, leaving Shimi somewhat astonished at these developments.

Rav Schwab on One-self

AVI PULLS OUT a familiar book from his backpack. As he flips through the pages he says to Shimi:
"I brought with me *Rav Schwab on Prayer*. Let's see how he defines One, and then you will also come to a better appreciation of the self. Shimi, flashlight please.

> **V'Hu Echad ~ He is (One) alone.** *After affirming our faith in the eternity of the Holy One, blessed be He (V'Hu hayah V'Hu hoveh V'Hu yihiyeh ~ He was, is and will be, from the previous stanza) here we affirm His absolute Oneness, which is called Achdus Hapeshutah. This concept is very difficult for the human mind to comprehend because, to our minds, any number can be subdivided. Even the number one . . . can be subdivided into smaller units. However, the Oneness of the Holy One, blessed be He is absolute; nothing comparable exists.*[204]

Natan slaps Shimi's shoulder in a friendly manner and then says, "Remember the words *bli dimyon*, which appear in the Sephardic rendition of this stanza. They translate as 'without comparison'. Like Avi just quoted from Rav Schwab, there is nothing comparable to Hashem. As you look around you now you see nothing with which to compare anything to. There

---

204 The words of Rabbi Schwab have been slightly adapted to enable easier reading for those unfamiliar with certain Hebrew terms.

is nothing to see. There is nothing you can perceive except yourself—and what is that self? We'll deal with that soon."

"Excellent, Natan" says Avi. "That's the same concept which Rav Schwab refers to when he states:

> There is none other to compare Him to, to declare as His equal. God is not definable. Nor does He have a colleague to share His Divinity.

"Rabbi Schwab is relating to the Hebrew word להמשיל ~ l'hamshil, which appears in both the Ashkenazic and Sephardic renditions of this stanza of ADON OLAM. It means a practical comparison or, better put, an evaluation of similar things. In the Sephardic rendition the words bli erech, without evaluation, and bli chibur, without a cooperative relationship, are added. Whether you are Sephardic or Ashkenazic, the point is the same. When dealing with Hashem, there is nothing to put on the other end of the scale. It is not just that there would need to be a lot more put on the other side, but that there is nothing to put on the other side at all. Not even if we multiply the whole world by a billion."

"Shimi," explains Shalom, "since there is nothing other than Hashem, then there is no outside existence, whether spiritual or physical. ADON OLAM is not only informing us that polytheism is false. It is explaining what monotheism really is."

And Natan completes the idea: "Monotheism is complete oneness."

The Error

"AT FIRST," says Avi, "when I started to delve into other faiths, I was disturbed by the multiplicity of gods even among the 'monotheistic' faiths. Some of these so-called monotheistic faiths have gods with family members, i.e., a father, a mother. Some of these gods were supposedly born and died. Some of these deities are so weak that they were recorded to have been killed at the hands of finite man. Most of these faiths have the concept of an anti-god that we discussed on our walk in the woods, and nearly every one of these faiths has the concept of praying to intermediaries, which are kind of like semi-gods. All this really sounded to me like bad versions of Greek mythology. So I started to look around and eventually found Judaism. At those beginning stages of my search I was satisfied with what I thought Judaism meant: finally, I had found a religion that really believed in One God instead of a few. But then Yehudah brought me to this beach. It was here in the middle of the fog that my own fog started to lift."

Let's now see how Yehudah and Ovadiah are doing in the middle of the lake . . . .

When One Really Equals One

YEHUDAH AND OVADIAH are sitting in the dark, on the flimsy raft. The only sound heard is little waves lapping around them. Yehudah breaks the spell: "So here we are on this little raft, in the middle of nowhere, and here we will learn together about a very central issue. You have come a long way since your conversation with Laibel Weiss. Now that you are well on your way to becoming an accomplished Torah scholar, I think it is time to take what you think to be simple and uncover its depths."

"Excuse me for being so foolish, but why here in the middle of a lake at night in this heavy fog?"

"This is the scene that your grandfather depicts in order to help his readers understand the third stanza of ADON OLAM which describes Hashem's Oneness. In order to fully grasp the implications of true monotheism, you need to know that there is no escape from the one and only existence. Besides knowing that there is nothing else out there, you need to be forced to deal with the ultimate and singular existence of Hashem, and what that means in your life.

"What do you mean by the only existence? Don't you and I exist too?" asks Ovadiah.

Yehudah pulls out a small but powerful flashlight from his shirt pocket. He points it horizontally towards the right and flicks it on.

"Like we discussed in the woods," he says, "we can only understand light from darkness, life from death, truth from falsehood. You can only see the beam of light because there is the opposing darkness around it. Similarly, we are here on the water. The only thing that separates us from the water is a very thin piece of synthetic rubber, yet we know that above the water is life and that under the surface of the water we cannot survive. The difference between life and death is a few millimeters. In order to understand Hashem's Unity, and therefore truth itself, we need to understand the fine lines of what it would mean if there was no complete unity. By morning you will understand why any other perceptions of Hashem are not that of complete unity and therefore are in actuality darkness. So instead of generating true faith, they lead to falsehood."

And with that, Yehudah turns off the flashlight and puts it away.

But Ovadiah persists: "Isn't it already so obvious that Hashem is One? I mean, really! After having understood all that we have from ADON OLAM, I have no doubt about the unity of Hashem. What do you think that I don't yet understand about the implications of Hashem's Oneness?"

Self-centered Idolatry

"KEEP IN MIND, Ovadiah, that when our sages authored ADON OLAM, they were experiencing a time period where many of our people were missing some major aspects of faith. For example, we know that there were numerous intermarried couples among those returning from the Babylonian exile. At that time, the prophet Ezra ben Serayah, who started and led the Great Assembly, made the very unpopular decision to expel all of the non-Jewish wives and their resulting children.[205] We must remember that these same intermarried Jewish men had made arduous efforts to return home to the Holy Land despite all odds. These efforts were obviously expended because of their belief that Hashem is One; they were not idolaters. Yet they had made the grave mistake of not following Hashem's commandment of not engaging in intermarriage.

"Obviously, there were many factors that led to Ezra's decision to enact such a difficult edict. Now, consider that it was the Sanhedrin that he established that wrote this stanza of ADON OLAM. Making such an edict is possibly the strongest expression of Hashem being One and of there being no other; for accepting this Oneness means that there isn't any place for our own wills in the face of His. This edict taught our people, then, that their wants had to melt in front of His commandments, even when it came to their own wives and children.

"This stanza deals with the absolute singularity of Hashem, and thereby emphasizes that there is nothing outside of Him. It clarifies to us that attributing importance to the self or having selfish desires of any shade is tantamount to idolatry. And so, Ovadiah, I brought you here on this foggy night to show how the illustrious authors of ADON OLAM enable us to remove the fog of the self."

"How? I still don't understand."

"I'll explain, don't worry."

The Finger that Must Point at Nothing

*H*OLD ON TO YOURSELF, *Searching Soul, because Yehudah is about to toss the self overboard. But don't worry: as the evening progresses he'll fish both Ovadiah's and your sense of self worth back up, to the surface. How? Just listen . . . .*

205 Ezra, chapters 9–10.

"Your grandfather explains how Rabbeinu Pinchas of Plutsk[206] understood that it is inconceivable, after all the vast depths that the Great Assembly has shown us in ADON OLAM till this point, that the authors are not merely speaking in this stanza against the foolishness of polytheism. Rather, he informs us that they were expressing a much greater concept: Not that Hashem's Oneness means His being not two or three gods, but that there is absolutely nothing other or outside of Hashem's existence."

"Didn't we discuss this in the woods?" Ovadiah pipes up.

"Yes, but there are many implication of what we learned then, that you may not have understood. It is with the intention of helping people like you that Chacham Yashar continues with these words . . . .

In order for my readers to fully grasp the full significance of monotheism, I ask you to do as Rabbeinu Pinchas' words suggested. When you say the words of ADON OLAM 'And He is One', point your fingers upwards towards the heavens, and when you say its next words, of 'and there is no other', point them towards yourselves."

"The message is clear; Hashem's Oneness means that our significance is null and void if not recognized to be part of Hashem Himself. "

We Have Entered Deep Waters and the Current Sweeps Us Away

"**B**UT RABBEINU PINCHAS' statement is very brief," continues Yehudah, "and so, to better appreciate his message, *The Hidden Master* has us take a look at the Ashkenazic *Selichos*[207] which further explain the same point:

206 Remember, he is one of the main disciples of the Vilna Gaon. His book includes a commentary on ADON OLAM.

207 Prayers in which we ask for atonement. This particular one is said on the day before Rosh Hashanah. See Artscroll translation of the Ashkenazic *Selichos* for *Erev Rosh Hashanah*, No. 31, pp. 343, 419.

True—You are the first and nothing precedes Your precedence; and You are the last, and there is no end to Your finality. And I and Your Law testify that there is none besides You . . . (But) we have chosen defilement instead of purity . . . We have traded an eternal world for an ephemeral one . . . we have entered deep waters and the current sweeps us away. (In so doing) we have not done harm to You, Hashem, our God, but to our own souls . . . (For) if man should sin, what has he accomplished against You.

"Here Chacham Yashar tells us that the current which can 'sweep us away' is not outside the boat; it is inside."

Never been to Morocco before, have you? Well, let's turn the clock back approximately forty years, Searching Soul. There, in the back room of that small but sturdy stone home sits a man who looks just like Rabbeinu Reuven. Yes, it's Chacham Yashar. He now sits with his black Moroccan cape covering his head. Under him is a simple ceramic chair. With quill in hand, he is starting his chapter on "V'Hu Echad ~ והוא אחד (And He is One)". After a few moments of deliberation, he dips his quill into the inkwell and scrawls a long note under the title of the third section.

Every time that we choose our desires over Hashem's, we are showing that we lack understanding of His Oneness. When ADON OLAM teaches us that He is One and that there is no other, our Sages are telling us that nothing exists outside of Hashem's Will, not even the self. This is what the authors meant by One and no other. My beloved people, the tides of our times have brought with them a thick cloud that does not allow us to navigate through the deep waters. In order to avoid drowning, we must cast our errant concepts of the self to the depths, and then we will be able to see beyond the fog. Our Yemenite brothers and my beloved and holy teacher and friend, the great Baba Sali, help us lift the fog. They include in ADON OLAM the passage "He is the first and He is the last to all matter and form," to inform us that Hashem's Oneness is the *source and destination of all.*

Run, my brethren; run through the fog straight to your destination, to the only destination. Do not veer off the path and serve yourselves. Rather, serve ONLY Hashem.

Back on the lake the silence is only broken by the gentle ripple of the water against the rounded sides of the rubber raft. Ovadiah looks out over the nothingness. No shore, no sky, nothing can be seen. There is just this little raft.

Hold On For Dear Life

"IT'S STRANGE THAT YOU brought me that passage now," remarks Ovadiah.

"Why?"

"Last week we learned in *yeshivah* from "the chapter of 'The Boat',[208] which speaks of our Rabbis being lost in a torrent in the raging sea. The only thing that they had to hold onto was a small wooden raft. The commentators[209] there tell us that this is all a parable to teach us that there is nothing that can help us other than this raft, and we must hold on to it for dear life. It is the only thing that keeps us alive. Outside is an unknown darkness with unknown depths of morbid ends. The raft, they tell us, is the Torah. They depict how without the Torah the Jew is lost and has no hope. For the Jew there is nothing outside of Torah. Like a raft, it was given to the Jews to bring them home from even the deepest and foggiest eras of our dispersion.

"Tonight, as we are tossed about on our own rubber raft, I realize that the only way to stay afloat in the turbulence is to never let go of the raft that Hashem gave us, the Torah, which we know to be His Will. The fog, or feelings of being lost, does not come from the raft, but rather from holding onto something that is outside of the raft, outside of reality. My grandfather's

208 Gemara, Tractate *Baba Basra*, Chapter '*HaSefinah*'.

209 Maharal and Maharasha.

message is speaking to me through the fog and telling me that when I go after my own will I am missing the truth. In the midst of the fog of the self his message is so clear; there is nothing outside of the raft: all is just the Will of Hashem, His Torah. My grandfather is telling me to never let go. The Torah is the only raft which can bring us back safely to Hashem."

"I am amazed at your perception, Ovadiah."

"What do you mean, Yehudah?"

"The example of the chapter of 'The Boat', with those commentaries that you quoted, is what appears next in your grandfather's book, immediately after that paragraph that I just read you!"

Learning How to Fly

*T*HINGS AREN'T GOING *as easily on the beach as they are on the raft. Hashem's absolute Oneness as described by Rabbi Schwab seems to have flown way over Shimi's head. Avi has another plan of action.*

"Don't give up, Shimi. Just because you didn't yet understand Rabbi Schwab, that does not mean that all hope is lost. Let's take a close look at what the Sephardic Jews include in the text of ADON OLAM. I think that will help you understand more clearly what the absolute Oneness of Hashem means.

"They add the words: בלי ערך, בלי דמיון, בלי שינוי ותמורה, בלי חיבור, בלי פירוד ~ *Bli erech, bli dimyon, bli shinui u'temura, bli chibbur, bli peirud* . . . Let's start to translate and understand these words. 'Hashem cannot be **defined or estimated** because He is also **unable to be compared** to anything since there is nothing other than Him.' Think about that: without being compared to something how could He be defined? Remember that Yehudah spoke about this on our walk in the woods when he picked up a few stones from the riverbed and asked you to identify the most round one?"

"Yeah, I remember that," says Shimi. "He told us that since Hashem is Infinite He is not like the rocks because there is nothing outside of Him. There are no other rocks to compare Him to. There is no one outside to estimate Him."

Avi then continues, "Let's continue with our translation. 'He also **cannot be changed** into something else as there is nothing else, **nor can He be switched** for another as there is no other. And in turn, He is **unable to be connected** to anything outside of Himself since there is nothing other than Him, and finally, He **cannot be separated** into parts, for He is really One and has no separate parts.'"

"So, Shimi, think of one tree. Can it be divided?"

"Yes, of course. It has many branches, leaves, cells, molecules, atoms etc."

"What could I **compare it** to in order to be able to judge whether it is a big or small, strong or weak, beautiful or an ugly tree?" asks Avi.

"You could compare it to another tree."

"Can you **define** a tree for me, either by its essence or by its use?"

Shimi thinks a moment. "I could define the tree in many ways. For example you could think of it as a living organism, as a source of wood and shade. This tree can also be thought of as part of a greater whole as we see it working as part of a larger ecosystem in a forest, among other trees."

Avi presses on: "Could you describe the tree in a way that we will be able to understand its limitation?"

"Every tree has a definite height and width. A tree starts life at a certain time and will die eventually. And even if the tree is a two-thousand-year-old sequoia, taller than many buildings, I can still control it. If I want to, I can plant a seed of a tree, and/or chop it down," answers Shimi.

"But you, the tree planter and wood chopper, are finite, and therefore nothing that you described about the tree or yourself has anything to do with ADON OLAM's definitions of Hashem. So what ADON OLAM is telling us is that infinity is not just a larger form of the finite. Hashem is not just a powerful god that is bigger than me. Rather, He encompasses all physical and spiritual realities. As ADON OLAM tells us, **He has no beginning and no end**. This means that He cannot be born, nor can He die. He can have no father or mother; neither can He have an enemy or cohort. These descriptions would define something that is not absolutely One.

"So when Yehudah and I sat here in the middle of a fog, very similar to tonight's fog, I started to realize that I was not only sitting physically in the fog, but that I, like so many other inhabitants of our world, had been sucked into a spiritual man-made fog of faith. My earlier beliefs had been so tainted by the non-Jewish world around me that I had never really appreciated what true monotheism is. As Yehudah explained the words of ADON OLAM, I felt my fog begin to lift. I began to realize that my upcoming conversion to Judaism was not going to be just a move to a belief more monotheistic than the errant faiths which I had inculcated. This was not merely a one-step-up improvement. I was undergoing a complete metamorphosis, a continental shift. I was deleting my previous beliefs just like the larva must have its previous body dissolve before it can metamorphosize into something completely different. On this beach I stopped crawling like a larva through the fog and learned how to fly above it, to the clear blue sky."

The Sky is Not the Limit, You Are

AVI PAUSES, and then continues. "But, guys, it doesn't even end there. Yehudah and I have recently learned a lot more than any of us had on this beach in the past. In monotheism, the sky is not the limit—rather, your will is."

"Your will?" asks Shalom blankly.

Avi is thinking of how to bring across Rabbeinu Pinchas' explanation where Chacham Yashar used the metaphor of the pointing finger. He has an idea.

"ADON OLAM exposes that even the loftiest notions in

other 'monotheistic' faiths, are really self-centered desires. This is found most clearly in a certain faith whose proposed afterlife reveals its core error. In its doctrines, this faith speaks of curtailing our own wills during our lives in order to receive a great reward in what they conceive of as the world to come. And what is that great reward?"

No guesses from the guys, so Avi continues.

"Their distorted view of the world to come consists of having all physical desires met beyond man's wildest imagination."

"Their service, then," says Natan, "is not really of Hashem but rather of the self."

"Exactly! When they live their lives only to ensure their own future reward of fulfilling personal physical desires, they are showing their belief that individuals can have an existence outside of Hashem. What they mean is that 'If I fulfill His desires, there will be a chance for me to make it big, to cash in on my desires.' Their faith is self-centered, a manipulation of the deity for the purpose of one's own desires. In their eyes, the essence and existence of the self is very much important in and of itself."

"This is a warped form of monotheism, at best," says Shimi thoughtfully.

"They certainly have not accomplished what Ethics of the Fathers demands—to cancel our wills in face of Hashem's Will,"[210] says Shalom.

"If anything," notes Natan, "they have made their own wills much more important than Hashem's. Their goal seems to be to aggrandize their own lowly physical desires."

"Right," says Avi. "And, on the other hand, ADON OLAM is telling us that the only thing of any importance is not our will but Hashem's Will. 'He is One and there is no other'—not even you."

"Wait a minute," says Shimi. "Don't we have any importance?"

Back to the raft, where Ovadiah is asking the same question . . . .

210 Ethics of the Fathers 2:4.

Ponder Your Worth

"FOR THE NEXT FEW MOMENTS," says Yehudah to Ovadi-ah, as they float silently, "ponder these words: Hashem's Oneness is the source and destination of all. Not only the source, but also the destination. This is an enormous distinction. Not only did Hashem originally create everything —and presently allows it to exist continually—but the creations never become a goal in and of themselves. Even after Creation, the only existence is Hashem. He is above all of the physicality of the finite world that we experience. The Sages of yore instilled these thoughts into ADON OLAM's essence and they were vocalized by some of the Sephardim and the Yemenites. Many centuries later, the *Derech Hashem* tried to further vocalize the depths of this thought when he stated . . . .

> *The only reason all other things have the possibility of existence is that God wills them to exist. All other things therefore depend on Him, and do not have intrinsic existence.*[211]

"The meaning of One is therefore that the only intrinsic existence is Hashem. You may now be wondering what you really are."

"Does my 'existence' have any meaning? Am I just a big zero?"

"Don't come to the false conclusion that I am trying to tell you that you are insignificant. You can actually become infinitely significant. Rabbeinu Pinchas states:

> *The Holy One, blessed be He—His Holiness comes from Himself and He does not need another, but the righteous ones are lacking any [holiness] of their own—their holiness is only from the Blessed and Holy One. And without Him there isn't holiness etc.*[212]

"So now let's see what holiness is, and then we will come to understand your infinite worth . . ."

---

211   *Derech Hashem* 1:1:6.

212   Rabbeinu Pinchas is quoting the Rabbi Moshe Alshich.

The Holy Distinction

"NOW OVADIAH, we are going to touch upon a very common but generally misunderstood Hebrew word. *kadosh*. What is its translation into English?"

"Holy."

"Very good," says Yehudah. "What does holy mean?"

"Spiritual. Ethereal. Angelic. Lofty."

"I see you have a Hollywood-based definition and not a Torah definition. But don't worry—so do many others. English is actually lacking a single word that captures the concept of what *kadosh* or holy really means, but some of the Latin-based languages have such a word: *sancta*. This word means separate and distinct from all that which is commonly-known and experienced. This is the definition of *kadosh*.

"In order for something to be considered to have holiness, it has to be separate and distinct from the finite world that we experience. It has to be above an existence that is a mere fleeting breath.

"Let's focus on and combine two concepts. The Torah teaches us that 'there is nothing other than Hashem,'[213] and ADON OLAM tells us that **He has no beginning and no end.** Unlike Hashem, we were both born and will die. If we are not defined by His holiness, then, since there is nothing other than Him, we never were. So when Rabbeinu Pinchas tells us that 'The righteous people's holiness is only from the Blessed and Holy One, and without Him there isn't holiness, etc.,' this means that our ability to raise ourselves above the finite, above the meaninglessness of a passing moment called physical life, is only through Hashem, Who is the singular source and destination of all. In order to attach to His Oneness, to His Holiness, we first have to learn how to let go of our errant concept of the self."

---

213   Deuteronomy 4:35.

When Zero Equals One

OVADIAH IS STARTING to internalize a new clarity of Hashem's Oneness, but he is wondering about his own importance in it all. As old foggy concepts start to drift away, a strong spring breeze suddenly passes over Lake Kinneret, and with its passing the fog is removed. The nighttime scene is suddenly changed. Now the lights from Tiberius are visible in the distance. A bonfire is seen a few hundred meters away from the raft, on a secluded beach opposite the city.

"The fog is gone, I see the whole shoreline, but I still do not have my bearings," he says.

Yehudah points. "There's Tiberius, there's the Kinar Hotel, and that fire a few hundred meters away is where the guys are."

"How do you know?"

Yehudah pulls his cellphone out of its watertight case, puts it on speakerphone and dials.

"Hey, Avi, who knows One?"[214]

Avi's voice echoes back over the cell phone: "I know One! One is our God in the Heaven and on the Earth!"

"And does Shimi know One?"

"We're getting there. He's a tough nut to crack. Hey, where are you now?"

"Look straight out over the water."

"Hey, the fog is gone. When did that happen? O.K., I am looking. What am I supposed to see?"

Shalom and Natan are heard snickering in the background, as if they all know what is coming next.

"In a moment you will see Ovadiah making a large zero with a flashlight."

Ovadiah duly flicks on a flashlight and makes a large circle in the air, pointing at the bonfire. Three flashlights on the beach respond, with two parallel lines going back and forth horizontally, while to the right of them the other light starts to quickly go up and down.

---

214 A play on words, hinting at "Who Knows One? I Know One," a liturgical song found in the Passover *Haggadah*.

"They are signaling 'Equals One'," says Ovadiah softly.

From the speakerphone, the guys can be heard in unison saying:

"This is ADON OLAM's higher mathematics, 0=1!"

"Good job, Avi," says Yehudah. "Keep staying on schedule. See you soon."

The phone is turned off.

"So what's 0=1?" asks Ovadiah.

"You are not a zero. You are extremely important. When the Zohar tells us that "The Holy One, blessed be He and the Torah and Israel are One",[215] it is saying that your potential importance, as a member of the Jewish People, can be infinite, but this can only occur if you are attached to the Torah, for we know that without the Torah there is no way for us to comprehend Hashem at all."[216]

"Through the Torah? Why not through direct connection with Hashem?"

"Tomorrow. Wait until tomorrow and you will know. In the meantime, let's move on.

"When Jews say **Hear O Israel, Hashem is your God, Hashem is One,**[217] they are recognizing that their own existences are completely dependent upon the only true existence, the Oneness of Hashem. Zero can equal one if you attach to Hashem's Oneness, but only on His terms."

Yehudah lights a battery camp light which he takes out of his backpack. Ovadiah thinks that he is doing so just so that they will be able to see each other better. Yehudah, though, is going along with his secret plan.

In the meantime, back on shore . . . .

---

215 Zohar, Achrei 73a.

216 This concept is related to multiple times throughout Torah literature and more specifically by Rabbi Chaim of Volozhin in his book, *Nefesh HaChaim.*

217 Deuteronomy 6:4.

Ashes, Worms, and What?

SHIMI IS SAYING PLAINTIVELY: "Do you know what you're saying? Nothing other than Hashem? Nothing? Aren't we all sitting on a beach? Don't you all hear me speaking to you? Doesn't that mean that we exist? Yes, of course Hashem is One, but there is still a big world out there. You guys and I are on this beach, and supposedly Yehudah and Ovadiah are somewhere out there, so doesn't this mean that there is something other than just Hashem?"

Avi grabs the second, much smaller, inflated raft and an oar and starts moving towards the shore. Over his shoulder, he calls back, "I think it's time for you guys to give Shimi back his self. Keep the bonfire lit. I'll need it later to light my way home. Hope to see you soon. *Aufwiedersehen!*"

And, with a splash, he sets off.

"It's amazing that the raft didn't sink with all of his weight," observes Natan.

Shalom is watching him. "Look at him move."

"Where does he think he is going? What is this, the nighttime Olympics?" Shimi is thrown by this further development.

"He has something that he has to clarify with Yehudah and Ovadiah," explains Natan.

"How will he find them out there?"

"Don't worry, he'll find them and he will find his way back. Right now there's someone here you have to find," says Natan.

"Who?"

It is Shalom who answers: "Yourself. After all of this talk you may be wondering where you fit in to all of this."

And Natan continues: "We are not the first to wonder about the meaning and importance of the self. Avraham *Avinu* said that he was dust and ash."[218]

"And King David stated that he was a worm and not a man,"[219] Shalom seconds him.

"But Moshe Rabbeinu said it most extremely when he stated

218 Genesis 18:27.

219 Psalms 22:7.

that he and Aharon[220] were 'What?'[221] This then, is the Jewish definition of the self."

"What?"

"You got it, Shimi. Without our attachment to Hashem and His Will, we are zero. Whatever excuse you may have for not following Hashem's Will at any moment is a delusion that is pulling you out of permanent existence," says Shalom.

"But as we just showed Ovadiah with our flashlights, Zero can become One. An all-important One. An infinitely important One," says Natan.

"Your path away from zero," continues Shalom, "and towards One starts with your every action declaring that you are the servant of the Holy One, blessed be He. Become attached to His Torah and follow His ways, and you will not be meaningless; instead, you will have caused yourself to become important beyond your imagination."

My Choice vs. His Command

*A*s AVI ROWS *as swiftly and gracefully as the sculling champion he is, he contemplates his final appointment at the religious court two years before.*

RABBI:

So, young man, the court is quite impressed with your level of proficiency in Jewish Law. Your mentor, young Rabbi Stark, has told us that you are ready for conversion. But are you completely aware of the changes that will be happening to you once you convert?

ADOLPH REICH:

I am aware that now I only serve my Maker the way that I choose, but once I leave the waters of the mikvah[222] I will need to serve my Master the way He has commanded.

---

220 Aaron.

221 Exodus 16:7.

222 Ritual bath used for many religious purposes. Immersion in the mikvah is the final stage of the conversion process.

RABBI:

> That was quite a poetic mouthful. Could you explain to the court what you conceive to be the difference between choice and commandment.

Yehudah and Adolph look at each other with remembrances of their night at Lake Kinneret the week before the conversion. Yehudah winks at Adolph.

YEHUDAH:

> You're ready buddy, show them who you have become.

ADOLPH:

> For so long now I have longed to be commanded. I know that this sounds strange, especially coming from our modern "free" societies, but please allow me to explain. Over the past few years I have studied many of the philosophies of different religions. During this study, it has become clear to me that, logically, service to the Infinite can never be defined by finite servants, for such finite service would actually be incomplete. The only infinite, and therefore meaningful, service can be one dictated by the Infinite Will of Hashem, His Torah. I have experienced some of the errors of other faiths. I choose now to follow the only truthful path, but you see, Your Honors, that is exactly the problem.

RABBI:

> What problem are you referring to?

ADOLPH:

> I am the one choosing. For over a year now I have been the one choosing to follow the laws of the Torah. I have been staying kosher, praying with a minyan, observing Sabbath as much as a non-Jew is allowed, etc. I am observant. Although I am making good choices, that's not enough. What for you is a commandment, for me is a choice. I am asking for your help to eliminate the choice. If I truthfully wish to call Hashem my King, then as King He needs to be the One calling the shots and not me. As a follower of the Noahide commandments, this type of service is impossible.

RABBI:

> But you, along with the rest of the world are also commanded.

ADOLPH:

> Only partially . . . .

A Collision with Noah's Ark

"HEY, YEHUDAH, what's that splashing sound?" Ovadiah peers into the darkness, but not for long. The other raft, with Avi on board, has been quietly approaching them, and just at that moment it collides with theirs—exactly on schedule, of course. Ovadiah jumps nervously, and the battery-powered camp light tips overboard.

"What are you doing here??"

Avi's bulk looms in the darkness. "Ovadiah, according to my watch, it's time for me to tell you about the Jewish collision with Noahide ideology, but this time a little deeper than we did in the woods, *Yaah*."

"Speaking of deeply," observes Ovadiah, "I think the camp light has gone deep under. You are going to have to hold this discussion in the dark."

Unperturbed, Avi goes on. "It all came together a week before my conversion when Yehudah took me to that beach over there, and then to his office."

A harsh "Shhh!" comes from Yehudah's direction.

"Sorry, I forgot that it's a secret," Avi apologizes.

"Office? What office? Where?"

"Never mind," replies Avi. "You will find out at the proper time. Anyway, it was on that beach, at a barbeque late at night, that it all came together. We were discussing the number one. Then I realized what all of the past five years of my search for truth and meaning were all about. It all became so clear."

Back to the beach, two years before.

YEHUDAH:

"So, now that you are almost ready for the final meeting with the **Beis Din** (religious court), let me explain what you are about to embark upon. Right now you serve Hashem with all of your strength. You are as observant as any of the guys in the **Yeshivah**, but there is something missing in your service that you cannot have until you go through the final conversion. As a Noahide you choose to serve Hashem only *on your terms, not on Hashem's."*

ADOLPH:

I don't really get what you mean.

YEHUDAH:

Except for a few minimal guidelines, you are still the only one calling the shots; you are the one commanding yourself, and even if, as a follower of the Noahide commandments, you choose to go far beyond the minimal list of seven and fill your life with service, as you have already done, the choice is still not in the hands of Hashem but in your hands. Being a Jew means that Hashem must become your sole Commander and you the loyal servant.

Two years ahead, back on the rafts.

Avi continues to explain. "ADON OLAM expresses that Hashem is One and there is no other. What I learned from Yehudah that night on the beach is, that so long as I am the one calling the shots, then in my mind I imagine there is an other. ADON OLAM is telling us Jews that our service is recognizing Hashem's Oneness on a much higher level than any other type of service.

"And so I told the court just a few days later that I yearned to no longer be my own personal commander, but rather I long to have Hashem alone be my Commander."

Back to that day in court.

RABBI:

Very impressive, young man. Well, I speak for the whole court when I say that it is clear that Rabbi Stark is correct. Indeed, you are ready to complete your conversion. We will see you on Thursday at the mikvah.

Young Adolph bursts into tears of joy. After a few moments, the Rabbi speaks up again.

RABBI:

Adolph, I have a gift for you that I wish you to take with you for the rest of your life. With this you will understand how to serve Hashem constantly, at every moment. If you keep this story in your mind, you will always carry with you that feeling of being commanded that you so long for.

By now, not only Adolph's eyes, but those of Yehudah and the entire panel of rabbinical judges are wide open, waiting to see what this precious gift is.

RABBI:
   Listen well as I tell you how the great Chazon Ish[223] succeeded in making even coffee and biscuits into service to Hashem.

The Golem[224] of Bnei Brak[225] and the Chazon Ish

RABBI:
When the Chazon Ish was an elderly man, he was in the habit of talking to his body as if it were some sort of Golem, or guest. I'll try to reenact two of his conversations with his body, and from them you will learn a lifelong lesson. They went something like this:[226]

CHAZON ISH:
   Do you want some coffee? I will boil you some water.

He learns Torah as the water heats up, and the kettle begins to whistle. Then he busies himself making the coffee.

CHAZON ISH:
   O.K., here you are, I even put some sugar in it for you. Would you like some crackers? I will give you some margarine for them.

223 Rabbi Avraham Yeshayahu Karelitz, 1879–1954. He authored a multi volume compendium called "*Chazon Ish.*" As with many rabbis, he is lovingly and respectfully called by the name of his most famous book.

224 Literally, this means formless mass, but in this context, it means a non-thinking, almost monster-like creature.

225 The name of the city in the Land of Israel where the Chazon Ish lived.

226 Please refer to the Disclaimer.

He comes back to the table with the plate, and sits down to say his blessings and eats and drinks his breakfast. Upon finishing, he grabs the prayer book and finds the proper blessing. Before uttering its words he says to his Golem—

CHAZON ISH:

Is there anything else that you would like? No. Then can you please leave me alone for a few hours so that I can learn some Torah?

A few hours have passed, and the Chazon Ish needs to rest his tired, old bones so that he can continue to learn Torah. The conversation between the Chazon Ish and his Golem continues.

CHAZON ISH:

Oh, you're tired? Lie down here. Take a pillow; it will make you more comfortable. Maybe a different position will create less pain, so that you will feel better. Are you O.K. now? Good. I am glad. Now leave me alone so that I can learn for a few more hours.

Not an Ascetic

RABBI:

Adolph, the greatness of the Chazon Ish was not in how much he ignored his body or was an ascetic. He took good care of himself, but not for selfish reasons. His entire reason for being was to serve Hashem and fulfill His commandments. He understood well that you need to recognize your physical needs and limitations, and cater to them. His lesson to us all and my gift to you is to constantly keep in mind your service to Hashem. A written sign, 'Know before Whom You stand',[227] should not only be placed in front of the community leader when he is leading the congregation in prayer, but it should be on the mind of the Jew in his every action. Know that there is only Hashem and nothing else and that we must live up to His demands. Use all of your strength, all of your days, not to serve your selfish desires, but rather to serve only Hashem.

227 Based on a statement from the Gemara Brachos 28b.

Back on Lake Kinneret

"Ovadiah, the gift that Rabbi gave me is a tool that has enabled me to bring alive the words of ADON OLAM. He is One and there is no other. Sure, I can have my coffee and biscuits, but I always need to remember that it's for Hashem and not for me," sums up Avi.

It's All an Excuse

"WOW! THANKS AVI. Now I understand how the Chazon Ish became such a giant." Ovadiah pauses for a moment and then interjects, "But I don't know if I can do the same. It seems a little too intense for me."

Yehudah breaks in: "When I was in *yeshivah* in Monsey, New York, I was taught how even the simple Jew can make himself great. Rabbi Yaakov showed how we can all take lessons like those of the Chazon Ish into our own lives, even beginners like we were at the time. I remember when he came to me one cold winter morning. I had not gotten out of bed in time and had missed morning prayers."

Knock, Knock. Knock.

YEHUDAH:
   Ahhhhhhhhhhhhhh. Who is that? I mean, come in.

The door slowly opens

RABBI YAAKOV:
   Yehudah, are you feeling well? I did not see you in synagogue this morning. Can I get you something?

YEHUDAH:
   No don't worry. I'm fine. I heard my alarm and started to get up. When I felt the cold out there, I used it as an excuse to stay under the warm covers.

RABBI YAAKOV:

> The power of excuse is great. It can be used to pull you down or you can use it to pull yourself up.

YEHUDAH (BY NOW FULLY AWAKE):

> I know that it can pull me down, but how can an excuse pull me up?

RABBI YAAKOV:

> We don't have to spend our lives using many excuses not to serve Hashem. Instead, we can be proactive and decide to look for excuses for how to still serve Hashem even though there are obstacles.

YEHUDAH:

> Rabbi, you are correct, but sometimes I need to pamper myself.

RABBI YAAKOV:

> You mean you care about yourself. That's fine. But you should keep in mind that if you really care about yourself then you would use the excuses to get yourself to greatness. I remember when I was just starting out at yeshivah. My rabbi saw that I was not using my time optimally. I would waste some time here or there with the best of excuses. He told me that instead of using excuses for why not to learn, I should use excuses for why to learn.

YEHUDAH:

> Hey, I never thought of it that way. It all just depends which end of the excuse that you decide to take.

Back to the boats

"Great story, Yehudah," Avi says appreciatively. "That's true Judaism: constantly down to business with an upbeat striving to become complete servants of Hashem. Ovadiah, remember when I was explaining to you about the service of non-Jews, in the study hall, and I brought that verse from Psalms, where King David informed us that one of the requirements to be a good Jew is to be requesting peace, that is, requesting completion?

"Yes, I remember."

"That's exactly what we learn from the Chazon Ish, and that is what we learn from Rabbi Yaakov: to reach completion in your service to Hashem, you need to simply replace the excuse. When we realize that Hashem is absolutely One, then the only place to find ourselves is in our relationship with Him. And that is where we will find our own greatness as well. He is the only Commander, and it is only to Him that we should devote our every strength. This is the collision between the Noahide fleet and our Jewish raft."

And with that, Avi slowly starts to row away.

"Why are you leaving now?" Ovadiah wants to know.

"Yehudah needs to continue with you alone. See you in the morning."

Avi's raft disappears rapidly, and soon not even the splash of the oars can be heard.

Without a Beginning and Without an End

*A*FTER AVI'S RAFT *ebbs out of sight, Ovadiah notices that the sound of the night breeze has quieted down. The crickets and cicadas on shore are faintly heard on the raft. The mini-waves that earlier were lapping on the sides of the raft have abated, and the water surface now appears smooth as a sheet of silvery glass. Ovadiah seems deep in thought. He is beginning to understand that even the simplest of his actions can be both highly positive and meaningful—or extremely detrimental. Listen, Searching Soul, as Yehudah grabs the moment and helps Ovadiah, and you along with him, to move on to an even deeper appreciation of my words.*

"Your grandfather had an agenda when he wrote his book. In his introduction, he speaks of the many new ideologies at that time that were pulling many of his people away from the faith of their fathers—especially the young and the searching. Your father, his son, was among those youths being led astray. The following segment of his book, which discusses the next few words of ADON OLAM, is where he gives his readers the tools to combat what he calls the waves of falshood. As we discuss this, imagine what may have led him to write these words."

Come with me, Searching Soul, and I'll show you what led Chacham Yashar to write the next segment of his book.

It's late at night in Chacham Yashar's modest home. The old sage is studying Torah by candlelight. Suddenly the front door opens quietly. Binyamin thinks that he will not be detected. As he sneaks in and heads for bed, he hears his saintly father calling him.

"Binyamin, my sweet Binyamin, please come to me."

Binyamin has no choice but to respond. "Yes, father, how can I help you?"

"Where have you been?"

"With friends."

"What type of friends?" asks Chacham Yashar. "And what were you doing with them?"

Binyamin speaks boldly: "New friends, learning of a new world. Father, I know you want me to be like you and like my eldest brother, Reuven, studying Torah all day. But that is just not for me. There is a big world out there and I want to see it. These friends and I want to open ourselves up a little to the enlightenment that is evident around us."

Chacham Yashar is perturbed. "But what about serving Hashem? How will that fit into your new lifestyle with your new friends?"

"The Rambam[228] tells us that the best path is the middle road—he calls it the golden path. You are special, father, but I cannot duplicate your life. It is just not for me. I need compromise, a little mediocrity, the middle path. Not everything needs to be so black-and-white. It is just beyond where I see myself going. I need the freedom."

Chacham Yashar frowns. "That's not the intention of the Rambam. There is a difference between the middle, golden path, and mediocrity. Mediocrity is being satisfied with being half-religious.

---

228 An acronym for Rabbi Moshe ben Maimon. Born in 1135 in Cordova, Spain, and died 1204, in Cairo, Egypt. He was a great Talmudic commentator, halachic authority, codifier, and philosopher. Also known as Maimonides.

ADON OLAM tells us that "He is the first and last to all matter and form," so there isn't anything else to search for other than Him. "He has no beginning and no end," but the ideologies that you are now tasting do have an end. Watch out, my son, before you and your friends are swallowed up in the waves of falsity and mediocrity that you call 'freedom'."

As Binyamin goes to bed, Chacham Yashar realizes that since his own son is beginning to be swept away by the waves of falsity, the time has come to write a message to his son and this generation.

Back to Lake Kinneret with Yehudah and Ovadiah.

"So Chacham Yashar's readers," Yehudah tells Ovadiah, "now find themselves on a raft in the midst of very turbulent waters. Imagine that our flimsy raft was in the midst of a torrent. If you were to fall out of the boat it would be certain death, so you cling to the raft and to life itself with all of your strength. This analogy, he tells his readers, depicts the experience of the Jewish people from ancient times until the present. The raft, he tells us, is the Torah, and the torrent represents the various cults, mutant forms of Judaism and offshoot religions that have persistently tossed our people's faith and disturbed it throughout our long history.

"He posits that this next message of ADON OLAM is what has given our people the strength to cling to the raft against the barrage of false waves. ADON OLAM states:

בלי ראשית, בלי תכלית, ולו העוז והמשרה ~ *Bli reishis, bli tachlis, v'lo Ha'oz v'hamisrah* ~ He is without beginning and He is without end. We recognize that to Him is the Eternal Will and ultimate dominion.

He dissects the sentence like this: 'He is without beginning'—He is before any of the newfangled ideas, cults, or offshoots. And 'He is without end.' When all 'isms' will be dead and buried, when the last wave has dried up into oblivion, we who held on tightly to His faith through the torrents will still recognize that His Will has always reigned—continually with ultimate dominion.

"Your grandfather reminds us that this same concept was given to our people, long before the writing of ADON OLAM, by King Solomon, z"l, who informed us that 'There are many devices in a man's heart: but the counsel of the Lord, that alone shall stand.'[229] Chacham Yashar notifies us that although the winds of time may bring in fleeting, meaningless thoughts that sweep the masses of the world off their feet, we should still hold onto our faith. He tells us that just as these waves of falsity came with a wind, so too, they will ebb out of existence with a mere puff of air. But, unlike the winds or the waves that they brought along, Hashem did not begin, and His existence can never ebb. His thoughts and Will are beyond the limitations of time. He will never be blown away, no matter what storm will come or leave. His will, His Torah, which we hold onto for dear life, rules alone over all with ultimate dominion.

"Now, Ovadiah, I will quote for you *The Hidden Master*'s next plea to your father's generation . . . .

> *Woe to those of you who numbly shout the mantra that is so commonly heard today on the shores of Morocco, "We need to be free—free thinkers and free men." Remember that there is no less free a man than he who is controlled by his own animalistic desires. And these desires, like those who hold them, will pass out of memory, while those who live by His Torah will have chosen the freedom that is eternal."*

The Downward Escalator

*M*EANWHILE, BACK ON SHORE, *Natan and Shalom are still hard at work . . . .*

"O.K., Shimi, let's give it another try. Pretend that you are standing on a downward escalator. Your goal is to reach the top."

"If you stand, you will go down. If you stroll leisurely, then you will stay where you are, and although you will not go down, you will certainly not achieve your goal of arriving at the top. The only way to reach the top is to run with all of your might," elaborates Natan.

"So too," continues Shalom, "with life as a servant of Hashem. If you are happy with the level you're at and are not trying so hard to improve yourself, if you are a complacent, mediocre Jew who likes to be casual, who enjoys his 'freedom'. . ."

"Then you will be pulled down by the forces of this world that you were put into," concludes Natan.

"So life is a downward escalator," says Shimi disconsolately. "What a dismal outlook!"

Suddenly, a deep voice is heard.

"It's not dismal, that's the spice that life needs."

All are startled to see a very wet Avi, holding his raft.

"I guess that you found your way back," remarks Shimi, somewhat unnecessarily.

"How could I miss you? You guys have the only campfire in town tonight," grins Avi.

"Avi, what do you mean that the spice of life is being on a downward escalator?"

"Do you remember the underground sepulcher that night in the woods?"

"Who could ever forget that and its bats?"

"Do you remember what we learned there?"

Shimi does: "Free choice is the name of the game, that's why we were created."

"And so, if you choose to stand still, it is also a choice, albeit the wrong one," Natan breaks in.

"Inertia brings us down because it is the choice to not grow," adds Shalom.

Shimi understands: "So if we sit inertly and are not trying to perfect ourselves by trying to emulate Hashem's ways, then I guess we are not going up the escalator of life. Only by plugging into the only Source of all existence do we actually grow—though it takes effort. And it is for that growth that Hashem gave us life in the first place."

"Wunderbar," says Avi. "I mean, wow. I see the evening was a success both at sea and on shore."

Of Man and God, of Man and Man

ORANGE AND CRIMSON HUES of light start to paint the eastern sky. Morning is on the way. A few moments before, Yehudah and Ovadiah paddled gently through the reeds and arrived at a secluded enclave. Avi has come through yet again by having set up a small tent, towels, dry clothes and, of course, a thermos of hot coffee. After drying off and changing into dry clothes, the twosome pack everything away and wait on the side of the nearby path, each with his wet towel thrown over his shoulder, sipping hot coffee.

"Something's missing in all of this, Yehudah."

"What do you mean, Ovadiah?"

"I was told by one of the rabbis soon after I arrived at *yeshivah* that you cannot serve Hashem properly as a monk. There aren't just commandments between us and Hashem but also commandments between us and our fellow people. True and complete service must encompass both of these."

"Who said anything different? What are you saying is missing?"

"I understand how Hashem being One without any comparison and without any beginning or end fits into my relationship with Hashem, but how do these concepts fit into my relationships with people? In order to really understand the unity of Hashem, we must also put this concept into practice in our daily, interpersonal lives. It is becoming clearer to me how to do this in the commandments between man and God, but how do I use the commandments between man and man to heighten my awareness of Hashem's unity?"

Yehudah thinks for a moment. "Do you ever get angry, frustrated, envious, vindictive, or just fed up with the people around you?

"Don't we all?"

"Well, unfortunately, yes. One of the ways that so many people choose to deal with these emotions is to give up on a relationship. But if we constantly remember that Hashem is the ultimate cause of all, if we remember that He is the One sending us these people and their particular tests, then our anger, frustration, envy and vindictiveness should be focused on Hashem, rather than on them."

"But that would be ridiculous! How could we be angry at Hashem? Everything that He does is for our good, isn't it?"

"Right, Ovadiah. And that includes the tests that people bring our way. Remember that no test is insurmountable. Hashem is not testing you to make you fail but rather to make you grow. Instead of throwing in the towel, you need to make the situation work. Do not go through relationships seeing if they can work, but rather look at interpersonal relationships as being a commandment like any other. You do not go into the Sabbath, with all of its complicated rules, and say, "Let me see if I can make it through this Sabbath and follow all of the rules, or if I will give up in the middle.""

"Of course not. You go in knowing that there will be some challenges that you must overcome."

"And the same thing," says Yehudah, "is true in relationships. Realizing Hashem's hand in all life's events and interactions is living up to the knowledge that He is One."

The unmistakable sound of Yehudah's *yeshivah*-mobile making its way along the dirt path ahead is heard. The van stops and honks. The doors open. It's 5:14 and 50 seconds.

"We made it on time with precisely ten seconds to spare . . ." Avi and the guys inside are pleased with themselves. "Hey Ovadiah, how was the nighttime swim?"

"Kind of like a tidal wave. I now know a little better what it means that Hashem is One."

"So do I, Bud, so do I," says Shimi.

Avi breaks in: "We need to keep on schedule. The sun will not wait for us, and therefore neither will the sunrise *minyan*."[230]

---

230   As stated before, this is a quorum of ten needed for public prayer.

V'lo Ha'oz V'hamisrah—
We're Off to See the Wizard of *Oz*

THEY ARRIVE AT A HOTEL parking lot and run to join the
vacationers for the morning prayers. Forty-five minutes
later, all except for Ovadiah are back at the van. Ten minutes
later Ovadiah arrives to see the guys setting the tents up outside
the van for an early morning snooze.

Shalom looks at Ovadiah and remarks: "I see by the length
of time it took you in the synagogue and the look on your face
during prayer, that Yehudah's twilight boating service has left
its impression on you."

Natan slaps Ovadiah on the back. "Keep growing, buddy,
keep growing, the sky is the limit."

"Ovadiah," says Avi, "none of us ever went on this raft ride;
maybe you could tell us about it on our way to the Banyas."[231]

Ovadiah looks at Yehudah. "I don't think that there is any
way to duplicate the magic of last night. How could I describe
it to them?"

"First let's go to sleep for a few hours," advises Yehudah.

Five hours pass. 11:15 am. A couple of snacks are bought at
the nearby food stand, and away the van goes.

Once in the van, Yehudah says, "Ovadiah, according to the
GPS, we have an hour and 45 minutes till we get to the spot
I am bringing you to. Try to give over what we discussed and
see how it goes."

"O.K., guys, imagine being out there in the middle of . . ."

An hour and 42 minutes later, he concludes his description
with, "So that's a little of what I internalized last night."

A short silence follows. There are looks of wonderment on
the faces of all the guys, except for Yehudah, who is smiling
from ear to ear.

Shimi is the first to speak. "You call that a little. I only
understood part of it, but I am dumbfounded."

Avi, whose head keeps bumping into the ceiling and who

needs to push back the driver's seat almost all the way in order to fit into it, says, "Boy, do I feel small now."

As they all laugh, the van hits a large bump in the road, and the power of the impact sends the van airborne.

Before the scene continues, Searching Soul, it's time for me—yes, ADON OLAM—to speak. I hope you are enjoying your adventures with the guys. But before you continue with them there is still perhaps something missing in your understanding of how to relate to Hashem's unity.

From the bonfire in the woods you already learned that it is impossible for the finite to relate to the Infinite Essence of Hashem, but, rather, we can only relate to Hashem through His Torah. Now watch as Yehudah further unravels my words to bring Ovadiah—and you as well—to a deeper understanding of how to forge your attachment to Hashem through attaching yourself to His Holy Will.

Those wishing for an easy fix will try to work out short-cuts to connect with Hashem. Yehudah will show you through my words that these are not shortcuts; they are actually wrong turns. Any other path to Hashem other than through the Torah itself is a path going in the wrong direction. And now, back to the van.

Powerful Impact

THE VAN LANDS back down with a bump. Then they all hear the GPS's computerized British voice saying, "Recalculating," prompting a U-turn and the foot on the gas. Eventually, the van parks on the side of the road at the designated place, and the group of friends follow their teacher, Yehudah Stark, into what looks like a Middle-Eastern jungle.

"Hey Yehudah, what's that sound? The 'jungle' seems to be roaring," notes Shimi.

"It's the Banyas waterfall. There was a lot of rain and snow this year, so it's really gushing now that the sun is melting all of the snow on the mountains. Avi, you take the guys for a freezing and rather exhilarating swim in that pool of white water way down there, after the second, smaller fall. They'll have the time of their lives. We will meet you in the pool in about an hour and a half. While there, discuss Hashem's power and dominion. O.K., guys, each to his own road. In the meantime, Chacham Ovadiah and I will also try to understand Hashem's power and dominion."

"Did you call me **Chacham** Ovadiah?"

Yehudah looks at him fondly. "You're getting there, buddy, just you wait."

And as they walk away, Avi shouts over his shoulder, "See you later, Chacham Ovadiah. You will never experience anything like this!"

While the guys, led by Avi, go downstream, away from the smaller falls, the twosome forge upstream through the dense forest and undergrowth, trying to follow the almost imperceptible path through some of the richest foliage in the Land of Israel. After a few minutes, they begin their approach to the upper, more magnificent waterfall. As they make their way, the path becomes increasingly more misty and many mini-streams cross it. Soon they can see the source of all this water: a twenty-five meter high waterfall. The sound becomes increasingly thunderous. Ovadiah stands with his feet in the froth, looking up, gaping at it.

Ovadiah has to shout above the noise: "Hey, Yehudah, the ground is vibrating, and there are gusts of wind. I feel like the power from the falls is enveloping us."

Yehudah shouts back: "And all the more so are the power and dominion of Hashem." Then he grabs Ovadiah's hand. "Don't let go of my hand. I am going to pull you through the falls to my cave, my private office."

The Bubble Cave

YEHUDAH NOW PULLS Ovadiah over the slippery rocks, against the powerful downstream current of the Banyas River. Searching Soul, sometimes we have to go over massive hurdles in order to realize our potentials. These hurdles may go against the currents of our minds. Ovadiah and you are about to go against the most powerful currents in your faith. Many never dare to try to get over these hurdles. Let's follow Yehudah and Ovadiah and find out how to tap into the power needed for such an endeavor.

"Through the falls? Private office? You've gotta be kidding. And what do you mean **your** cave? What cave, and why is it yours?

"Just hold on. We are going to my favorite haven, the best place I know to explain to you what ADON OLAM calls **the power and the dominion** of Hashem."

As they approach the cascading deluge of water, Yehudah notices his skinny friend's inability to withstand the downstream force of the water. The pelting mist starts to actually hurt the skin of Ovadiah's face. He cannot see anything now. Yehudah grabs him around the waist and holds his arm around his own neck and shoulder. With a rush and holler, Ovadiah is through the crashing water in a whisk.

They are now in a cave behind the falls. And there, sopped to the gills and trying to catch his breath, Yehudah says graciously, "Welcome to my office, I mean my cave."

Yehudah puts his hand into his pocket and replaces Ovadiah's *yarmulke* that he removed so that it would not get washed away. Although the sounds of the waterfall are still roaring behind them, there is comparative calm in the cave.

"Let's go in a little further. It's much quieter further in, plus I have two lounge chairs set up for us."

Ovadiah gives a quizzical, but 'I'm-already-used-to-it' look.

Further inside, there are two rocks covered with thick moss next to a break in the walls of the cave, through which sunlight streams. Through this crack in the rock, which seems like a window between the two mossy rocks or 'lounge chairs', a gentle stream of froth pours in steadily. A rippling pool of backwash from the falls covers most of the floor of the cave. On the wall near the crevice, opposite the 'lounge chairs', the sunlight shines on some Hebrew letters scratched in the wall: ולו העוז והמשרה ~ *V'lo Ha'oz v'hamisrah* ~ To Hashem alone are the power and dominion.

Yehudah looks perfectly comfortable in this strange setting. "The members of the Great Assembly," he says, "longed for you and for every Jew to understand the meaning of the next words of ADON OLAM which I have scratched on this wall."

Ovadiah wonders about those words, as he perches on one of the sopping, moss-covered 'lounge chairs'. The thunderous water surrounds them on all sides. Water drips from various points in the ceiling. The ground underneath them rumbles.

"Touch the walls, Ovadiah. Feel the massive rocks quivering under the power of the water. You are surrounded by an awesome power, yet from this seemingly encapsulated setting you do not see its source. Is there a source to this power?"

"Of course there is."

"Look over there, at the far end of the cave—there's an almost impenetrable wall of water which blocks your view of the outside world. And likewise you cannot see out of this small crevice because there is yet another barrier of frothy water blocking it. If you were born in this cave and had never been out of it; if your only tools for understanding were those that you received in this bubble of a cave, then you would understand the power of the water but you would not be able to comprehend its source. Your perceptions would be based only on the information you had received here in this bubble. Your definitions of reality would be limited by the power that encapsulates you. Because of the unsurpassable barriers, your knowledge of the source would be attained through the power that you experience."

Ovadiah says in wonder: "I feel totally encapsulated. The outside world seems to be unfathomable from amidst this thunderous bubble. As you said, I can't see anything outside of here, nor can I hear anything outside. The wall of continuous, cutting water closes off all other existence. But why did you bring me here?"

"As we have spoken about many times before, nothing finite can comprehend the Infinite. Because you are physical, and limited by the barriers of the finite physical world, therefore you wonder how you can hope to comprehend Hashem, Who is infinitely greater than you. Your mind simply has no tools to conceive of that which is beyond its grasp. This cave represents exactly this situation. You find yourself in a physical world, cut off from the Spiritual Essence of Hashem. Can you find Him? Can you relate to Him? With all of the barriers between you and the Infinite, what hope is there to know Him? How can you hope to strive to become a servant of what you are blocked from?"

"But we are told that we have to know Hashem in all of our ways.[232] How could we be commanded to do something that is beyond our capacity?" asks Ovadiah.

And then Yehudah drops a bombshell: "Although you can never understand His Essence, He still has enabled you to know Him through His *oz*, His power."

"What exactly do you mean by His power, and how can his power enable me to understand His Essence? Aren't His power and His Essence different?" wonders Ovadiah.

"Actually they are one, and that's why one enables the connection with the other. Make yourself comfortable on that moss, and I'll show you how. For starters, we already know that Hashem and His Will and His Word are One .[233]

"Yeah, but that statement does not mention anything about Hashem's power that we can understand in our physical world." Ovadiah wipes off some of the drops of water that have landed on his face from the roof of the cave.

"Oh yes it does; and that's where ADON OLAM comes in— *V'lo ha'oz v'hamisrah* ~ To Him is the power and the dominion. It's time for you to discover what power and dominion are.

232 Proverbs 3:6.

233 *Nefesh HaChaim* 4:10. There he brings as his source *Shemos Rabbah* 33.

Oz translates as power. But there are other words for power. There is something special about the word oz that made the authors of ADON OLAM choose it over the other words. Our sages of blessed memory told us that 'Ein oz ela Torah'[234]—that whenever the Torah uses the word oz it is actually a signal word for Torah itself."

"A signal word? Why not just say Torah instead of oz, power? What do we gain by this word game? And what could it mean that power equals Torah?" asks Ovadiah.

"It's not just a game, Ovadiah. It's a lesson. "The Holy One, blessed be He is called Torah . . . and the Torah is none other than the Holy One, blessed be He."[235] We have no way of comprehending His completely Infinite and Spiritual Essence from within our bubble or barrier of physicality. We can relate directly only to His Torah, His power, from which our bubble, our physical world, was created. Hashem's Essence is not felt or understood through the barriers of physicality, but His power through which He constantly recreates the physical world penetrates those barriers. When we are commanded to know Hashem in all of our ways, we are not being commanded to grasp the ethereal. Rather, we are being told to know and live by His Torah in all our ways. "

Inside the rumbling cave there seems to be more that's being shaken up than just the walls.

"So," continues Yehudah, "ADON OLAM's words V'lo ha'oz v'hamisrah are telling us that what is Hashem's in this world (lo ~ to Him) is the Torah (ha'oz ~ the power).[236] Now let's start discussing misrah, Hashem's dominion."

Ovadiah leans back on the wet and powerfully vibrating wall and sees the beam of light illuminating the words on the wall opposite him.

---

234 Shir HaShirim Rabbah 2:10.

235 Nefesh HaChaim brings this statement from the Zohar, *Parshas B'shalach*, p. 60a.

236 Nefesh HaChaim in the commentary *U'vacharta Ba'Chaim*, p. 252.

The Go-betweens Must Go

SHIMI IS, AS USUAL, complaining. "I never swam in such cold water in my life. I am so numb that my head is spinning."

Natan is not perturbed. "Well, we have some more info to spin your head. Tell me, after last night do you feel that you are starting to understand what it means that Hashem is One?"

"Yeah, and Ovadiah seems to have put it all together for us in the van. I am sure that one day he is going to become someone special. Mark my words. I will then say that the great Ovadiah Yashar was once my roommate."

"Right now let's just work on making Shimi someone special," says Avi.

"Right now all you seem to be working on is making me into a really special ice cube," Shimi continues to grumble.

Shalom gets into the conversation with, "Let's break the ice on this subject. Last night we learned that Hashem's Oneness is infinite and therefore indivisible. Since you are finite and not even miniscule compared to Him, how can you conceive of Him?"

"Good question," says Shimi. "We spoke about this at the bonfire, didn't we? It was warmer then!"

"Hey, your memory is improving!" Natan is pleased.

But Shimi won't let go of his grievance. "No, I am just so cold that my memory banks are preserved."

"You remember that at the bonfire we discovered that only through the Torah can we relate to Hashem," says Shalom.

"So the Torah is considered some type of go-between, an intermediary? Sounds a little like so many of the other religions out there."

But Avi makes things clear: "The go-betweens must go. Many other religions felt the need for go-betweens between themselves and Hashem. This is one of the reasons for the formation of idol worship. Whether it was pagans or the wayward people who formed the cults that became some of our well-known modern-day 'monotheistic' religions, all have one thing in common. They understand that we cannot connect to Hashem with only our finite brains, and therefore, they want to conjure up the concept of these go-betweens, which are god-like or semi-god-like characters that we can relate to.

"The difference between these false religions and Torah Judaism is that we have no concept of a fallible or killable god or god-like creature as a go-between. We understand, like ADON OLAM tells us, that He is One and that there is no other. Rather, the only method of connection to Hashem is via His own Will. Only through the Will of Hashem Himself do we bridge the finite and the Infinite. And He and His Will are One."

Shimi muses. "Hashem and His Will are One. I've heard that many times, especially in the last few months, but still don't really get it."

"Maybe this will help you," says Avi. "The Torah says[237] that in the middle of the night, Hashem came to smite the Egyptian firstborn."

"And we all know from the *Hagaddah*[238] that this means Hashem and not some other go-between," Natan points out.

Avi continues. "Yet *Targum Yonasan ben Uziel*[239] translates this sentence as 'the **Word of Hashem** came to smite the Egyptians.' The Word of Hashem and Hashem are One. There are no go-betweens, no middlemen. Hashem and His Will and His Word are One.[240] This is the same message of Unkelus's that we went over in the woods. Remember?

"Now let's talk about Hashem's *misrah*, dominion . . ."

---

237 Exodus 12:29.

238 This is the liturgical composition used on the first nights of Passover. It tells of the Exodus from Egyptian bondage, through the miracles that Hashem performed to save His people.

239 He is among the most ancient and authoritative translators and commentators of the Torah.

240 *Shemos Rabbah* 33, *Nefesh HaChaim* 4:10 and many sources in the Zohar.

There's No Escaping It

WHILE SHIMI IS BEING introduced to the concept of Hashem's dominion, Yehudah and Ovadiah start to make their way towards the opening of the bubble cave, when Yehudah says:

"Misrah translates basically as dominion. Rabbeinu Pinchas of Plutsk clarifies that the intention of ADON OLAM's authors when using the word misrah was to show us that there is no way to escape from Him through any worldly scheme.

"As thunderous as these falls may be, they are still passable. But there is no passing by Hashem, because, unlike the falls, His dominion encompasses all."

The closer they get to the thunderous sound of the falls, the more Yehudah needs to raise his voice. They now stand just inches from the crashing waters.

"It just became unmistakably clear why you brought me here. Not only can we know Hashem through His power, which is His Torah; but as we learned from Yonah[241] the prophet, there is no escape from Hashem, not even in the recesses of your mind. Although we can escape from this cave, there is no escape from Hashem's dominion. Therefore we must spend our every moment coming to terms with this inescapable dominion. 'The Torah is the Tree of Life to those who hold onto her; and happy are those who hold her fast.'[242] Hold onto the Torah through the turbulence, and the power of the Torah will hold onto you."

"You got it, buddy! Ovadiah, it's time to move on. Hold on tight, and let's make a dash for it. 1,2,3 . . ."

241 In English this name is "Jonah."

242 Proverbs 3:18.

The Plunge

AVI IS STILL TRYING. "So, Shimi, do you understand now a little about what *V'lo ha'oz v'hamisrah* means?"

Shimi replies: "Hashem's dominion is inescapable. Yet our only connection to that infinite dominion is through His Torah, which He sent down from above."

Shouts are heard as Yehudah and Ovadiah plummet into the water from above.

After this 'refreshing' splash, the guys are soon back in the van and start to head off back home.

While in the van, the conversation continues, of course.

"ADON OLAM has explained to us in the previous stanza, '*V'Acharei*', about the plight of the community. But I know that some of you may still be wondering whether there is an answer in ADON OLAM for the plight of the individual? Maybe my petty problems are not important to the Master of all. Maybe Hashem is too far above me to care about my personal predicaments while He is busy dealing with the greater global picture.'"

"Yeah I've wondered about that," remarks Ovadiah.

"Remember that Avraham *Avinu* said that he is dust and ashes,[243] yet he called Hashem *Adon*, personal Master. When the members of the Great Assembly started their message to the generations specifically with that name of *Adon* they were shouting through the millennia directly into our ears. Hashem is *Adon Olam*, which means *Ein Sof*, Infinity. There is no force other than Him. Yet this same *Adon Olam* is also אלי ~ *Eli* ~ my personal God, Who is constantly involved in everything that is coming my way, no matter how petty I may think I am. This is the message that we are going to be tackling now as we delve into the ancient words of ADON OLAM's fourth stanza, *V'Hu Eli*."

Sometimes, Searching Soul, we have trouble seeing the bigger forest because the individual trees are standing in our way. Consequently, my authors included in my second stanza the concept of tifarah, the perfect bal-

243 Genesis 18:27.

ance which gave us an understanding of Hashem's running the bigger picture in the most perfect balance. Then they showed our people how to properly serve the Master of this perfect balance through understanding His oneness more deeply. But, like Ovadiah, we sometimes feel lost in the bigger picture and wind up having the opposite problem: We find ourselves unable to distinguish the individual trees in the bigger forest. But my next words will show you that Hashem has no such trouble. Although He is the One God Who runs the larger picture, He uncompromisingly picks each one out of the crowd. Come with me, as I show you through my fourth stanza, V'Hu Eli, just how important little old you are in the eyes of the singular Master of the splendorously hidden world.

SECTION FOUR

V'HU ELI:
Taking Global Theory and Making It Personal

וְהוּא אֵלִי וְחַי גּוֹאֲלִי, וְצוּר חֶבְלִי בְּעֵת צָרָה
וְהוּא נִסִּי וּמָנוֹס לִי, מְנַת כּוֹסִי בְּיוֹם אֶקְרָא

~

V'Hu Eli,[244] v'chai goali, v'tzur chevli b'eis tzarah,
V'Hu nisi, u'manos li, menas cosi b'yom ekra.

~

And He is my personal God and my living Redeemer, and He
is the rock of my distress at the time of my troubles.
And He is my banner, the One testing me[245], and my refuge.
He is the portion of my cup on the day that I call.

*H*EY, OVER HERE. *Yes, Searching Soul, it's me again,
ADON OLAM. So you wonder why I am here today.
You see, I know you well, as did my holy authors. Even
though you are committed to an observant lifestyle,
you often come away from your performance of com-*

---

244 Since Eli is one of the Holy Names of God, when it is not used liturgically it must not be
pronounced as written. The custom is to pronounce it Keli instead of Eli. The author chose
to not do this here, for the name is not being said aloud, but merely read.

245 In order to understand why the Hebrew was translated in this manner, please refer to the
Disclaimer.

mandments with a sense of emptiness. It's clear that those feelings stem from not understanding just how important you, your thoughts and your actions really are to the Master of the Universe. So if you are interested in changing lifeless practice into vibrant service, if you crave for the bland to become flavorful, if you yearn for your now-feeble efforts to develop into strong labors of faith, then it's time for you to understand my fourth stanza, V'Hu Eli.

Let's start by listening as Yehudah Stark confronts Rabbeinu Reuven with a dilemma . . . .

"I called this meeting with you tonight, because I don't have the answers to your nephew's questions. I think maybe it's time for Rabbeinu Reuven to meet him and answer the questions face to face."

"What troubles the young man now?"

Yehudah tells Rabbeinu Reuven about what Ovadiah asked him earlier that day:

"'Yehudah, after the towers went down you explained to me that ADON OLAM's words, 'Hashem was, is and always will be in *tifarah*', mean that the world's events are never haphazard, but, rather, they are always in a perfect balance. From those words I learned how Hashem is always in constant control of the larger picture. But that was a little too global for me. It did not answer my questions about my personal faith. You told me to wait to understand the personal until we learned the stanza, V'Hu Eli, which translates as 'He is my personal God'. That is the next stanza, and you said that we would be starting it soon. Before we start, I want to give you a feeling of just how blurry my understanding is of this personal-God stuff. I still don't understand why Hashem cares if, for example, I learn His Torah, stay kosher, observe the Sabbath, pray, wear a Yarmulke, put on Tzitzis,[246] lay Tefillin[247] or do any of the other commandments.

---

246 Strings entwined on the corners of a four-cornered garment.

247 Literally phylacteries. These are leather boxes that contain certain paragraphs from the Torah. They are worn by Jewish men when they pray the daily morning prayers.

"Don't get me wrong. From ADON OLAM I do understand why the Master of the Universe matters to me, but I have no idea why I or my actions matter to the Master of the Universe. Personal God? I just don't understand the Master of All's involvement in the life of the lowly individual. What am I missing???"

Rabbeinu Reuven listens intently to Yehudah's report, and then sighs. Yehudah waits as the old rabbi, covered in his black, hooded garb, covers his eyes with his hand as he rocks back and forth.

"No. Not yet. It's not yet time for us to meet. He must finish this part of his search for meaning with his friends. I will teach you what my father wanted Ovadiah's father to know. With that knowledge, Ovadiah will be equipped to handle the last leg of his search for meaning. Only then will it be the right time for us to finally meet.

"This is not the first time that I have heard these questions, you should know. They are the same questions that his father Binyamin asked our father. I remember that day well. It was a short time before our father passed on from this world . . ."

Chacham Yashar has recently fallen quite ill. As seventeen-year-old Binyamin cares for his frail father he senses that he will not survive this illness. He is fearful that soon he will be left an orphan. Recently he has had so many questions about his faith. Why does his father have to be ill now, when he is going through so much turmoil? There is so much that he still needs his father to answer. But he knows that it won't be. As Chacham Yashar looks at Binyamin, he discerns the trouble on the teenager's face.

"My son, please speak to me while I can still be of help to you. What is bothering you?"

Binyamin's brother, Reuven, enters to assist in the care of his ailing father. Binyamin is now doubly embarrassed about his questions, but he realizes that 'if not now, when?'[248] So he musters up the courage to ask questions that he never asked before.

"Father, please do not take my questions as disrespect for your beliefs. But I am very confused now. You taught me the words of King David, 'Hashem, what is man that You take knowledge of him, or the son of man that You make account of him? Man is like a breath; his days are like a shadow that passes away.'[249] Hashem is Infinite. So why would my limited actions matter to Him? Why should I follow the commandments of the Torah if my life is but a breath and shadow that passes away? I understand why the Master of the Universe matters to me, but I have no idea why I matter to the Master of the Universe."

"Go on; do you have more good questions, like this?"

"Yes. Father; I do . . ."

For the next few minutes Binyamin pours out to his dying father all of his quandaries. All the while, Reuven listens quietly from the other room. After a small pause, Chacham Yashar responds . . . .

"These are excellent questions Binyamin. Don't worry; there are also ancient and excellent answers."

"Where, father?" Binyamin is desperate to know.

"We find them in ADON OLAM, in the stanza V'Hu Eli."

"So the answers are found in Father's *The Hidden Master*? I will read it, Father, I promise."

Chacham Yashar closes his eyes in deep concentration for a few moments. He then opens them and speaks.

"Not all the answers are there. Until now I thought that I had finished my book. Now, after your heartfelt questions, I see that there is still something missing. With God's help I will compose some answers especially for you."

"But, Father, you are weak and need your rest. It is not time to write. It is time to regain strength."

But Chacham Yashar shakes his head. "While I am still alive I will put all of my strength into the answers for your questions. I want you to carry the answer to your soul's pain with you when I am gone. May it be His Will that these words that I hope to compose will hold you tightly and lovingly to your Father in Heaven even when your father on earth has left you. Please bring me some sheets of paper and a quill. I need to start . . ."

---

249 Psalms 144:3–4.

Five Worn Sheets

*F*ORTY-ONE YEARS LATER, *eighty-year-old Reuven Yashar sits with Yehudah Stark in his study in his yeshivah in Jerusalem. In his hand are five sheets of yellowed paper that he has just pulled out from between the pages of Ovadiah's copy of The Hidden Master.*

"These sheets are the last writings of my father. He completed them with the last ounces of his strength. They were to be his last determined effort to try to bring my brother back. He knew that he would never have the chance to share these thoughts properly and at length with Binyamin. So instead he wrote them as his last legacy, hoping that his son and others like him would be drawn to their personal God through them. Just days before he died, he handed me these sheets and told me to teach them to Binyamin and to then include them in *The Hidden Master*."

Rabbeinu Reuven sighs sadly. "I never had the opportunity to read these sheets. Caring for our father during his illness for those next few days took all of our time until he breathed his last breath. During the shivah[250] Binyamin kept to himself. He was unapproachable. Something in him snapped when he became an orphan. He showed the utmost respect for our father's memory, but when the shivah for our holy father was completed, he left us. But before he went, he took our father's copy of *The Hidden Master* with him. I ran after him to the dock with that final letter and told him that our father had written this for him. He looked at me blankly with a tear in his eye and respectfully placed them in between the pages of the volume in his hands.

"I discovered them only recently, when you gave me the book. They were still folded neatly but I saw from the worn edges that Binyamin eventually did review them many times. It is clear to me that Binyamin's last words, "*Adon Olam,*" his message to his only son, were the product of the soul-searching that these

---

250 The week of mourning following burial.

sheets ultimately produced in him. Now you and I will learn the messages which will answer Ovadiah's questions as they seem to have answered Binyamin's. Then you will give these messages over to Ovadiah and his friends."

Yehudah is curious. "Before Rabbeinu starts, is it known what prompted Binyamin to leave?"

As the Community Crumbled

RABBEINU REUVEN ANSWERS: "You wonder how my brother went so far off the path of our father when I stayed on this path. For me it is no wonder. As I told you many months ago, there were more than twenty years between us, but it may as well have been twenty generations. I was born in 1921. I was raised before the Holocaust, and before the subsequent formation of the State of Israel, I was already married with children. Throughout my youth, our community in Morocco was filled with scholars, Kabbalists, and many righteous people. For thousands of years, the Jews of Morocco were an untainted stronghold of Torah learning and a bastion for the observance of its commandments.

"But that all changed. With the birth of the secular State, many of the youth gave up religion for nationalism. It was almost like a frenzy of change, it happened so fast. The entire religious societal structure that our people had had for a millennium fell apart in front of our eyes. Secularism hit Morocco like a devastating hurricane.

"Binyamin was born in 1943 and was raised in the midst of this frenzy. He did not have memories of the stable Torah community that I was raised in. Instead, he experienced a community that was caving in and needed its leader, our father, to fight a losing battle alone. Binyamin and I had many conversations about the 'new ways'. He saw the battle being lost and concluded that his father's ways were to be left respectfully in the past.

"Of course he was raised on the high thoughts of ADON

OLAM. They were the breath of our humble home for everyone but Binyamin. They seemed to him as just theory. They never affected him personally. My father's world was crumbling around him, yet my father stayed strong, for he knew that his every action and thought was important to Hashem. Binyamin, on the other hand, didn't grasp why his seemingly petty actions and thoughts could matter to the Infinite Master of all worlds. When he heard Binyamin's questions, he knew that he must do something to enable Binyamin to understand the personal impetus needed to stay a good Jew. He could not just watch Binyamin being washed away with the tides of time. But what could he say that would enter the ears of his young son who wanted to 'move on'?"

With the five ancient, worn sheets spread out before him on his large mahogany desk, Rabbeinu Reuven's right hand supports his forehead as his left hand holds his white straggly beard.

"For some unknown reason, Hashem deemed it that it should take forty-one years until I would have the opportunity to read these words. Yehudah, the time has come to breach the painful chasm that came into being so many years ago. Young Ovadiah is now ready to hear that last message to Binyamin. Listen well and give these words over to my nephew. So together, let's start to go over that last letter . . ."

You Deserve Good Answers

My Dear Binyamin, I hope that my words will fall gently and warmly upon your heart.

You asked me so many good questions today and you deserve good answers. May Hashem give me strength to write you the answers before He reclaims my soul. Our sages taught us that our every action and thought is of ultimate importance to our personal God, for they state in ADON OLAM: HE IS MY GOD (ELI), MY LIVING REDEEMER. HE—this infinite, incomprehensible, supremely powerful

Being, which defies our power of conception—is MY GOD! He has a personal relationship with me.[251]

Notice, my son, that the holy ancient authors purposely chose to use the name Eli, which is the name that refers to Hashem's attribute of mercy. This they did to teach us that it is necessary for each Jew to realize that the fact that my mother conceived me, that I was born, and that I am able to function as a viable human being, is all because of His mercy.[252] We constantly need to have recognition of the good, of the continuous acts of mercy that our personal God, Eli, showers upon each and every one of us.

The choice is ours; if we choose to open our eyes and look honestly at even the mundane details of our lives, we immediately recognize the continual acts of mercy directed personally at us. From this we should discern that we and our actions are important in His infinite eyes.

"But my father was aware that this would not be enough to satisfy Binyamin who had just asked him. 'If Hashem is so powerful why has He deserted us for so long? Why are we so downtrodden in this long and bitter exile? Has Hashem deserted us for another nation, or has His strength ebbed as would happen to an elderly man?'[253] So, in response, my father continued:

My son, we all see that the exile is long and painful. But this does not mean that our God has deserted us. ADON OLAM tells us each day that He is Eli, my personal God. This name Eli was chosen by the members of the Great Assembly to express that He, Who is the God of Mercy, is each and every person's personal God. This is why Hashem has also attached this specific name of His to ours, hence the name YisraEL—to show that through all of our bitterness, He is still our personal God and has not left us.[254]

251 This passage ("He is my God . . . with me") was brought from *Rav Schwab on Prayer*. Page 9

252 This passage ("my mother . . . His mercy") was brought from *Rav Schwab on Prayer*. Page 9

253 Rabbeinu Pinchas of Plutsk in *Siddur Shaar HaRachamim*. Pages 71–72.

254 This passage was adapted from Rabbeinu Pinchas of Plutsk in *Siddur Shaar HaRachamim*. Pages 71–72.

A few hours later, Yehudah Stark leaves Rabbeinu Reuven's study with a much more insightful view of just why and how the individual matters to our personal God. As he walks through the empty streets and alleyways, he ponders over just how to give over these new messages to Ovadiah and the guys.

"I got it!" he exclaims to himself jubilantly. "I'll tell them about when the KGB was on my tail."

Rushing Through Russia

COME WITH ME, Searching Soul. We're now back in 1984, and Communism isn't showing any signs of crumbling. Eighteen-year-old Yehudah waits deep below the earth's surface in the Soviet Metro at the station near the Cosmos Hotel in Moscow. What's he doing in communist Russia? This was Yehudah's first adventure. He was sent by a Jewish activist group to help some of his fellow Jews behind the Iron Curtain. Presently he is waiting with a brave young man named Pesach Moshe who has endangered his life many times for what he calls "a breath of Judaism." His father was sent to Siberia two years before for the crime of teaching the Holy Tongue, Hebrew. His mother was removed from the home to some institution. With both his parents away, he is compelled to brave the enemy world alone. Surrounded by Russian-speaking passengers, he speaks to Yehudah in Hebrew. Yehudah interrupts him:

"Maybe we should not speak in Hebrew. People will notice and it will cause more attention to be focused on you. You are in enough trouble as it is."

"No, my friend. I barely get an opportunity to speak my language. I am imprisoned in an enemy land, and they have stolen my people, my religion, my language, my parents, and most of all, my freedom to serve Eli, my God. I don't want to be taken to Siberia, but I still need to stay sane. If I do not have this small piece of Judaism, then I will die of suffocation.

"ADON OLAM tells us that Hashem is my God, Eli. This has become my motto through all of my predicaments. I know that I cannot possibly get out of the mess that I am in without Him. And while I am in this torture of an imprisoned life, I hold on to anything that attaches me to Him. I am YisraEL, and Hashem is ELI. They can never take my identity from me. They can never take my God from me. Never!"

Yehudah has been looking around all the while. "There he is. My cohort from America is coming with an entire suitcase full of expensive merchandise just for you."

They spot Zalman at the top of a steep stairway leading down into the Metro. There is enough loot in that suitcase that, if it were all sold on the black market, would give Pesach Moshe enough money to bribe his way through the paperwork that would set him free. Pesach Moshe's eyes light up in longing.

"Who's that following Zalman?" Yehudah wonders.

Two men in black are following Zalman down the stairs. Zalman keeps looking over his shoulder, and then spots Yehudah. His look is a silent scream: *What should I do???*

Pesach Moshe utters something between a groan and a sigh. "It's the KGB. There is no escape. They will take me away. You are foreigners, so nothing will happen to you. But I will be sent to Siberia."

The thunderous roll of the Metro is heard. Zalman's eyes again meet Yehudah's. Yehudah points with his head towards the incoming subway car. They both understand. They were told to expect something like this. Their only chance is to lose the KGB.

Grabbing Pesach Moshe's trembling hand, Yehudah says, "Just follow me."

Zalman dashes down the long steep staircase, pushing people to the side. They are too startled to react; such behavior is unheard of in the Soviet Union.

"Zalman," commands Yehudah, "run into this car."

The three of them enter the car and dash through it into the next one, and from there onward—through car after car. The KGB also enters after them. But they are slightly slower—never a push. As they approach the next station, the KGB agents close in on them. Again Yehuda's authoritative voice is heard: "Out of the car; run towards the other end."

The scurry seems hopeless. But then, just before the Metro doors close, Yehudah, Zalman and Pesach Moshe disappear among the exiting crowd into the now exiting train. The KGB is left on the platform searching for them.

Yehudah's tale has captivated the guys so much that no one has touched their dinners, which now lie cold on their plates in the *yeshivah* dining hall.

Shalom just can't hold in his curiosity, "So what happened next, Yehudah?"

"Thank God, our escape was quick and successful, and so was the selling of all the merchandise on the black market. When the KGB came to Pesach Moshe's home that night, the money was stashed away safely. Hope was not lost; it was tucked away, waiting for a break in the darkness.

"Six months later, I picked up Pesach Moshe at Ben Gurion Airport in Tev Aviv. He became a free man.

"But it did not stop there. A little over a year later, at the age of nineteen, he was already teaching a beginners' class in this *yeshivah*."

"How did he get to such a level so fast?" asks Ovadiah in awe.

"He held onto his motto in his new life as well. Many times he told me, 'He is my God, Eli. If you live knowing that the whole world is run by Hashem and that He looks out for you personally in every event that He sends your way, then you can accomplish anything. When you realize that your actions count to 'He Who spoke' and the world came into being,[255] then not even the mighty KGB can stop you.'

"Today, he runs his own *yeshivah for Russian speakers*," concludes Yehudah triumphantly. "The voice of Torah is heard among the descendents of expatriats of the former Soviet Union because of his efforts.

255 From *Baruch She'amar*, a blessing in the morning prayers.

"His success and the success of his *yeshivah* were made possible by understanding how each of us really does count. In observing him, I have taken note that he teaches his students to view their Torah learning as important in the eyes of Hashem."

"Although Pesach Moshe's story and attitude are inspiring," exclaims Ovadiah, "I still do not understand why individuals should count to Hashem."

"When we were in the woods, we discussed why Hashem created the world in the first place. Do you remember what we learned there?" Yehudah asks.

"Yes, I do. You taught us there the *Derech Hashem* that explained that the world was created in order to bestow good."

"And that good," Yehudah cuts in, "we learned, is defined as our ability to choose to serve Hashem, and to therefore earn closeness with Him. I can think of nothing which explains Hashem's beckoning us to choose this closeness with Him more than the words of ADON OLAM."

Ovadiah is still somewhat unconvinced. "Where do ADON OLAM's words show us that Hashem is beckoning us to choose this closeness and that we actually matter in the bigger scheme of things?"

Just then a grumpy voice booms across the dining hall. "This is not an all-night diner," proclaims the middle-aged cleaning man. "Please continue your conversation outside. I have to clean up and get home to my family."

"Let's sit in the playground across the street. We'll pick up the conversation there," suggests Yehudah.

As they walk to the playground, Ovadiah's questions ring in Yehudah's mind. He thinks back to his lesson last night with Rabbeinu Reuven and is amazed at how Ovadiah used the same words that Binyamin Yashar did 41 years before.

"So," he thinks to himself, "I guess I should answer Ovadiah just as Chacham Yashar responded to Binyamin on those sheets."

"*V'chai goali*," he says to the guys trailing after him. "ADON OLAM expresses that not only is Hashem 'my God' but also that He is 'my living Redeemer'."

"I guess a living redeemer is better than a dead one, but how does that answer Ovadiah's question?"

"I'd like to add to Shimi's question," says Shalom. "Why would anyone need to be redeemed if they have a personal God who is looking after them?"

"Do you even know what the Torah's definition of a redeemer is?" shoots back Yehudah.

Natan, the team's walking concordance, is quick on the draw, as usual: "In the Torah, the term *goel*, or redeemer, speaks of a living relative who is responsible to bail out his destitute family member."[256]

"Very good, Natan. Let's go on with that thought . . . ."

My Closest Living Relative

AS THE GUYS GET SEATED on the swings, seesaws, and other assorted playground equipment, Yehudah quickly reviews in his mind the previous night's lesson with Rabbeinu Reuven:

"Yehudah, before I continue with this letter, I must fill you in on one of Binyamin's questions that prompted my father to write what he did. Binyamin asked our father that heart-wrenching night: 'How can we say that He is El, the God of mercy, when nearly half of our people were killed just 15 years ago by the Nazis?'

"You have to admit, it was a good question," says Yehudah. "I don't know if anyone has the answer to that."

"ADON OLAM does. Be patient, and you will see. Binyamin was not alone. Throughout human history, questions of this nature have been prevalent. The text of ADON OLAM's fourth stanza was written not only to depict the personal side of our faith, but also to answer the dichotomy of Hashem's mercy as opposed to His strict justice. This is why its authors chose to use the name El or Eli here, which refers not only to mercy, but also to strict justice. El is the Divine Name that describes how God shows mercy to those who either have not sinned or to those who sinned and then repented. He will save them, regardless of any natural causes.[257] Many times in our long history we have seen this mercy.

"As for the aspect of strict justice, let's look at how my father answered Binyamin."

Rabbeinu Reuven picks up the yellowing sheets and continues . . . .

Yet, my son, you should know that many times we as a people have turned away from His ways. And although some of us might hold on tightly, we Jews are all responsible for one another. We are judged not only individually, but also as a whole nation. So, if many of our people have ignored His commandments and started to stray from His paths to join the paths of those surrounding us, then we as a nation push away the divine attribute of mercy and cause our nation as a whole to become deserving of the attribute of strict justice.

But even in those situations where strict justice is delivered, all is not lost, for if the attribute of justice strikes, ADON OLAM informs us that "He is also my living Redeemer . . . chai goali,"[258] Who, if He wishes, will redeem us through His mercy and loving-kindness.[259]

"I am sorry to interrupt," says Yehudah, "but can this dichotomy of mercy versus justice also be seen in the personal?"

"Of course it can, Yehudah. My father only wrote about the Holocaust in this letter because he was responding to Binyamin's question. But in *The Hidden Master* he related this dichotomy to the individual. There he told his readers that if the individual falters and does not merit mercy, then the attribute of strict justice takes over. But both in his book and in this letter to Binyamin, my father goes on to explain why the authors of ADON OLAM chose the word *goel*, redeemer, as the next description of Hashem. He refers to Exodus 6:6, where

257 Rav Huminer, *Olas Tamid*, p. 17.

258 *Rav Schwab on Prayer.*

259 Rabbeinu Pinchas in *Siddur Shaar HaRachamim*.

Hashem says, 'I redeemed—*ga'alti*—you with an outstretched arm . . .' To further understand this term, my father points to Leviticus 25:25. Open to it now, Yehudah, and tell me what you see."

Yehudah checks the reference. "The Torah is speaking of a situation where someone is so deeply in debt that he is forced to sell his property. We are then told that the closest living relative, or *goel*, should come to 'bail him out', to redeem his property for him."

"So you see, Yehudah, the *goel* of a person is his closest living relative. And so, my father continues in his letter to Binyamin . . . .

"If I am the recipient of mercy in my life, then Hashem is its source. But, if His strict justice strikes, then I can look to Him as chai goali, my closest living relative, Who will redeem me.[260]

"So," says Rabbeinu Reuven, "now that you understand what is meant by Hashem being *chai goali*, my Living Redeemer, let's continue on in these sheets to see what my father wrote about the next words in ADON OLAM, וצור חבלי ~ *v'tzur chevli* ~ the Rock of my suffering . . ."

The Rock of My Suffering

"SPEAKING ABOUT REDEEMERS, can someone get the thug off the bottom end of the seesaw? I'm stuck up here in the air," says Shimi, who has been perched on the top end during Yehudah's explanation of 'Living Redeemer'.

"Why didn't you say you wanted to go down?" asks Avi, getting up and sending Shimi crashing to the ground.

"Living Redeemer. Let's see if I got this straight. From what you just explained, I am supposed to look upon Hashem's relationship with me as that of my closest living Redeemer, the One Who will bail me out of jail, or other troubles. That's pretty intense," notes Natan from the swing.

"Sorry to burst your intense bubble," asserts Shalom, from the top of the monkey bars, "but I am not impressed. What Yehudah just told us about Hashem being our 'Living Redeemer' is an incomplete view. How can we be expected to view Hashem as our Living Redeemer when we all know of many who have met up with suffering that they were not redeemed from?"

Ovadiah, who is not in a playful mood, just sits on the bench, waiting for Yehudah to give an answer, which he does.

"If, in His Infinite Wisdom, He decides not to redeem me, and I do not experience mercy, and I suffer, then ADON OLAM tells us that Hashem is צור חבלי בעת צרה ~ *tzur chevli b'eis tzarah* ~ the Rock of my pain or suffering in time of distress.[261] In other words, Ovadiah, Hashem gives me the strength to be able to bear and accept my suffering."

"So חבלי ~ *chevli*, means my pain. Why does ADON OLAM use that word for pain? There are so many other words for that, more commonly used in scripture," queries Ovadiah.

"*Chevli* does not describe a normal pain;" adds Natan from the swing, "rather, it refers to the type of pain that grips you so severely that there is no escape from it."

"Like labor pains, *chevlei leidah*."

"Exactly. I see again that you're taking your Hebrew lessons seriously," Yehudah praises Shimi. "Here ADON OLAM describes these pains as being not only gripping and inescapable, but also specifically mine, hence *chev-li*, my gripping pain. We must endure our hardships while knowing that the pain is specifically ours, because it was either caused by us or intended specifically for us. These pains are sometimes inescapable in order to force us to learn a necessary lesson."

Ovadiah considers this for a moment. "This seems similar to what we mentioned when discussing *tifarah*. There you explained that nothing happens haphazardly; everything is part of a larger and complete picture of cause and effect, run completely by Hashem, Who does everything for a precise reason. Why does ADON OLAM bother to then state the same point again in the fourth stanza?"

And Yehuda explains: "Here, in the fourth stanza, we are given a very different view of how these black parts of the picture, the dots on the vase that we described in b'tifarah, are not just global but are also specifically mine. Whether the pain is caused by my straying from Hashem's paths, or is sent to teach me a necessary personal lesson, ADON OLAM informs us that Hashem is *tzur chevli*, the Rock when I suffer."

"But you just said that He is the cause of my suffering. Why call Him the Rock of that suffering?" asks Shalom.

And Natan adds, "I'm with Shalom. Doesn't the word rock imply something that you lean on, or depend upon? What could it mean that Hashem is both the Source of the pain, and the One upon Whom I depend when the pain comes?"

"There is no contradiction. Like I just said, Hashem causes my suffering for a reason. In the midst of experiencing a gripping, seemingly inescapable suffering, the person is actually being steered from above to the necessary realization that there is no one to rely upon other than Hashem. He is the only 'Rock of my suffering.' We were all put in this world in order to strive to get closer to Hashem. If I stray from this path or need an extra push, then Hashem sends these seemingly-inescapable ordeals, so that I will look to my only Living Redeemer, Who is the Rock when I suffer."

A Rocky Eulogy

OVADIAH PUTS ACROSS a thought that he has been holding back during Yehudah's explanation of Hashem as 'the Rock of my pain'.

"Tzur *chevli*, the Rock of my pain. This was the main point of the eulogy at my dad's funeral. The presiding rabbi said . . . .

We are told that "He is the Rock (Tzur). His work is perfect: for all His
ways are justice: He is the God (El) of truth and without iniquity,
He is just and right,"[262] even in His mysterious ways, like this
seemingly senseless murder.

In these words of the Torah, there is a message for the bereaved
family. They come to inform you, Estelle and Ovadiah, that when
your troubles seem to grip you in a hold that you cannot escape,
when seeming injustice smacks you in the face, still we need to
remember that somehow Hashem is the Rock of justice.

I was told that the dearly departed Binyamin's last words were "Adon
Olam". ADON OLAM also describes Hashem as a Rock. וצור חבלי
בעת צרה ~ V'Tzur chevli b'eis tzara ~ Hashem is the Rock of my
gripping pain at times of distress. The authors seem to have
understood that when enduring difficulties it is not enough to
know that there is a Rock somewhere out there Who is perfect
in His deeds, His great plans, as described by the Torah. They
understood that many times, like today, we would need to know
and experience that He is the Rock of our personal pain.

The members of the Great Assembly set down that we should thank
Hashem three times a day in the blessing of Modim (thanks).
Surely they knew that there would be many, many days when
the Jews praying would see nothing to thank their God for. Yet
they set down in words for the ages that we must always thank
Hashem for both that which we view as good and that which we
think of as bad.

If you recognize Hashem's hand dealing with you personally, even
when you are in distress, then you will feel what King David said,[263]
"Hashem is my Rock , and my Fortress, and my Deliverer; my
God (Eli), my Rock (Tzuri) in Whom I will trust; my shield, and
the horn of my salvation, and my high tower."

Yehudah nods appreciatively. "Hold on to that thought.
Tomorrow I am taking you guys up to Mt. Hermon. There we
will discuss this point in greater detail. See you all tomorrow
at 3:30 am."

"Where did you say that we are going tomorrow, and when???"

262 Deuteronomy 32:4.

263 Psalms 18:3

Mt. Hermon

*Y*EHUDAH PICKS UP *the guys at 3:30 am promptly and starts heading up north to Mt. Hermon. After stopping at Katzrin²⁶⁴ for morning prayers, the guys are back in the van at 7:45 am. A few minutes later . . . .*

"O.K., we are at the foothills. We'll be there in 15 minutes. I have a question for you all before we get there. Our people had to go down to Egypt before they would receive the Torah. Does anyone know why we were required to endure 210 years of slavery?"

Avi rubs his eyes sleepily, but nevertheless comes through. "It looks like cause and effect to me. That slavery was eventually going to lead to salvation. Because Hashem saved us, we became indebted to Him for having saved us. It was this indebtedness that enabled us to readily accept the Torah from our Savior."

"Excellent. And that same lesson of our ancestors is still true for us today. We all have to view life as constantly having its own personal Egypts. And in the midst of these personal Egypts we must recognize Hashem as our personal Redeemer Whom we lean upon like a rock."

"Oh come on, let's not exaggerate," blurts out Shimi. "Egyptian slavery was quite bad. Babies were ground into the mortar, physical labor took on new meanings. I don't know about you guys, but I don't think that we all have our own Egypts happening to us on a daily basis. We owe thanks to Hashem for redeeming our ancestors way back then. But that was thousands of years ago. I don't feel that I am leaning on any rock. In fact, I feel quite capable of standing on my own two feet, thank you."

Yehudah raises his eyebrows in a knowing manner. "I don't think that you will say that after this morning's little show. I brought you all up here to Mt. Hermon to understand—in a much more poignant way than you may have ever understood—that Hashem really does save each and every one of us miraculously every day. And we are all quite unaware of most

264 Town in the Golan Heights, near Mt. Hermon.

of the things He saves us from. But before the show, let's look again at the text of ADON OLAM.

"In the fourth stanza Hashem is described as the Rock that we depend upon in times of personal trouble. But most of us are unaware of just how much trouble we are in and therefore are oblivious to what extent we need to depend upon our Rock. As we approach our destination, I want you all to reflect upon the blessing of *Modim* found in our daily prayers. The text of that blessing instructs us to thank Hashem for 'His miracles that are with us every day.' You see, Shimi—it says 'every day'."

"Every day?" Shimi is still quite skeptical. "Who says that there are miracles that happen to us every day?"

"Hey, Shimi, remember that the authors of that blessing were also the Great Assembly. And remember that many of its members were actually prophets," responds Natan.

Shimi grudgingly realizes that Natan has a point.

Yehudah continues. "And it's not a coincidence that the Great Assembly composed both the 'blessing of thanks' and ADON OLAM. One of our most basic beliefs is that Hashem is watching over each of us personally. There isn't any individual Jew for whom hidden miracles don't happen every day."[265]

By now the windshield wipers are swishing to and fro rapidly and the defogger is on high. Wind throws fine remnants of the past winter's snow onto the windshield. Outside, all that can be seen is walls of snow made by the plows on either side. Now Yehudah stops the car at the heavily guarded gate of an army intelligence base. He rolls down the window and two soldiers in heavy winter attire covered with frost peer in. One of the soldiers relays the message through a microphone. "It's Yehudah , open up."

To the utter bewilderment of the guys, the soldiers move to the side, and the heavy gate lifts up, allowing the van to enter.

Shimi expresses it all for everyone: "How does he do this?"

"I think that this is one of those times that we should just stay put and shut up," advises Avi.

265 *Pathway to Prayer* by Mayer Birnbaum on the blessing of '*Modim*'. This quote is from R. Bachyei (Rabbi Bachyei ben Asher, 14th century), in his introduction of *Parshas Ki Sisa*.

Huge radar disks are seen bolted to the cliffs surrounding them. The van pulls to a halt.

Before they get out, Yehudah instructs them: "Just act naturally, like you own the place, and follow me. But don't touch anything."

After going through quite a labyrinth in the massive, high-tech structure, welcoming calls are heard from the personnel manning the place, each in his own particular way:

"Hi Yud."

"Yo Bro!"

"It's Mighty Stark."[266]

"What's up, Mr. Bond?"

They reach a door, and Yehudah calmly puts his whole hand upon a fingerprint sensor, just as if it were something he did every day.

"Quickly, guys, come into my office. The door will remain open for only seven seconds."

Among the computer monitors and multiple-colored phones are neatly-placed photos of familiar faces—Yehudah's wife and kids. Ovadiah looks around. "Oh, so this is where you went by helicopter that day, after the Towers fell."

"Right."

"I always wondered why your schedule at the *yeshivah* isn't exactly fixed in time."

"It seems," remarks Shalom, "as though you have a more important job than teaching little old us."

Yehudah smiles wryly. "I won't ever tell you exactly what I do here, but let it be clear to you all that there is nothing more important than the Torah that we learn. I brought you here today to watch a set of films that I put together for my coworkers. Look at that wall with the 18 screens."

He types a few commands into his computer and multiple scenes of terrorists attempting to cross borders or infiltrate into high-population areas pop up.

"Each of these events could have caused massive tragedy, but they were not separate events. They were a single-day of pre-planned, multiple terror attacks."

266 This is a play on words. Stark is a common Jewish name, and means "mighty" in Yiddish.

"When was this?" asks Shalom. "I don't remember this showing up on the news."

"It didn't make the news," explains Yehudah. "This type of stuff happens on different scales on a daily basis."

Ovadiah says thoughtfully, "You mean that the army stopped all of these attacks successfully."

"I didn't say that," says Yehudah quietly.

"Then what did happen?" questions Avi.

Frogmen and Fishing Nets

"WE INFORMED the armed forces of the few incidents that we detected that day, but later on we started getting reports of the demise of a great many other terrorists, complete with the footage. That one on the bottom middle screen was bitten by a snake as he tried to cross the border. The top left screen shows a submerged boat of explosives with two dead frogmen who drowned after they became entangled in a stray fishing net off the shores of Rafiach.[267] The car in the left bottom screen contained enough explosives to destroy the settlement it was heading toward. It hit a telephone pole and the rest is history, along with the pole; etc., etc. We could not have detected all of these and dealt with all of them simultaneously."

"So it could happen again, anytime, anywhere. I feel so unsafe," Shimi frowns.

Yehudah goes on. "ADON OLAM's words, V'tzur chevli ~ And He is the Rock of my distress, teach us that Hashem has always been our holy nation's Rock. Avi was on the right track when he told us that we needed to go down to Egypt so that we would have to be saved. This salvation created a feeling of indebtedness to Hashem. The Holy One, blessed be He, took us to be His people specifically when we were in Egypt, and not at a time of peace. We needed to be saved from the inescapable hardships of Egypt so that we should come to believe in and depend only upon Hashem at all times, and especially

267 A town in the Gaza Strip that borders on the Mediterranean Sea.

in the midst of troubles. Having this lesson in mind since the inception of our people, we have learned to never give up or lose hope in the face of other difficulties.[268]

"We must peer through the terrifying façade of oppression and gain a firm recognition that Hashem stands ready and even eager to alter the reality of each moment—for the sake of our care and protection. With this in mind, we can stare into the face of any enemy and declare, 'Whether we live or die, we have no fear of you. Only God will determine our fate.'"[269]

Ovadiah is pleased. "After having seen your 'little show', I understand the message of the 'blessing of thanks'. Clearly, there really are miracles that happen every day to each of us, disasters that are averted that we may never even know about,and it is Hashem Who saves us from all of them."

"Mission accomplished," Yehudah asserts. "O.K. guys, the class trip is moving on. Let's go for a hike in the Golan Heights . . ."

Binyamin Breaks Down
His Old Barriers

COCA COLA—It's the real thing. As the empty words of the midnight commercial echo through the basement TV room, Binyamin Yashar's middle-aged eyes catch a 'chance' glimpse at the very dusty holy book on the top shelf, above the large screen.
"No it's not. It's not the real thing; there is so much more."
As he thinks back to the depth and warmth of his father's home and thinks of the emptiness that he lives, he feels his stomach churning. Reaching for the remote control, he flicks the TV off. On the coffee table are a few beers and the remainders of the breaded pork chops Estelle had prepared for dinner. Again he looks at *The Hidden Master*.
"I don't even stay kosher anymore."
He tries to ignore the book. It's too painful. He grabs something from

268 Rabbeinu Pinchas, *Siddur Shaar HaRachamim*. Pages 71–72.
269 Wegbreit, *The Power of Aleinu*, pp. 67–68.

the magazine rack. It's a brochure sent by the college placement service. There's a picture of a boy and a girl; they seem rather young to be in graduation attire. Behind them is a red Lamborghini, parked in front of an oversized, overdone home. The caption reads: "Save now. Your child's success is in your hands."

Once more his eyes catch the fading letters on the old binding. They seem to beckon him.

"A large home, a fancy car, that's what they call success? My father didn't even have a horse, and a meager hut was his abode, yet his success remains eternal."

Binyamin looks around to make sure that no one has woken up. His wife and 13-year-old son, Ovadiah, are fast asleep in their bedrooms. Even the poodle is asleep in the corner. He musters up the courage, and as he rises from his La-Z-Boy, he feels like he is breaking through the cobwebs of time. His hand reaches for it. As he opens the front cover, five aged and yellowed sheets fall to the floor.

"I promised you, Father, that one day I would read your message. Now that day has come."

He kisses the sheets as he picks them up. For the first few seconds of reading, his hands are trembling.

My Dear Binyamin, I hope that my words will fall gently and warmly upon your heart . . . .

Tears begin to fall from his eyes. Nearly an hour passes as he reads the words that have been waiting for him all those years. His father's message, though thirty-five years old, pierces him as if it were newly composed.

"Oh, Hashem, what have I done? The confusion and pain that led me away from You now seem dwarfed by the pain of being so far from You. Will You want me back even after my disloyal behavior toward You?

"Hashem, my father wrote in this letter that it's never too late, that no matter how far I may stray, You will still be my Rock, Who will pull me out of the predicaments that I have created. Where do I even dare start?"

His eyes look down once more at some of his father's words . . . .

All you have to do, Binyamin, is listen to the words of ADON OLAM. "Hashem is my banner and refuge; He is the portion of my cup." But, as the text continues, my beloved son, this can only be "on the day that you call." Wherever you may wander, remember it is never too late to call. I believe in you, Binyamin. Hashem gave you the strength to return to Him. It's all in your hands. It's never too late. Remember that I love you, and remember how much more infinitely Hashem loves you and beckons you to come home."

My Banner and My Refuge

IT'S BEEN A LONG DAY up at the Hermon and the Golan Heights. As dusk turns into evening, Yehudah's van putters its way southward down the dusty road from Beit She'an[270] to Jerusalem. Ovadiah leans forward to speak to Yehudah.

"You told us this morning, when we watched that set of films you prepared, that Hashem constantly saves us in very unexpected or even unnoticed ways. But doesn't it take a lot of gall for us to think that the Master of the Universe would still want us back after all of our wrong turns? How do we know that He would still want us after all that we have done against His Will? Shouldn't we consider ourselves a lost cause?"

Yehudah waits until they have gotten over a sudden, stomach-wrenching dip in the road, and then answers: "The second half of the fourth stanza answers your question. It states, והוא נסי ומנוס לי ~ V'Hu nisi u'manos li ~ He is my banner and my refuge. He is my banner that I look to for encouragement in the midst of the battle, and my refuge."

"A battle banner?" wonders Shalom. "Who needs a flag during a battle? And what does this battle have to do with Hashem wanting us back after all of our errors?"

"The battles spoken of are not just military," explains Yehu-

270   Name of a town in the Jordan River Valley.

dah. "They even include the battles against the temptations to sin.[271]"

Just then the van approaches a poorly-lit sign. Yehudah slows down. As he passes and reads the sign, tension is heard in his voice:

"ENTERING AQABAT JABER REFUGEE CAMP."

Ambushed

YEHUDAH CLOSES ALL THE WINDOWS, and turns out the lights both inside and outside the van. He is intensely serious and alert, a mood picked up by everyone else as well. They all remember that just a few weeks before Yehudah told them that he was almost killed in this place. Now they sit in utter silence as they witness a most unusual scene: Yehudah peering into every tiny alleyway. These dilapidated mud huts noticeably send chills down Yehudah's spine. For a quick moment the van almost stops. Yehudah points to the left.

"It happened there when I was just nineteen. That's where I needed my banner and my refuge the most . . ."

It's nearly two decades before, and the time is 2:00 a.m. Twenty-eight cold and frightened soldiers maneuver their way slowly and unsurely through the unfamiliar and seemingly deserted streets of Aqabat Jaber refugee camp, nestled at the base of the Judean Mountains. The stench of freely flowing sewage wafts through the damp cool alleyways. Tonight the streets are hauntingly quiet. Last night they were full of the blood of fellow soldiers. Here and there, low murmurs are heard from dwellings. A baby cries, and then is hushed by its mother. A cat crosses the road and startles the soldiers laden with machine guns and grenades. All seem afraid of their shadows. There are no streetlights. The small sliver of the remaining moon sheds insufficient light on the dismal, unpaved paths. Most of the structures surrounding them are one-story mud huts.

271   *Rav Schwab on Prayer.* Page 10.

Commander Eyal stops suddenly. "Just a minute, I think that we have taken a wrong turn. Where are we?"

He pulls a folded map from his pocket as young Yehudah Stark shines his flashlight upon the crinkled sheet. A guess is made—it seems that the 211th brigade has just made a fatal mistake. They have taken a wrong turn. Now they come to a two-story stone structure on the right. It is at right angles to an identical building in front of them. This one, though, seems to have electricity. There is a light shining from the second floor. The curtain is quickly drawn open as the enemy strives to divert the soldiers' attention from the garbage can to their left. Then, as the soldiers look towards the distraction, machine gun fire is suddenly directed towards the Israeli soldiers, coming from a terrorist who has popped out of the garbage can. Screams are heard:

"Stark, watch out!!!"

As the bullets whiz, cinderblocks rain down on the unsuspecting group from the roof of the structure to their right.

"Goldberg, quick—Nachum's been hit."

Thump.

The calls ring out:

"Daniel, duck!"

"Medic, Yitzhak's shoulder's been broken by a block."

More screams. The bullets keep coming, as does falling debris. The soldiers run. Chaos.

"Where's Commander Eyal?" asks Yehudah. "How do we escape from this ambush? Where do we find refuge?"

The commander has dashed away from the group—to the outskirts of the camp, where the huts end suddenly, and all that is there is the wide open space of the Judean Desert. He has now removed his shirt and set it on fire. He starts screaming and waving it in the air like a banner: "Over here, over here, follow me. Here it's safe. Run fast, it's your only chance of escape."

The van has just left Aqabat Jaber behind. The lights go back on and the windows open. They are safely back on their way down the Jordan River Valley road towards Jerusalem.

You're Not a Lost Cause

"DID THAT REALLY HAPPEN TO YOU?" Shimi wants to know.

"Yes, it is a true story. Now that you all understand a little better what the power of a banner in battle can be, let's try to imagine what the author's intentions were when they wrote the word נסי ~ *nisi* ~ my banner, into ADON OLAM. That will enable us to answer Ovadiah's questions of how we know that Hashem still wants us back after all we have done.

"Soldiers may fall into seemingly inescapable pickles. They can make 'wrong turns'. Similarly, we can make wrong turns in life. Our wrong turns as soldiers in Hashem's army are the sins that we commit. With each turn away from the proper paths of Torah we get increasingly lost, and consequently entangled in our own web of confusion. Our desires can ambush us into situations where all hope may seem to be lost. Who will help us out of our blunders? If we have strayed, can we still hope to look to Hashem for help? Can we hope that He will be our refuge even from the troubles that we have brought upon ourselves time and again?"

Yehudah pauses, and then goes on. "ADON OLAM announces loudly and clearly that we are not a lost cause. Sin is cause for embarrassment, but never for despair—and certainly not for surrender. Hashem is always there, before and after the sin, with His support and open arms. He, like a waving banner, awaits the return of His fallen children,[272] and when they awake from their stupor and follow the banner, then He becomes their only refuge.

"And now, let's take a closer look at the root of *nisi*, my banner, and compare it to another word with the same root. Natan, is there another word with the same root as *nisi* that you can think of?"

272 ArtScroll *Selichos*, Overview, p. XXVII.

Just Testing

"Yes," ANSWERS NATAN. "Nisi shares the same root as the word *nisayon*, which means test. But that can't be what you are referring to, Yehudah. There is no similarity between the words banner and test."

"Actually," says Yehudah, "you got the right word and there is a connection. Ramban explains[273] that even when we find ourselves in a chaotic situation, the banner can still be raised to help us refocus and regroup. He writes that 'Hashem is the One giving the *nisayon* (the test) . . . for the good of the ones being tested.' He is the One **testing** me, and He is also the **banner** (*nes*) that can even pull me out of my failed tests.

"When I was that young ambushed soldier, surrounded by certain death, the banner seemed to me to rise out of the dark like the sun bursting through the clouds, to point the direction homeward, toward life. Commander Eyal's shirt in flames showed us how to get out of the mess that we had gotten ourselves into. The same is true for every servant of Hashem. While life is full of tests of our faith, ADON OLAM speaks of Hashem being my banner, *nisi*, which can help me find the only path out of the web that I have entangled myself in.

"ADON OLAM then calls Hashem מנוס לי ~ *manos li* ~ my refuge. But to escape to that refuge, we first need to remember that our Source, our Rock, and our Banner is Hashem. He is the One Who tests us, and He is the banner that we must follow to our refuge. והוא נסי ומנוס לי ~ *V'Hu nisi u'manos li*."

As the guys contemplate this idea, the van starts the long climb from the Jordan River Valley toward Jerusalem.

"So far we've defined *nisi* as referring to banners and tests," Yehudah notes, "but that's still not the complete picture . . ."

A Flag, a Test, and a Miracle

THE VAN SEEMS to be having a little trouble making the steep climb. The temperature gauge starts to flash and steam is seen coming from under the hood. Yehudah stops to open the hood to allow the engine to cool down.

"According to the sign that we just passed, we have hit sea level,[274] so at least we're out of danger of floods," Shimi comments sarcastically, as usual.

Using a flashlight, Avi peers through the steam emanating from the engine block and states categorically, "We need a miracle to get this van to climb the mountains of Jerusalem."

"Avi, that's a perfect lead into what I was about to say," says Yehudah jubilantly. "Let's give the engine a few minutes to cool down. In the meantime, we'll sit on the side of the road and wait for a miracle."

Once the guys are all seated on the shoulder of the road, Yehudah continues.

"Speaking of miracles, we see the word *nisi* is used in the Torah where it describes our ancestors facing the surprise attack of the nation of Amalek—and winning the battle miraculously.[275] After that battle they built an altar to thank Hashem for saving them from that attack. Moshe Rabbeinu gave this altar the name, '*Hashem Nisi*'. Anyone have any ideas as to what the meaning of *nisi* is in that context?"

Natan, who seems comfortable sitting on the still warm asphalt, interjects, "Now that I think about it, you're right, Yehudah. The root of the word *nisi* actually has more than the two meanings—banner and test—that we discussed already. *Nisi* could also mean the miracle that was performed for me. This seems to be the best of the three possible meanings for the name of the altar. We know that as a result of their lack of faith in Hashem, the Jews wandering in the wilderness fell into the hands of their enemy, Amalek. Hashem miraculously saved them from the enemy even though they were undeserv-

274 The entire Jordan River Valley (including the town of Aqabat Jaber) is far below sea level.
275 Exodus 17:15.

ing. Therefore, the altar was given the name, 'HaShem Nisi, 'God Is My Miracle.'"

"Natan seems to be on to something," declares Shalom.

"I agree," says Yehudah, "and what's more important, so do both Rashi and Unkelos.[276] They inform us that the name of the altar, *Hashem Nisi*, is a proclamation that Hashem performed a great miracle for us. The Baal HaTurim,[277] on the other hand, says that the word *nisi*, as used in that context, means that Hashem is actually *digli*, which is another way of saying 'my flag', similar to *nisi*. So what definition of *nisi* does ADON OLAM intend, flag, test, or miracle?"

"It's obviously all three," says Ovadiah definitively. "Is there any **flag** as high and meaningful as knowing that even after we have failed our **tests** and sinned, if we return to Him, Hashem performs **miracles** to save us?"

"Hey, is everything O.K. over here?" says a deep voice from a border patrol vehicle that has just pulled up. "Yehudah, is that you? I know better than to ask what you are doing here at this time of night."

"Could you give us a lift home and call a truck to tow the van?" asks Yehudah in an almost expectant tone. The stranger acquiesces, and all six of them squish into the back seat meant for three, and let's not forget that Avi takes the place of two. Ovadiah's voice is heard from under a pile of arms and legs. "Yehudah, aren't you going to introduce us to your friend?"

Yehudah smiles. "Of course. This is my friend, Nisim."[278]

Hashem's Always on the Lookout

BACK TO *Rabbeinu Reuven . . . .*

276 A nephew of Titus, this convert translated the Torah into Aramaic (1st Century C.E.)

277 Name of a commentary on the Torah written by Rabbi Yaakov Ben Asher (1275–1349) of Cologne, Germany.

278 This is a common Hebrew name meaning miracles, which shares the same root as the word, nisi, from ADON OLAM.

"So, Yehudah," says Rabbeinu Reuven, "after all of these sessions we have come to the fourth page of the five sheets of my father's last letter. This is the one most worn out. There are many water stains upon it. It seems like my brother cried over this sheet. I think I understand why."

Several years earlier . . . .

Binyamin Yashar sits down after morning services to learn in the synagogue with his new friend, Laibel Weiss. Today, again, Binyamin brings his father's letter with him.

"Laibel, I need your help. I don't yet grasp all the implications of this sheet."

"Well, Binyamin, I will need your help with translation. As you know, my Arabic is less than rusty; it is non-existent."

"First of all, the message here is based on the Sephardic addition to והוא אלי ~ V'Hu Eli.

"I've been learning my lessons well, too. You must mean, והוא רופא והוא מרפא, והוא צופה והוא עזרה ~ V'Hu rofeh V'Hu marpeh, V'Hu tzofeh V'Hu ezrah."

"Exactly."

"What was his message? What words of wisdom does Chacham Yashar have for us today?" asks Laibel. And Binyamin reads:

My dearest Binyamin, look at the sweet words of V'Hu rofeh. ADON OLAM tells us that "He is the One Who heals and the One Who causes healing to come. He is the One Who is constantly on the lookout to be the One to help." In those words is an eternal message just for you. When you will look into yourself and understand how large a healing you need, don't despair of the seemingly-impenetrable doors that are in the way. They can be opened, but not by you alone. Know that only Hashem can cause them to open wide for you. Hashem wants you and is looking to help you, once your tears have penetrated these doors.

"Very wise words, very wise indeed. Your father was a wise and righteous man."

But Binyamin is puzzled: "What did he mean by healing? What type of lookout, what type of help did my father mean? What doors, and how can they be penetrated by tears?"

Laibel puts his hand gently on Binyamin's.

"My new friend, you are just starting the return to the ways of God. You have a long way to go. I won't let go of you until we finish. I promise. Don't worry, you will understand everything eventually.

"I remember that you told me how sick you felt that night two weeks ago when you watched that soda commercial and ate the non-kosher food. Horrible thing, horrible. Don't do it again. You realized that something was wrong. Remember."

Binyamin winces at the memory. "Yes."

"Your father was telling you that not only is something wrong, but that you need a healing. Being far from Hashem makes you spiritually sick."

"I feel that is true, but what could it mean that 'He is the One Who causes the healing? Aren't we the ones to choose to return and not Hashem? Don't we cause our own healing?"

Colossal Chasms and Pinholes

LAIBEL LEANS BACK and relaxes a moment.

"True, you make the original choice. But sometimes we stray so far that we think that there is no way home. For example, think of your father's home and how he raised you. Now think about how you are raising your own son. What a colossal chasm. Can you imagine healing such a breach?"

"It . . . it'll never happen. There's no hope. I will never be able to get my son to understand . . ."

Binyamin starts to shed tears, and some of them fall onto the yellowed sheet.

"May Hashem guard your tears in a flask to be remembered forever. Binyamin, this is what your holy father was showing you. You cannot be expected to do it alone. You and all of us are far too small. Little peas, that's all we are. Little peas. Only Hashem has the strength to cause the healing, only He can breach the chasms."

"What about the doors? I remember that my father used to speak about putting up doors, but I never paid attention to him then. I was a young, foolish lad. What were these doors that he was referring to?"

"Your father gave a wonderful metaphor of a door, but he was not the first to use it. No, it was not his original idea. That metaphor was used long, long ago by our holy sages. They tell us that if we open a hole of return the size of a pinhole in the walls we have placed between us and Hashem, that Hashem will open a wide door for us.[279] Your job, Binyamin, which you are just starting to work on, is to create that pinhole, and this is what your father's message was to you: Hashem has been waiting to help you, but you need to make the pinhole."

"Waiting for 35 years? How much patience does Hashem have? You'd think He would have forgotten about me by now."

"Yes, He has enough patience—35 years worth of it—to wait for you to return and open up your own pinhole. You think that's a long time, right? Well, He has been waiting for the Jewish people for 2,000 years, so I think that He can handle your 35 years. And I think that your father would agree that your tears have already started to open that pinhole."

"I think that they have also dampened my father's letter. Do you have a handkerchief? I want to dry it off . . ."

If at First You Don't Succeed . . . .

"So, Yehudah," says Rabbeinu Reuven, sitting in his study in Jerusalem, "let's continue to my father's next message. He warns Binyamin to stay strong on the path back to Hashem. He speaks of pitfalls along the process and urges him not to give up. *V'Hu rofeh*, he states, was placed by the Sephardim at the end of the fourth stanza of *V'Hu Eli* to show us that—

279 *Midrash Rabbah*, Song of Songs 5:2.

If during the process of return you succeed, Hashem is the cause of your victory. However, if you lose the battle, know that He is ma-nos li, my refuge and my escape. I will run right back to Him; I will try to return again and again. He is the One Who causes the healing. You just have to keep trying. Leave the success up to Him. He is on the lookout for your return.[280]

Back to the synagogue with Laibel and Binyamin . . . .

Concluding Conclusions

"Well, Binyamin, we have been learning together for more than five years now. It has been my pleasure. You have become a fine man."

Binyamin smiles appreciatively. "You kept your promise, you never let go of me. It's been a long, hard path. I am well on my way to becoming a good Jew. Even my wife has mellowed over the years."

"Yes, you told me that she let you make the home kosher—no more pork chops."

"She no longer even complains about me going to synagogue in the morning."

"Actually, I took care of that one."

"What do you mean, Laibel?"

"I took the liberty of going to your home one day when you were at work and having a talk with her. She agreed that she saw a major change in you for the good. She knows that you are happier. I told her that what she was doing was not good. She was holding you back. She didn't respond, but I could see that my words meant something to her. They hit a nerve."

"So that's what happened . . ." Binyamin is thoughtful. "Thanks. Let's say the situation has improved."

"Now we have to deal with your son. He also needs to become a fine man like his father and grandfather. You have to try. Send him to yeshivah. God-willing, we'll talk about it more next time, but now our time is up; I have to go."

280 *Rav Schwab on Prayer.* Page 10.

Binyamin walks slowly towards his car in the synagogue's parking lot. He carries a small bag of uncut diamonds in his pocket. A few minutes later he is already parking his car in his driveway. After turning off the engine, he speaks out loud to himself:

"Hashem, my father wrote me the message that it is never too late. He was right. Look how far I have come already. I finished his letter and the entire book many times, and now I feel that I finally have internalized their messages. I have even tried to hint at some of them to my own son, but that's not enough anymore. The time has come. I must speak to him about going to *yeshivah*. This is my next stage; this is how I will make You מנת כוסי ביום אקרא—my portion on the day that I will call, as it says in ADON OLAM. Today is that day that I will finally call . . ."

As he enters the house and shuts the door, a man sneaks into the house behind him with a gun.

"The rocks. Hand me the rocks or this will be your last day . . ."

My Cup's Shadow

*Y*EHUDAH SITS WITH OVADIAH *at a quiet café. The small wooden table has a glass jar with a floating candle in its center.*

"It's time for us to finish up those five sheets that I told you were written to your father, and, with them we will conclude our learning of the forth stanza, והוא אלי ~ V'Hu Eli. So far, we have seen how V'Hu Eli emphasizes how Hashem is our personal God Who saves us from our troubles. In the last phrase of this stanza, we will now learn about a different aspect of this personal God. In order to understand this phrase, let's first look at Psalm 121:4, where King David explains to us how Hashem relates to what we've personally earned. He says, '*Hashem tzilcha*'—Hashem is your protector. But the word *tzilcha* has another meaning besides 'your protector'. It also means Hashem is your shadow. Why did King David choose this word, tzilcha, where there are numerous other words which express Hashem's ability to save us or remove us from our troubles?"

"Protector and shadow? Hmmm. I don't see any connection between these two words. All we know about shadows is that they're dependent on what casts them. It doesn't seem to me that the shadows save or protect anything."

"Look at the shadow of my finger in the candlelight as I move it back and forth. King David wanted us to know that just as a shadow follows and imitates the actions of a person, so God is, in a sense, the shadow of a person's deeds. If we are kind, He is kind to us. If we are forgiving, He is forgiving to us.[281] This is ADON OLAM's message when it tells us that Hashem is מנת כוסי ביום אקרא ~ *menas cosi b'yom ekra* ~ the portion of my cup—or better stated, the cup that I earned—on the day that I call. Hashem gives us a portion which, like a shadow, mimics how we strive to follow Him."

Yehudah now pulls the neatly folded sheets from his bag.

"Your grandfather ends his letter to your father with these two paragraphs . . . .

ADON OLAM states that Hashem is the portion of my cup on the day that I call. When someone holds up his cup to be filled, sometimes it is filled with something sweet, sometimes with something bitter, or a mixture of both. Sometimes the cup overflows and sometimes it barely receives anything. Some people receive what they call a very hard life: they may view themselves as never making it. This phrase, "He is the portion in my cup on the day I call," means that I know that whenever I call to Him, and I hold up my cup for His answer, He always responds appropriately. Cosi, my cup, is the earned personal portion of each individual. This personal portion is the result of our efforts to emulate our Master.[282]

But why is Hashem considered our portion only "on the day that we call"? Reflect now on the end of the first stanza of ADON OLAM, where it says 'Azai melech shemo nikra'—only after the physical world and free choice were created, can Hashem be

281 ArtScroll Selichos, Overview, XXV, citing Kedushas HaLevi.

282 *Rav Schwab on Prayer.* Page 10.

called King. There ADON OLAM uses the word **nikra**, will be called; here it uses a slightly different form of the same root and states **ekra**, I will call. The message is clear, Binyamin. We need to spend our day, which is our short life in this world of free choice, calling Hashem King in every way we can. As my strength is ebbing, I know that I have not missed my chance to call out Hashem's Kingship, but your day is just starting. My message to you is that every choice you will make is ultimately important. May it be the will of the Master of the Universe that you merit to call Hashem King during your day.

Your loving Father

Yehudah folds the pages and puts them away. "That is the end of the letter, and that is where I end with teaching you. I am not going to be the one to teach the last stanza of ADON OLAM to you."

Ovadiah is understandably astonished. "Why not? It is going so well. Who else could do the job?"

"There is someone who has been waiting to meet you, and it's he who will finish the job. We should leave now, as he is waiting for us."

Comprehension dawns on Ovadiah. "Are you referring to the mysterious rabbi who has been teaching you?"

"Well, yes. And . . . there is something you should know about him. He's actually your . . ."

So, Searching Soul, Yehudah is finally bringing Ovadiah to meet his Uncle Reuven.

In the meantime, let me help you get your bearings.

You remember that in my first stanza I introduced you to the notion of Hashem being a personal Master Who created the physical world from His Spiritual Will, but then in V'Acharei (2nd stanza) you were taught to understand Hashem as the universal King, Who glob-

ally guides all of Creation in perfect splendor. This left you perplexed. How can you relate to the King of such a global model, as your personal master? In order for you to conceive of Hashem as both the universal Ruler and your personal Master, you needed to first understand that there is no dichotomy between these concepts. So in V'Hu echad (3rd stanza) I came to meet just that challenge by helping you achieve a better appreciation of Hashem's absolute Oneness. I then came to you with my words of V'Hu Eli (4th stanza) to highlight for you how you can properly relate to this single, infinite, personal and corresponding global God as being involved in your life. I opened the doors for you to come to understand how every action in your life does matter. All was alluded to in my first stanza, but you still needed my subsequent stanzas to give you a hand. Now that you are starting to get a handle on life, let me give you a handle on death . . . .

SECTION FIVE

B'YADO,
Into His Hand

HELLO AGAIN, SEARCHING SOUL. Yes, of course it's me, ADON OLAM. Who else did you think it was? It's time for us to discuss my concluding words, which deal with the conclusion of physical life. Yes, I know that we discussed some of this when Yehudah took the guys into that underground sepulcher in the woods. But there is so much more for you to learn from me about death and the afterlife.

There are so many people who are confused as to exactly what is in store for us upon death. I don't blame them, because the topic is indeed confusing: Torah sources speak about many different aspects of the afterlife, such as Gan Eden, The World to Come, The Yeshivah in Heaven, Gehinom (Hell) The Messianic era, The Resurrection of the Dead, and, of course, The Great Day of Judgment and beyond. Sometimes these terms are mistakenly thought of as being synonymous. You ponder: How do all these fit together, if they really do?

You admit that you do not yet know it all and consequently tuck your secret uncertainties away. I sense that you are uncomfortable. Admit it: some of these beliefs bother you. You cannot honestly believe in that which you view as contradictory or illogical. You are not alone in your frustration, my friend. My text was written to clear up the haziness of many of these concepts, but not everything can be explained logically. There are beliefs that are beyond the human grasp. For these, my words come to ease your fears. Follow me as my last stanza raises the dead, calms your fears and lowers your uncertainties with these concluding words . . . .

בְּיָדוֹ אַפְקִיד רוּחִי, בְּעֵת אִישַׁן וְאָעִירָה
וְעִם רוּחִי גְוִיָתִי, אֲדֹנָי לִי וְלֹא אִירָא

~

**B'yado Afkid Ruchi, B'eis Ishan V'a'ira
V'im Ruchi Gviyasi, Adonai Li V'lo Ira**

~

Into His hand I will deposit my spirit,
at the time that I will sleep and I trust Him that I will awake.
And with my spirit will be my body,
Hashem is for me, therefore I will not fear.

Sephardim include:

בְּמִקְדָּשׁוֹ תָּגֵל נַפְשִׁי, מְשִׁיחֵנוּ יִשְׁלַח מְהֵרָה,
וְאָז נָשִׁיר בְּבֵית קָדְשִׁי, אָמֵן אָמֵן שֵׁם הַנּוֹרָא

~

**Bemikdasho Tagel Nafshi, Meshichainu Yishlach Mehera,
Ve'az Nashir Beveit Kodshi, Amen Amen Shem Hanorah.**

~

In His Sanctuary my life-force will eventually elate.[283]
Our Anointed Messiah He will send speedily.
And then We will sing in My Sanctum.
Amen Amen is the Awesome Name.

---

283 In order to understand why the Hebrew was translated in this manner, please refer to the Disclaimer.

Dispelling Confusions

*S*EARCHING SOUL, *you might be wondering what hand is being referred to in the first words of my last stanza, '***Into His hand I will deposit my spirit***'. Since we know that Hashem cannot be limited in any way by a body, you know that this must not be taken literally, and is merely an allegory, but what precisely is this allegory coming to teach?*

Come with me to Rabbeinu Reuven's study. Just a week ago, Ovadiah was introduced to his Uncle Reuven for the first time. That was an intense moment, and the timing was perfect. With the help of his friends, Ovadiah had already become quite strong in his understanding and observance of Judaism. All these adventures with Yehudah and The Hidden Master have made Torah alive and vibrant for him. He feels like a new fledgling comfortably flapping his wings in the new world shown him by ADON OLAM. Now Uncle Reuven will help his nephew, and you along with him, not only to flap your wings, but to soar to higher heights. Presently, they are sitting together in Rabbeinu Reuven's study.

"So, Ovadiah, the last words that you learned with Yehudah taught that Hashem is the 'portion of your cup on the day that you call.' What did you glean from those words?"

By now Ovadiah understands Hebrew well, but is still slow in his speech.

"I appreciate Uncle's patience, as this will be hard for me to express in Hebrew. When ADON OLAM states that Hashem is the portion of my cup on the day that I call, it means that if I will live my life according to His Will, by having His Torah as my constant guide, then my relationship with Hashem will be my earned portion during my life, which is referred to as 'my day of calling'."

Uncle Reuven smiles. "You are much too self-conscious. You

express yourself beautifully in Hebrew. You just spoke about how this life is your day of calling. What about after this life? Are you clear as to what the Torah tells us about that?"

As Uncle Reuven awaits Ovadiah's response, he opens a crisp, new, Hebrew version of *The Hidden Master* which lies upon his desk, and starts to turn the pages slowly.

Ovadiah chooses his words carefully. "I have heard differing opinions about what the afterlife holds for us. Some of these beliefs still seem unclear and others actually appear to me to be contradictory or even illogical. For example, we are told of a completely spiritual World to Come, a World of Souls also called *Gan Eden*, yet we also learn of the times of the Messiah (a physical state of being), which is to come after this World of Souls. I don't understand this. Why would there be a need to return to physicality after the spiritual world of the souls? Also, there are the concepts of the Resurrection of the Dead and the Final Day of Judgment, which I must admit, still confuse me. I'm supposed to trust Hashem with my spirit, but I am still uncertain as to what exactly is in store for me at the end of my days. What will Hashem be doing with my spirit? Where, pray tell, is the spirit going, and is it coming back to the body, and if so, why? And if the soul lives forever, then what does death, the separation of the spiritual from the physical, really mean?"

"I see that you really are a Yashar. Your questions show your intelligence, honest searching and concern. *The Hidden Master* tells us that our Sages composed the final stanza of ADON OLAM, B'Yado, to clarify our conceptualization of the afterlife. Although there are some varying opinions on certain points, ADON OLAM successfully synthesizes many of them into a very clear picture of what happens after death."

Trusting Hand

TAKING A SIP from the cup of tea in front of him, Uncle Reuven continues.

"Let's start by exploring the roots of the beginning words of this last stanza. You may have noticed that these words are not original, but rather are borrowed from King David who wrote: '**Into Your hand I deposit my spirit**: You have redeemed me, Hashem, the God of Truth.'"[284]

"What is the lesson that we are supposed to learn by using this analogy? Why describe the Infinite Being as having hands, and why only a deposit?" questions Ovadiah.

"Let's start first with the hands, and later we will deal with the deposit. Most of your actions are done through your hands. With them you can build and destroy, push down or support. Hands are often used as an anthropomorphic metaphor to explain that Hashem is acting upon the physical world. But what would it mean to deposit not the physical body, but rather the spirit into this Hand?

"For the answers, let's take yet another look at ADON OLAM's previous stanza, where Hashem is described as each individual's Rock in times of personal distress. You already learned with Yehudah that this Rock, like a hand, is the trusted support that is needed and experienced throughout life's trials.

"Rashi explains King David's words like this: '**I will deposit or entrust my spirit into Your hand** forever because You have already rescued me (in this world) from distress.' In other words, I have come to trust this hand through my every distress, which is the same message of the previous stanza—that Hashem is my trusted Rock in times of distress (צור חבלי בעת צרה ~ *tzur chevli b'eis tzarah*).

"There are so many situations where we need to trust in Hashem's hand. Through learning this next stanza of ADON OLAM we will begin to deal with many of them." And then, Rabbeinu Reuven drops a bombshell: "We meet up with one of these situations every night."

284 Psalms 31:6.

Sweet Dreams

"**E**VERY NIGHT?" Ovadiah is curious as to what his uncle is referring to.

"Yes. Each night, as we fall asleep and leave our conscious existence, ADON OLAM informs us that we must fully entrust our 'soul', our conscious life, to Hashem. Then it tells us that when we are awake, we trust that He will keep us alive, as long as He sees fit."[285]

"But, Uncle Reuven, what's to be afraid of in going to sleep? It's a natural process, which we do all the time."

"Actually, according to our Sages, sleep is considered 'one sixtieth of death.'[286] That means that each night when we go to sleep we are in a small way, tasting death."

Ovadiah can't help but think of his roommate, Shimi, and he smiles in spite of himself.

"What are you smiling about?" asks his uncle gently.

"Please excuse me, Uncle. Anyone who knows a certain friend of mine knows that trying to wake him up is like trying to wake the dead, but I know this is no joking matter. What could we possibly gain from tasting death each night?"

"We know,"[287] answers Rabbeinu Reuven, "that when we lose consciousness, the soul and the body separate somewhat, and we are told that we undergo a form of judgment[288] each time that we sleep. Through this judgment, the soul, which during sleep is somewhat separated from the body, draws nearer to Hashem. In this state, it can gain understanding of matters that it cannot understand while awake."

After letting that thought sink in for a few moments, Rabbeinu Reuven continues.

"I am assuming that you have read some sources that place importance on certain types of dreams?"

"Yes," says Ovadiah, "but these sources bother me. Aren't dreams just random thoughts, sometimes even foolish?"

285 Rav Schwab on Prayer, pp. 10–11.

286 Berachos 57b.

287 Derech Hashem 3:1:6.

288 Zohar Chayei Sarah, 121.

"Some are. In fact, many of them are, but our Sages tell us[289] that, under specific circumstances, dreams may actually have a hint of prophecy in them. Although we certainly cannot rely upon our dreams as we would rely upon prophecy, certain types of dreams are not meant to be completely ignored.

"But ADON OLAM is not just telling us about sweet dreams. There is so much more about trusting Hashem that we are supposed to learn from sleeping."

Ovadiah waits patiently, while Rabbeinu Reuven takes another sip of tea.

"When we wake up each morning, we say a blessing which states, 'Blessed are You, Hashem, Who restores souls to dead bodies'. In other words, each morning we experience a mini-awakening of the dead. ADON OLAM informs us that upon dying we will need to deposit our souls, our most precious possession, into Hashem's hand. That deposit, death, is referred to in ADON OLAM's fifth stanza as sleep."

Your Most Precious Possession

"WHERE ELSE," asks Rabbeinu Reuven, "can we trust to deposit our most precious possession, our very spirit at the moment of the death of our body, other than into the same hand that was there for us through our many distresses when our body and spirit were together?"

Ovadiah is looking uneasy. "Uncle Reuven, before you speak of the spirit leaving the body and being entrusted to Hashem, I have a problem. I still do not quite grasp the connection between the spirit and the body while together. Spirituality and physicality seem to me to be two opposites."

"The connection of the spiritual to the physical," answers his uncle, "is described by the Zohar[290] as being not a natural connection but rather as the soul temporarily coming down from a lofty place for a sublime intention. While in this world,

289 *Derech Hashem*, 3:1:6.

290 *Zohar Chayei Sarah*, 130b.

the body becomes the soul's temporary home; the soul merely 'hangs onto' the body like the flame of a candle hangs onto its wick.

"At the time that a person is departing from this world, both the soul and the body have to each give an accounting of all of their actions, and then the soul leaves the body.

"Upon the spirit leaving its physical home, the body returns to the dust from which it was created. This disintegration is the body's method of being purified from whatever sins it was involved in. Soon we will be discussing the purification of the soul as well. The Zohar tells us that while the body is undergoing this process of purification, the soul is guarded until the time that Hashem will give life to the dead."

Uncle Reuven discerns from Ovadiah's expression of half-hearted acceptance that the words of the Zohar have not yet achieved results. He turns one last page in *The Hidden Master* and places his finger on the subtitle . . . .

Candles and Souls

"I will read you my father's embellished version of a *midrash*.[291]

"Now, my readers, it is time for us to go back in time to the Garden of Eden.[292] Imagine that it's now nearly six thousand years ago. Open your ears and hearts to hear this eternal message of the Creator to the world's first man:

"Adam!"

"Yes, Creator, I am here."

"My candle is in your hand, and your candle is in My Hand."

Adam thinks to himself, "*B'Yado*, in His hand?" Then he speaks:

"What is the Creator referring to? I see no candle in my hand, and I don't recall having turned over any candle to Your hand. Furthermore, You, God, have no hand, for You are beyond the barriers of physicality. I am afraid that I do not understand."

291 *Devarim Rabbah, Reeh*, 4:4; *Likkutim*, p. 74.

292 Please refer to the Disclaimer.

"I am referring to that which is beyond the physical. When I tell you that My candle is in your hand, I am referring to My Torah which I have given over to you to live by its ways. And when I say that your candle is in My hand I am referring to the life-force, the spirit which I have placed within your physical body. You will eventually deposit it into My hand, for in My hand is the life-force of all who live.'"[293]

"Why has the Almighty God entrusted His spiritual Torah into my physical hands, and what high purpose is attained by my life-force being entrusted to the Almighty?"

And the Creator answers: "You are the progenitor of the human race. Know and teach your children that if you guard My candle, My Torah and its ways, then I will preserve your candle into the future. But also teach them to beware: if they extinguish My candle and do not follow the Torah, I will extinguish their candles."

"A candle or flame," explains Uncle Reuven as he looks up from *The Hidden Master*, "has two parts. One is the wick; the other is the light, which is joined to the wick. The wick is mere physical threads spun together. The light, on the other hand, is not purely physical like the wick. The midrash alludes to this symbiotic dichotomy of the physical and the non-physical working together in both the example of the soul and that of the Torah. The Zohar tells us that the spirit of a person is temporarily linked to the body and is enabled to function through using it, but its essence remains completely spiritual, and therefore, it is very much not the body. The message of the midrash is that if the spirit guards the Torah while it is appended to the body, then upon detachment from the body it will be able to return to its spiritual source, where Hashem's trusted hand will guard it for the future."

After turning that thought over a few times, Ovadiah says, "I think that we can summarize the lessons of that midrash like this: 'Those who use the light of the Torah, the light of the Torah will give them life.'"[294]

Uncle Reuven seems impressed, but before he has a chance

293 Maharzu Commentary on the midrash.

294 Kesubos 111b. See also Nefesh HaChaim 4:24.

to continue, Ovadiah asks, "What happens if the person did not guard the Torah during his or her life?"

"I'll state your question a little differently. We are told[295] that there is no one who has never sinned. We know that nearly all people need to go through a process of judgment and purification through punishment before they are able to bask in the light of the Divine Presence.[296] This process is called *Gehinom*.[297] But before you start thinking of Hashem's punishment as being vindictive and purposeless let's get a better overview."

Veiled Reward

A ND RABBEINU REUVEN CONTINUES: "The rewards for living life according to Hashem's Torah are somewhat veiled. At first glance it appears that the Torah only speaks about reward in this world. For example, the Torah tells us[298] that 'if you live according to Hashem's will and follow His commandments . . . then you will have the early and the late rains, and you shall gather in your grain, wine, and oil'. You may wonder if this is the entire reward. To make things more confusing, our Sages tell us that 'there is no reward for the mitzvahs in this world.'[299] So it seems that we have to redefine the 'rewards' mentioned in the Torah.

"Instead of viewing the blessings that the Torah gives for good conduct as rewards, let's instead call them **tools** to enable us to build up merit. As our Sages say, 'the merit of a mitzvah is a mitzvah.'[300] If we conduct ourselves in this world according to His Will, then certain barriers to our successful service

295 *Shabbos* 55b.

296 This concept is mentioned numerous times by our Sages; see *Eruvin* 19a and *Rosh Hashanah* 17a.

297 In English this is loosely translated as 'Hell', although the term describes something quite different from what other religions conceive Hell to be.

298 Deuteronomy 11:13.

299 *Hullin* 142a.

300 Ethics of the Fathers 4:2.

of Hashem are either removed, and/or we are given tools and strength to pass the next tests.

"You will see what I mean when we look at this next statement of our Sages.[301] They tell us that one moment of the pleasures of the World to Come is worth more than the conglomeration of all of the pleasures of this world. However, in the same mishnah, they also tell us a seemingly contradictory statement that 'One moment of mitzvahs in this world is worth the whole of the World to Come'. So Ovadiah, which is worth more—this world or the World to Come? You should be able to answer based on our new definition of reward."

"The purpose of this world is to gain closeness to Hashem through learning His Torah and acting according to its laws while being bombarded with many tests. This type of striving to serve Him is unique to this world; because once we die there are no more tests. This world is our chance to raise the level of our souls for all of eternity, so it seems clear that this temporary world has more importance than the eternal world."

"Very good, Ovadiah! But lest you think that death is a morbid end of the process, ADON OLAM has a lot to teach you. Death has a positive purpose, both for the body and for the soul. This purpose is to purify each of them respectively so that they can, together, eventually reach their full eternal reward. They must go through a stage of destruction before perfection can be attained. Man must therefore die, and his body, which was corrupted with him, must also be destroyed. The soul cannot purify the body until the body dies and deteriorates and a new structure is created, which the soul can enter and purify. The body thus returns to its element, decomposing and losing its form. Since the body originated from the dust, it must return to it, and this is what God told Adam (Genesis 3:19) 'You are dust, and to dust you must return'.

"Our Sages describe the preparation of the individual for the eternal reward as happening in stages. Upon death there are two stages of an 'interim state of being', in which the soul needs to become purified. In the first stage the soul undergoes

301 Ethics of the Fathers 4:22.

judgment and subsequent punishment. This is the stage of Gehinom. Once the stage of Gehinom is completed, then, through Hashem's kindness there is a further stage of purification."

Here Ovadiah interrupts: "For what is this purification needed, and what exactly is this stage of judgment?"

"The preparation is for a utopian state," explains Rabbeinu Reuven. "Into this utopian state neither a stained soul nor a stained body can enter. As for your question of what is this stage of Gehinom, think of it this way . . ."

To Distill a Soul

OVADIAH IS BACK at the Yeshivah late that night. Avi, Natan, Shalom and Shimi sit with him in the dormitory lounge, attentively listening to Ovadiah's rendition of his uncle's lesson.

"So now let's go over what we know about Gehinom. We are told[302] that this stage of judgment and punishment is a maximum of 12 months. It is important that you remember what I told you a few minutes ago about the body. Remember, Shimi?"

"Yeah! You said that while the soul is undergoing its judgment in Gehinom, the body is decomposing and going through its own purification in the grave. So what is happening to the soul? Is it also decomposing?"

"Shimi, come on, and take this stuff seriously," grumbles Shalom. "Let Ovadiah continue."

"No, Shimi, the soul is not decomposing. Rather, we learn that it is being distilled."

"What is this—a brewery?"

"I'm trying to pay attention, Shimi. Do you mind keeping quiet for a moment?" says Natan in a frustrated tone.

Ovadiah smiles and says, "Actually, Shimi's right. Just like many things need to be purified before we can use them: gold, other metals or minerals, beer, and even water, so too, does the soul need to get rid of its impurities. A stained and polluted soul cannot stand in the presence of Hashem in the perfected World to Come. The purpose of *Gehinom* is to purify the soul from the blemishes that it incurred during the period that is spent in this physical world, so that it will be ready for the utopian world."

No Eye Ever Saw It

"AFTER THE TWELVE MONTHS of *Gehinom* what happens to the cleansed soul?" wonders Shalom from a rickety rocking-chair, as he takes out a cloth to clean his glasses.

"The cleansed soul is then given an opportunity to prepare for the utopian state that will eventually come."

Natan, who's lying on the tattered couch with his hand on his forehead, seems deep in thought. "Prepare? What exactly do you mean by prepare? I need a clearer picture."

"It's a little hard to give a clear picture. My uncle brought a source[303] which teaches that . . . .

> Our earliest Sages have already informed us that people do not have the ability to explain or articulate the goodness of the life of the World to Come. Furthermore, there are none who know its greatness, beauty or power. This is because it cannot be appreciated, compared to anything or imagined. And so it is written,[304] No prophet's eye saw what the Holy One, blessed be He, will do for those who hope for Him except Your eyes, O God.'[305]

"Our Rabbis[306] inform us that not only is the World to Come (also called *Gan Eden*) beyond the understanding of regular people like us, but, in addition, none of the prophets prophesied except regarding the times of the Messiah, but with regard to the World to Come they use this verse to tell us that 'no eye

303 *Tanchuma, Vayikra* 8. The *Tanchuma* is a collection of *midrashim*, based upon the *midrashim* of Rabbi Tanchuma bar Abba, 350–375 C.E.

304 Isaiah 64:3.

305 This translation of the verse is based on Rashi.

306 *Berachos* 34a.

has ever seen it'.[307] What we do know is that *Gan Eden* is not a static state, but rather one where the soul is enabled to rise higher and higher."

"Just a minute." Shimi is starting to get a little more serious. "If everyone's soul will go through a purification process and then be enabled to rise higher, then why should we bother following Hashem's Torah in this world, when in the end it'll all work out the same?"

"Hey, Shimi, I asked my uncle the same question. He told me that not all souls are the same, nor will they all receive the same closeness to Hashem once purified. He quoted the *Derech Hashem*, who said that—

> When the soul leaves the body and enters the Soul World (another term that refers to the World to Come—Gan Eden), it can then radiate freely with a brightness that befits it as a result of its good deeds (performed while associated with the body). Through both this and what it can attain in the Soul World, the soul is able to regain the power that it lost while associated with the body. This, in turn, makes it more qualified for its ultimate function after the Resurrection, namely, the purification of the body.[308]

A Different Angle

AVI, WHO HAS BEEN PERCHED on the windowsill of the lounge, has something to add.

"The name of the game in this life is to earn closeness to Hashem. What we can all learn from the *Derech Hashem* that Ovadiah just quoted is that souls do not all reach equal levels of closeness to Hashem in *Gan Eden*. Think of it like this, guys. Let's imagine that the way to attain ultimate closeness to Hashem is to go on a path that is at a 90-degree angle upward. That is impossible to do, of course—no one is that perfect. So let's not talk in absolutes. Instead, let's visualize a person traveling

307 This is also brought from Rashi's commentary on Isaiah 64:3.

308 *Derech Hashem* 1,3,12.

on a path that is on an angle of one degree. As this person's path progresses he/she gets only somewhat closer to Hashem, but nevertheless does not achieve much height. On the other hand, if someone were to travel on a path that is on an angle of sixty degrees, then he/she will attain tremendous heights of closeness to Hashem. The righteous person is the one who has attained the 60-degree angle, while the less righteous one may have only attained the one-degree angle. Although the reward for every mitzvah is beyond our grasp, the difference between the reward for the more righteous individual and that of the less righteous one is without comparison."

"What Avi is saying helps us relate to the statement of our Sages that in the future world[309] we will be burnt from the position (chuppah) of our fellows." says Ovadiah.

"Burnt?" exclaims Shimi.

"Yes, in a way. We have our chance here and now to set the stage for what our future will be. What seems to us as small differences in our service of the Infinite Master in this world will become an unfathomable gap in the future.

"To understand this gap, my uncle told me that there is another name for Gan Eden or the World to Come. Although we learn that no eye ever saw the future world, and we are not able to fully conceive of it because it is beyond our scope of understanding, our Sages of blessed memory describe the process of Gan Eden as being like a yeshivah in Heaven, and so they call it. When we choose to sit and learn the Will of Hashem in a yeshivah down here, we are putting aside our foolish and empty desires in order to gain closeness to our Master through learning His ultimate wisdom. So, too, we are told[310] that the World to Come will be like a yeshivah, where we will continually grow closer to our Master through learning and knowing His Will. But in that yeshivah we will each start our process of getting closer to Hashem on our own level, or, as Avi puts it, our own angle. Each small effort that we put in down here will place us on a different angle whose end result we cannot even imagine."

309 Baba Basra 75a.
310 Yalkut Shimoni, Yeshayahu 429.

"This is all making sense, except . . ."

"Except for what, Shalom?"

"Well, what about the last sentence of that *Derech Hashem* that you quoted? It said that this stage of *Gan Eden* isn't the end result. Rather, it is only a stage that enables the soul to become more qualified for its ultimate function after the Resurrection of the Dead. Why is there a need for physical resurrection when *Gan Eden* seems to bring us to such lofty closeness to Hashem?"

"That's an excellent question. I've wondered about it myself. I'll have to ask my uncle tomorrow."

"Hey, could we all come with you?" asks Shimi.

"Why not?"

Leaving *Gan Eden*

THE BOYS, INCLUDING YEHUDAH, have all squeezed into Rabbeinu Reuven's study. Natan has been nominated as the simultaneous translator for those who need it and is doing a phenomenal job. After a few introductions, Ovadiah asks the previous night's question:

"Why is there a need for physical resurrection when *Gan Eden* seems to bring us to such lofty closeness to Hashem?"

"Our Sages tell us that 'Hashem created the world for His honor',[311] answers his uncle. "Once we discover how Hashem defines His honor, then it will become clear why it is imperative for the souls to leave *Gan Eden* after the coming of the Messianic era, and to then be resurrected again into bodies."

Shimi somehow doesn't need to be told that this is no place for his habitual sarcasm, and so he turns respectfully to Rabbeinu Reuven with a question of his own:

"Ummm. I have a problem understanding all of this. Resurrection of the Dead? Physical bodies rising from the graves? How can this all happen?"

"Your name is Shimi, right?"

"Yes, Rabbi."

311 Ethics of the Fathers 6:11; this concept is originally related to in Isaiah 43:7.

"You already learned with Yehudah how the physical world around you isn't quite what meets the eye."

"Yes, we learned how physical matter is just a relationship of forces and energies. And we learned in the first stanza of ADON OLAM how these energies and forces, emanating from the Torah, create a series of worlds that eventually become our physical state of existence."

"And, of course, you also know that creation of our world is reoccurring every split second."

"Yes, Yehudah explained that with his flashlight."

Rabbeinu Reuven smiles.

"So, if Hashem recreates physicality of the entire world every moment, why is it so difficult for you to conceive of Him reconstructing your decomposed body?

"That's a very good point," Shimi admits.

"Now, let's return to the previous question. What exactly does Hashem call 'His honor'? When Hashem rests His Presence upon His servants, the Jews, and upon the Temple, His Name is glorified and sanctified not only in the eyes of Israel but also in the eyes of all the nations. This is His honor. But, for most of world history, Hashem's honor has not been complete. Nearly all of the Kings of Israel (the Northern Kingdom) were wicked; a large number of the Kings of Yehudah (the Southern Kingdom) were likewise wicked. And even when we look at those short periods when the Judges and Kings were righteous, the nation's spiritual life was not perfect—the sin of idol worship was always present. In fact, we are told by the prophet Ezekiel that from the time of our leaving Egypt until the time of the destruction of the Temple, constant rebuke was needed. Even at the time that we were crossing the Sea of Reeds, people carried the idol of Micah right with them!"[312]

Now Shalom has a thought to give over:

"Interesting! Rabbi Yashar, you are pointing out to us that, for almost all the years since Creation, the physical world has not reached its target of revealing the honor of Hashem. Ob-

312 From *Aggados Rav Elhanan Wasserman, z"l*, in the *Kovetz Hearos* on Tractate *Yevamos*, 1:9, passage starting with "Mizeh muchrach"; brought down in *Sefer Shaarei Beis Hashem, Shaar Galus V'Geulah* by Yosef Stephanski.

viously nothing was hidden from Hashem, and He therefore knew exactly what was going to happen to the world that He was about to create. So why did He create this unsuccessful world?"

"The Ramchal explains that we are the ones who brought the world to its state of imperfection," replies Rabbeinu Reuven. "He tells us that:

> Since the beginning of Creation, however, this (perfected) state has not been attained . . . because of the numerous sins which caused the final rectification to be retarded and delayed.[313]

"Hashem enabled us to have free choice. Our wrong choices throughout history have damaged the world. The only logical conclusion is, therefore, that there must be a time in the future when the Creation will achieve its goal. If not, then you are correct that Hashem created the world for naught. We must conclude that the entire history of the world, as we know it, is only a preparation for a future, more truthful time.

"Returning the soul back to the physical body will be, as ADON OLAM taught us in its second stanza, ואחרי כללות הכל ~ V'Acharei kichlos hakol ~ after all evil will be shown for what it really is. Yehudah, you did teach them this in the second stanza, didn't you?"

Yehudah nods.

"All those who died and will die, from the time of the first man's sin until the time of the final redemption, have or will have lived before the conclusion of all evil, in the midst of the clouds. Many will have put their efforts in to serve Hashem through their own obstacle courses. And so, ADON OLAM teaches that they will be given a chance of living 'after the conclusion of all evil' where they will be able to serve Hashem uninhibited, without the cloud, at the level that they each wished and struggled to serve Him."

Shimi asks "Where does ADON OLAM speak of this chance of living again?"

---

313 Derech Hashem: Essay on Fundamentals in the subsection, "The Redemption."

No Deposit No Return

"Adon olam says, 'Into Hashem's hand I will deposit my spirit at the time that I sleep and I will awake.' What type of sleep are we referring to, Shimi?"

"I don't know. We came here to ask the Rabbi questions, not to give answers."

Shalom and Natan wince, and Ovadiah kicks Shimi under the table. Shimi gets the point, and looks somewhat abashed at his outburst.

Rabbeinu Reuven is not disconcerted. "Rabbeinu Pinchas[314] explains these words of ADON OLAM like this: '. . . And even when the time arrives that I will depart to sleep in the grave, in His hand I will deposit my spirit at the time that I will sleep. And I believe that I will eventually arise, if it be His Will, at the time of the Resurrection of the Dead.'

"ADON OLAM uses the term sleep to express death, for the sleep of death is not an eternal sleeping, but, rather, death is likened to a person sleeping for a while and then awakening."

"I don't get it," Shimi persists. "What is the purpose? To die only to be resurrected to the same situation? For what? It seems so illogical to me that the disintegrated bodies will be resurrected, and that is to be the reward. If that would be the reward, then why don't we just continue the way that we are already? Obviously, there's something I do not understand here."

"I like your questions, Shimi. You have a lot of spunk," says Rabbeinu Reuven. "It seems to me that what you do not understand is the times of the Messiah.

"*Gan Eden* is the state that the souls go into when, as ADON OLAM describes, 'we deposit them into His hands at the time we sleep (die).' The World of the Souls[315] is merely the deposit. This is where the souls are guarded for safekeeping until some future time. In that guarded stage, they continually become more purified and closer to Hashem as they get ready for the

---

314   In *Siddur Shaar HaRachamim*.

315   Remember this is the term that the *Derech Hashem* uses for the concept of The World to Come (also called *Gan Eden*).

next stage. It is only when ADON OLAM says V'aira, and I will awake, that it speaks of the withdrawal."

"What is this, a bank account? What does it mean that the soul will be guarded for the future?" Shimi wonders. "I thought that after death the spirit returns to its source and that's it."

Avi, who is always so sure of his beliefs, musters up the courage to ask a question that shows everyone that he has a missing link as well . . . .

"Don't get me wrong, Rabbi Yashar. When I converted, I meant it when I said that I believe in all of the Thirteen Articles of Faith[316], even the one about the Resurrection of the Dead. I had already come to realize that there were many things that I did not understand. I had come to trust the Torah and the rabbis, as my old beliefs melted in front of the flames of the truth of Torah. But I have not yet merited understanding why there is a need to return the souls to bodies. It does not bother me that the bodies could be resurrected. As you explained, Hashem renews the physical world every split moment with the forces coming from His Torah. So, to recreate what He already created—that does not bother me. I just don't know why this is necessary for eternal reward, or how this helps bring honor to Hashem."

Rabbeinu Reuven is very pleased. "Ovadiah, you have good friends, and you all deserve good answers. ADON OLAM tells us that 'into Hashem's hand I will **deposit** my spirit.' Let me help you understand why ADON OLAM uses the word deposit—afkid, instead of some other word.

"Gan Eden, the World of the Souls, is not defined as the totality of the afterlife.[317] When ADON OLAM tells us that the spirit is deposited into the hand of Hashem, it means that the spirit is temporarily deposited into the World of the Souls, or Gan Eden, which is also referred to as the 'World to Come'."

"Temporarily deposited?" Shimi is getting more confused. Natan, who has been translating all along, adds an explana-

---

316 The Thirteen Articles of Faith are based upon the Rambam's Commentary to the Mishna of Sanhedrin Chapter 10. These articles deal with three primary categories of belief: The nature of belief in God; the eternal, unchangeable truth of the Torah; and reward and punishment.

317 Ramban (Nachmanides), Shaar HaGemul.

tion of the Hebrew. "That is what ADON OLAM tells us when it states בידו אפקיד רוחי ~ B'Yado afkid ruchi ~ Into His hand I will deposit my spirit. By ADON OLAM using the word afkid ~ I will deposit (temporarily)—instead of, for instance, emsor ~ I will turn over (permanently)—it is telling us that the handing over of the spirit is only meant to be of a temporary, or, shall we say, transitory nature. The root of afkid is P·K·D.[318] A PiKaDon is a deposit. The nature of a deposit is that you have the ability to eventually withdraw that which was deposited.'"

Although Rabbeinu Reuven doesn't speak English well, he has understood Natan's explanation, nods approvingly and continues:

"So since we now know that there will be an eventual withdrawal, Gan Eden is clearly still not the final goal. The indescribable pleasures of getting closer to Hashem via continually increasing our knowledge of His Will in Gan Eden are still not the end goal. In Gan Eden, the soul is receiving only part of its reward while waiting to achieve its final lofty state of basking in the pure light of Hashem's Divine Presence."

"So let's pretend that I understand what you just said. If we are just returning to Earth, the way it is now, then what was gained?" asks Ovadiah.

Meanwhile Back on Earth . . . .

"OVADIAH," responds Rabbeinu Reuven, "remember I told you last time that we would get to this? Now I am going to keep my promise. We've already touched upon the fixing of the body and the soul, and now it's time to deal with the fixing of the world—to which the purified bodies and souls will return.

"Just like the body and the soul have to be purified and distilled of impurities, so, too, the physical world needs to return

318 The letters in Hebrew are פ·ק·ד—the peh at the beginning can be read as פ (p) or פ (f), depending on the grammatical construction. In the word, 'afkid' (to deposit) it's a פ (f) and in the word, 'pikadon' (a deposit), it's a פ (p).

to its original state, as it was before the sin of the first man. In this state, called the Messianic Era, there will be no hindrances stopping the servants of Hashem from serving Him."

Ovadiah now asks, "Uncle Reuven, we have all heard bits and pieces about the Messianic era. There have been false Messiahs throughout our long history. Cults, religions, and variant forms of Judaism have sprung up because of misguided perceptions of what this era will bring. I am confused as to what is in store for us then. Will it be a miraculous time, or what? Could you give us all clarity once and for all as to what the Torah tells us will happen in the days of the Messiah?"

"The Talmud tells us,[319] that there is no difference between the nature of this world and that of the times of the Messiah, except that in the time of the Messiah the people of Israel will not be oppressed any longer by the other nations of the world. This period will start when a flesh-and-blood man, a descendent from the lineage of King David, will be anointed King over the people of Israel. He will lead the battle in the final war of Gog and Magog. Upon the conclusion of this day of reckoning, peace will reign over the land, because we will not be controlled by any evil monarchy; we will be free to learn and perform all of the commandments of Hashem's Torah.

"All over the world, evil's reign will then be viewed as a circus of mockery. The truth of Hashem's Torah will become clear to all of Creation. The holy Sanhedrin will again establish court, and Torah law will be followed. Prophecy will be restored. The Temple will be rebuilt and its sacrificial service reinstated.

"Once all of this comes, then the dead from the times of the first man until the times of the Messiah will return to life. This is referred to in ADON OLAM with the words ועם רוחי גויתי ~ V'im ruchi guiyasi . . . And with my soul will be my body."

"Do we know when this is supposed to happen?" As usual, Natan likes to get to the bottom line.

"This will all take place by the end of the sixth millennium from the world's creation. May it be soon in our days. If the world had merited it through its good deeds, then the Messianic era could have come already, but that has not happened yet."

319 Pesachim 68a, also found in Rambam, Hilchos Teshuvah 9.

Avi instinctively looks at his watch and says, "We don't have much time left till the end of the 6000 years. Now it's 5761. That only leaves 239 years."

Ovadiah still seems incredulous. He wonders what the purpose of this resurrection really is.

"Uncle Reuven, what is so important about the souls being reincarnated? What will be achieved by their coming into the utopian world of the Messianic Era?"

"We all say every day at the end of the morning prayers the words, 'May it be Your Will, Hashem, our God and the God of our forefathers, that we observe Your decrees in this World, and merit that we live to see and inherit goodness and blessing in the years of the Messianic times and in the World to Come. So that my soul might sing to You and not be stilled . . .'[320] Let's see what it means that the soul will sing and not be stilled."

Singing Souls

"I know that some of you are Ashkenazic, and please know that I am not trying to dishonor your tradition, but we are presently going to be dealing with a stanza that only exists in the Sephardic version. For those who understand the intentions of the words of the shorter, Ashkenazic version, our words might be unnecessary, but for many, like Ovadiah and Avi, our added words clarify a very important point. We say,

בְּמִקְדָּשׁוֹ תָּגֵל נַפְשִׁי, מְשִׁיחֵנוּ יִשְׁלַח מְהֵרָה
וְאָז נָשִׁיר בְּבֵית קָדְשִׁי, אָמֵן אָמֵן שֵׁם הַנּוֹרָא

~

In His Sanctuary my life-force will eventually elate.
Our anointed Messiah He will send speedily.
And then We will sing in My Sanctum.
Amen Amen is the Awe-inspiring Name.

"When, according to all traditions, ADON OLAM states 'with my spirit will be my body,' it is informing us of the necessity of the Resurrection. Without the Resurrection we would never be able to, as the Sephardim add, sing in Hashem's Sanctum."

Shalom persists: "But this isn't answering Avi's question. Why do we need physical channels to attach to Hashem? Obviously, the World of the Souls is not limited by the barriers of physicality. Even the Holy Temple is still physical. The connection to Hashem is obviously much more direct in the lofty spiritual world than from way down here. Why would Hashem desire to have our relationship in *Gan Eden* interrupted by a long-distance call when we will be in the middle of making a local one?"

Rabbeinu Reuven responds: "It's the Rambam who tells us that 'the Holy One, blessed be He, gave us the Torah, which is the Tree of Life, and all who do everything which is written in it merit life in the World to Come'.[321] Our eternal reward depends upon our fulfillment of Hashem's Will through having followed His commandments.

"But from the time of the first man's sin, circumstances have inhibited Torah observance. Without the Temple, we are presently blocked from a large set of mitzvahs. What is more, because of the troubles of our times we need to struggle for survival. Our people have fallen away from the Torah and mitzvahs time and again. Sometimes they were even forced away. As a result of our struggles to survive throughout our long and arduous history, we have been unable to focus properly on the Torah, which is our Tree of Life.

"Only when our souls will return to the physically perfected world, will Hashem's honor be revealed, as the Jewish People will come to fully recognize His Kingship. All those who strove to serve Hashem while they were previously in this world of clouds will finally be given a chance, a perfected chance, to fulfill Hashem's complete will in this perfected future world. The righteous souls who were being purified in *Gan Eden* will

---

321 *Sefer HaMada, Hilchos Teshuvah,* 9:1,2. The same subject is covered concisely in *Sefer Shoftim, Hilchos Melachim U'Milchamoseihem* 12:4.

be resurrected so that they will be able to fulfill Hashem's Will without outside hindrance.

"Yehudah told me that you all learned from *Derech Hashem*[322] that Hashem created the world in order to bestow good. You also learned that our Sages tell us that the word *tov* (good) is used in the Torah as a signal word for Torah itself."

"Yeah, I remember that. We learned that in the woods," says Shimi.

"If Hashem is going to bestow good, not partial good, but complete good, then that would entail our fulfilling His complete Torah. When we enter His Sanctuary and are able to fulfill all of His Will, with no hindrance and no clouds, then we will be able to sing together.

"This is what ADON OLAM is describing with the words 'And then we will sing in My Sanctum. Amen Amen is the Awe-inspiring Name.' The 'we' in that stanza is referring to Hashem and the Jewish People. We will sing, or show our joy, in Hashem's holy sanctum. The joy is in experiencing the revelation of the honor of Hashem. Both the Creator and the created will see that Creation has arrived at its goal.

"There is still one final and eternal stage of the afterlife. But for now, young men, this old man needs to sleep. If Hashem permits it, we will meet together tomorrow."

The Great Day of No Fear

THE NEXT DAY, all are back in Rabbeinu Reuven's study. "So, young men, I am happy you have all returned. Now, let's speak of the unspeakable, the final and eternal stage of the after life.

"Once the Messianic period, including the Resurrection of the Dead, is finished by the year 6000, then there will be *Yom HaDin HaGadol*, the Great Day of Reckoning. The people will have been purified from the blemishes of sin, both physically and spiritually. They will have grown closer to Hashem, uninhibited by any body, and then will have had the chance to fulfill all of the mitzvahs in the renewed physical world: Only after all this will come that day of final judgment that will determine the reward that each individual will have into eternity.

"Torah and Chazal did not speak clearly about the nature of the eternal reward, also called L'Atid Lavo. Their language veiled these concepts from us just as if their words were heavy shrouds."

"Why?" asks Ovadiah.

"The Rambam states that in our physical form we cannot understand this form of reward. Obviously there is not much use in going into detail about something that is beyond our understanding. The Torah was given to us on Mt. Sinai in order to teach us how to live, and that is our job for now. So what will happen then, after the Messianic period? Just remember that Hashem has made all of Creation, including the far-flung galaxies, for you. As ADON OLAM's concluding words state, ה׳ לי ~ *Hashem li*, ולא אירא ~ *v'lo ira*. Hashem is there for me, so there is no need to fear.

"But how can we not fear the unknown, especially the eternal unknown?"

Uncle Reuven looks at Ovadiah with an intense, longing, and painful look. There is absolute silence in the room, as the other guys realize that something very deep is going on here. It is as if only the uncle and nephew are there.

"Uncle," Ovadiah finally says, "what are you thinking about?"

"Let me tell you first about the night that my holy father died."

The Lonely Boy

RABBEINU REUVEN STARES unseeingly at the wall opposite him, going back in time to the events of that night.

"My father lay on his deathbed, exhausted. I was warming some water for him on the stove as I listened to the conversation between your father and him. Binyamin was so afraid that he was beside himself. He knew that in just moments he would, as he put it, be left alone in the world. My father responded to his fear . . . .

CHACHAM YASHAR:

ADON OLAM tells us, Binyamin, that a Jew is never alone and need never be afraid. Hashem li v'lo ira, Hashem is there for me, and I will not fear. My son, He will always be there for you too.

BINYAMIN:

What will I do without you, Father? You have been both a father and a mother to me. Now I will be left alone. Alone. What will become of me?

CHACHAM YASHAR:

Our Sages tell us[323] of a boat that was being violently tossed at sea.[324] There seemed to be no hope. All of the idol worshippers prayed to their false gods to no avail. The storm increased its rage and the boat was about to sink. In the hull of the boat was a young, lone Jewish boy. When the peril-stricken passengers heard that there was a Jew on board the ship, they said to him, "Pray to your God, maybe He will answer you." So he prayed to Hashem to save them. Immediately the prayers of the boy were answered, and the storm subsided long enough for the boat to arrive safely at shore. When the passengers emerged from the ship to stock up on supplies for the continuation of their journey, they asked the boy why he did not come with them. He replied that he was afraid, for he had no one. He was all alone in that strange place.

REUVEN YASHAR:

Father's voice is raspy. Here is some tea.

CHACHAM YASHAR:

Thank you, you are so kind.

After slowly and weakly taking just a few small sips, Chacham Yashar is out of breath. Binyamin who has been helping his father sit up, slowly and gently lowers him back to a lying position.

323 Jerusalem Talmud, Berachos, 9:1.
324 Please refer to the Disclaimer.

CHACHAM YASHAR:

> *Please listen, I have no more strength. You must hear my last message. The passengers laughed. You are not the one alone in this world. We are. We call to our gods and there is none to answer. You have your Father, the Creator of all watching over you. You need not fear, for you are never alone.*

Chacham Yashar wipes a tear from young Binyamin's face.

CHACHAM YASHAR:

> *Remember Binyamin, Hashem li v'lo ira. When I leave you, you will not be alone. You never have to fear, Hashem is always there for you . . . .*

Ovadiah has tears in his eyes. Until now, he had never been told the story of his father's last conversation with his own father. Uncle Reuven looks at Ovadiah with tears welling up in his own eyes. Then he speaks.

"For forty-one years I have been waiting for this very moment. After having heard my father's message, I wanted to give my brother a message that I knew he would be able to relate to, but there was never a chance. Moments later, my father started to have extreme difficulty breathing. We could do nothing to help him. He died late that night. Binyamin was unapproachable during the shivah,[325] and afterwards he left us so quickly that I never had the chance to give him my message. Now it is time for you, his son, to hear that message."

When Fear Becomes Your Greatest Treasure

"WE JEWS DO NOT FEAR what comes our way, because through our fear (or awe) of Hashem we already taste the World to Come in this world. We want—indeed, we struggle—our whole lives to attain this level of fear. Our fear of Hashem actually raises our sense of pleasure. For this is

325 Week of mourning.

the end purpose of the peace of the Jewish people—fearing Hashem and loving Him. The Jewish people's fear becomes their greatest treasure. We are considered to be belonging to the World to Come even while in this lowly physical world.[326]

"So, when the Sephardim end ADON OLAM with 'Amen Amen is the **fearful Name**,' it is no contradiction to the other statement of ADON OLAM that 'Hashem is for me and I will **not fear**.' I will fear nothing other than that which I was created to fear. This fear is my purpose, and this I cherish.

"What will happen in that final eternal reward? We cannot even conceive of it, but like the boy on the ship, we have nothing to fear of the 'unknown'. Whatever will happen, we know that our Rock, in whose hand we will deposit our souls, is Eli, our personal God, Who created the world to bestow good. Meanwhile, we struggle to gain closeness to the Master of the Hidden World, and we know that our efforts will bring the final Redemption, when all will fear His Name. And so, we say Amen in this world, and we have no fear, because we know we will be saying Amen in the World to Come."

The meeting is over, and the boys file out of Rabbeinu Reuven's study quietly, overwhelmed, still trying to digest all they have heard and witnessed.

On the way out, Ovadiah pulls Avi aside for a moment.

"Avi, I'm thinking back to the beginning. It's been a number of months now since I first sat with Yehudah in the study hall with my grandfather's book. You guys and Yehudah have really helped me a lot, and now Uncle Reuven, too. Thanks, buddy. I couldn't have done it without you."

"I see that ADON OLAM has helped you to understand what it really means to be a Jew," Avi interrupts him, slapping him on the back.

Ovadiah winces slightly at the hearty clap—but only slightly. "ADON OLAM opened up a whole new Judaism for me. Everything is so much more meaningful now. I must admit, when we first became friends I didn't understand you. You came from another nation; you left your people, your religion, and your

---

326 *Divrei Sofrim*, p. 27, *Takanas Hashavim*, p. 63, *Resisei Lailah*, p. 150. Mentioned in Schottenstein *Avodah Zarah* 65a, *he'arah* 7.

land. All this to come to our dispersed and dejected nation. I didn't know why anyone would do it. And now I understand that . . ."

"You understand ADON OLAM, so you can't understand why anyone wouldn't do it."

It's Never Goodbye

*O*VADIAH DECIDES TO WALK *home slowly on his own. You see him holding his father's copy of The Hidden Master under his arm. He looks down at it with a look of accomplishment, yet he feels a twinge of sadness. "So this is the end," he thinks to himself. Then he remembers that it is only the beginning. He will be saying my words every day in his prayers. He stops to sit at a park bench and gather his thoughts.*

"I have to put it all together in a complete picture so that when I say these words, I will remember what I learned," he says to himself. "O.K., it goes like this:

אֲדוֹן עוֹלָם אֲשֶׁר מָלַךְ בְּטֶרֶם כָּל יְצִיר נִבְרָא

The Infinite Master of the hidden world,[327] Who has reigned before all Creation and subsequent formation,

לְעֵת נַעֲשָׂה בְחֶפְצוֹ כֹּל אֲזַי מֶלֶךְ שְׁמוֹ נִקְרָא

Was enabled to be called King only upon His Will making everything come into being.

וְאַחֲרֵי כִּכְלוֹת הַכֹּל לְבַדּוֹ יִמְלֹךְ נוֹרָא

And when all evil will have completed its purpose, then He will reign alone, an unchallenged Kingship,

---

327 In order to understand why the Hebrew was translated in this manner, please refer to the Disclaimer.

וְהוּא הָיָה וְהוּא הֹוֶה, וְהוּא יִהְיֶה בְּתִפְאָרָה
He was, is, and will always be
in the perfect combination of splendor.

וְהוּא אֶחָד וְאֵין שֵׁנִי
And He is One and there is no other (not even **me**)

לְהַמְשִׁיל לוֹ לְהַחְבִּירָה
Who can compare to Him or be His comrade.

Yemenites and some Morocans add:

וְהוּא רִאשׁוֹן וְהוּא אַחֲרוֹן, לְכָל חֹמֶר וּלְכָל צוּרָה
And He is the First and He is the Last to every form and shape.

בְּלִי רֵאשִׁית, בְּלִי תַכְלִית,
He is without beginning and without end.

וְלוֹ הָעֹז וְהַמִּשְׂרָה
His is the power that is Torah and the dominion.

Sephardim add:

בְּלִי עֵרֶךְ בְּלִי דִמְיוֹן, בְּלִי שִׁנּוּי וּתְמוּרָה
He is without the ability to be evaluated,
and He has no ability to be compared to anything,
Neither can He be changed or exchanged.

בְּלִי חִבּוּר בְּלִי פֵרוּד, גְּדוֹל כֹּחַ וּגְבוּרָה
He can neither be attached to nor separated from anything
(as He is everything)
Great is the shown force and the restraining power.

וְהוּא אֵלִי וְחַי גוֹאֲלִי, וְצוּר חֶבְלִי בְּעֵת צָרָה
And He is my personal God and my living Redeemer,
and He is the Rock of my distress at the time of my troubles.

וְהוּא נִסִּי וּמָנוֹס לִי, מְנָת כּוֹסִי בְּיוֹם אֶקְרָא
And He is my battle banner, the One testing me,
and also the One Who performs miracles for me; He is my refuge.
He is the portion of my cup on the day that I call.

Sephardim add:

וְהוּא רוֹפֵא וְהוּא מַרְפֵּא, וְהוּא צוֹפֶה וְהוּא עֶזְרָה
He is the One Who heals and the One Who causes healing to come.
And He is the One Who is constantly on the lookout
to be the One to help.

בְּיָדוֹ אַפְקִיד רוּחִי, בְּעֵת אִישַׁן וְאָעִירָה
Into His hand I will deposit my spirit,
at the time that I will sleep and I trust Him that I will awake.

וְעִם רוּחִי גְוִיָּתִי, אֲדֹנָי לִי וְלֹא אִירָא
And the living existence of my body
is and will be dependent on my spirit.
Hashem is always for me, therefore I will never fear.

Sephardim include:

בְּמִקְדָּשׁוֹ תָּגֵל נַפְשִׁי, מְשִׁיחֵנוּ יִשְׁלַח מְהֵרָה
In His Sanctuary my life-force will eventually elate.
Our Anointed Messiah He will send speedily.

וְאָז נָשִׁיר בְּבֵית קָדְשִׁי, אָמֵן אָמֵן שֵׁם הַנּוֹרָא
And then We will sing in My Sanctum.
Amen Amen is the Awe-inspiring Name.

So, Searching Soul, through my words Ovadiah and his friends are well on their way to a more meaningful Torah life. It's now time for us to say goodbye to them, but don't worry—it's never time for you and me to say goodbye to each other.

I know that you see you are at the end of the book, but actually our time together is just beginning. You have only just begun to delve into the depths of my words which you will be saying every day of your life.

It's some 2,500 years after my composition by the Sanhedrin, who held court on top of the Temple Mount. Their sacred messages have been supporting every generation of our people until now. Every Jew who enters a synagogue, whether Sephardic, Ashkenazic, Persian, Chassidic or Yemenite has my words, the words of those great men, on his lips. Yes, my friend, the shards will last forever. You just have to do your job: Keep living by the words of ADON OLAM and you never need to fear.

My messages will not leave you, but rather will continuously provide you with the tools to peel back the clouds and find further depths of meaning hidden behind them. When you are lost in the storms, remember me; delve into my soul. I had the answers for you long before you ever had the questions. I'm just waiting for you to ask.

*May it be the Will of the **Adon** of the **Olam**, may His Name be blessed, that He open your heart to His Torah, and place in your heart to love and to fear only Him. May you make the rest of your life into the day that you call upon your personal Master. And together may we help bring the times when He alone will be recognized as the undoubted King of all. Together let's stand in the courtyard of His Holy Temple. Amen, Amen, Shem HaNora.*

Author's Biography

BS"D

Rabbi Zalman Weiss was born into a secular Jewish family in America, but early on yearned for a greater connection to his Creator. This quest took him to a variety of colleges and institutions, and involved him in a great many activities. After becoming an Ivy League graduate, he came on aliyah to Israel and served in the IDF. He later returned to America to attend Kol Yaakov Yeshiva in Monsey, New York, following which he learned at the yeshivas of Ohr Somayach and MiLi in Jerusalem, receiving *smicha* (rabbinical ordination) from Rabbi Zalman Nechemiah Goldberg. For the past twenty-two years, Rabbi Weiss has been in Kollel at Neve Yaakov, Israel.

Over the years, Rabbi Weiss has been involved in helping over 100 potential converts learn about Orthodox Judaism and prepare for their beis din appearances. Their journeys, their spiritual quests, re-ignited his own search for answers, as he himself admits:

"They asked questions about faith that I, the rabbi, did not know the answers to. I was embarrassed in front of them, and what is more important, I was embarrassed in front of G-d. I needed to find these answers—for myself as well as for them."

Eventually his research led him to the ancient prayer of Adon Olam, finding, to his surprise, that the answers to all of his students' questions about faith had been skillfully woven into the few short stanzas of that prayer. Over the next eight and one-half years, his findings and conclusions took the form of this present volume, a teaching novel, which elucidates these answers within the framework of a narrative. The stories contained herein are mostly true. They reflect real-life experiences and questions of Rabbi Weiss and his students. As is customary with such narratives, their names and identities have been changed.

Rabbi Weiss lives in Jerusalem with his wife and children.

Glossary

A   **Arizal**   Rabbi Yitzchak Luria (1534–1572). He enlightened the Jewish world as to the secrets of the Zohar that had remained hidden and elusive for so many generations.

Ashkenazic   A Jew of European descent.

Aufwedersehen   German term used like the English expression "See you soon".

Avraham Avinu   Literally, Abraham our Father. This is a term used to show respect.

B   **Ba'al HaTurim**   Name of a commentary on the Torah written by Rabbi Yaakov Ben Asher (1275–1349) of Cologne, Germany.

Ba'al teshuvah   This term literally means 'master of repentance'. It refers to Jews who were not born into a lifestyle of observing the laws of the Torah, but who later chose to become observant Jews.

Baba Sali   Rabbi Israel Abuhatzera (1890–1984), known as the Baba Sali, was a leading rabbi of Moroccan Jewry, and a world renowned kabbalist.

Baruch mechayeh hameisim   This literally translates as 'Blessed is He who enlivens the dead'. This statement is made whenever you haven't seen an acquaintance for a long time.

Beis Din   Court of Torah law

Bris bein Habesarim   The Covenant between the Parts. This is the covenant where Hashem promised Avraham that his descendants would inherit the Land of Israel.

C   **Chacham**   Literally: Wise man. This term is commonly used in Sephardic communities of Jews to describe the greatest rabbis of their generation.

Chazon Ish   Rabbi Avraham Yeshayahu Karelitz, (1879–1954). He authored a multi-volume compendium called "Chazon Ish". As with many rabbis, he is lovingly called by the name of his most famous book.

Chuppah   Canopy

D	**Derech Hashem**	"The Way of God", is a classic work on Jewish thought written by Rabbi Moshe Chaim Luzatto (1707–1746).
E	**Ein Sof**	A Kabbalistic term which literally translates as: without end.
	Eitam	The name of a place on the Jews journey out of Egypt
	Eliyahu HaNavi	Literally: Elijah the Prophet. In this book, it refers to a song which speaks about Elijah the Prophet coming to announce the future coming of the Messiah soon in our days.
	Ethics of the Fathers	This is a Tractate in the Mishna.
	Elokim	One of the Names of God
G	**Gan Eden**	Literally: the Garden of Eden. It is also one of the terms used for the World to Come.
	Gaon	The term 'Gaon' means 'genius'. Although it is officially used to refer to the Torah giants of the second half of the first millennium of the Common Era, it can be used for other great Torah scholars.
	Gehinom	In English this is loosely translated as 'Hell', although the term describes something quite different from what other religions conceive Hell to be.
	Gemara	Tractate, or volume of the Talmud. This term also is used to refer to the Talmud in general.
	Gematria	Using the numerical values of the Hebrew letters to show meanings hidden behind the text.
	Golem	Literally, this means 'formless mass', but in our context, it means a non-thinking, almost monster-like creature.
H	**Hagaddah**	This is the liturgical composition used on the first night(s) of Passover. It tells of the Exodus from Egyptian bondage, through the miracles that Hashem performed to save His people.
	Hallel	A set of specific Psalms recited on many of the Jewish holidays.
	HaMotzi	The blessing over bread

Hashem   Literally: The Name. It is a reference to the ineffable Name of God. This has become the traditional way that Jews refer to God.

Havdalah   Literally translated as 'separation' or 'distinction'. In this book, it is referring to the religious ceremony at the end of the Sabbath, performed with a braided candle, which marks the distinction between the holy Sabbath and the rest of the week.

K   **Kabbalah or Kabbalistic literature**   Rabbinical mystical literature

Kiddush   The sanctification of the Sabbath recited over wine

Kinos of Tisha B'Av   A kina is a lamentation. Many lamentations were written for Tisha B'Av, and collected in a book for use on that sad day which commemorates the date of the destruction of both the First and the Second Temples.

Kli Yakar   Shlomo Efraim Miloshitz (1540–1619). He was a Commentator on the Torah.

M   **Maharal**   Rabbi Yehuda Loeve ben Betzalel 1513–1609. He was a well-known commentator, known best for his explanations of Aggadic or story-like accounts.

Maror   Bitter herbs , which Jews are commanded to eat on the first nights of Passover in order to remember the bitterness of their bondage.

Mazel Tov   Congratulations

Megillah   Literally: scroll. In this book, it is refers to the Scroll of Esther.

Melaveh Malkah   This is a festive meal held after the conclusion of the Sabbath, which many times is accompanied with music and songs.

Midrash   Rabbinical homiletical interpretation(s) of the Torah

Midrashim   This is the plural form of the word Midrash.

Mikvah   Ritual bath used for many religious purposes. Immersion in the mikvah is the final stage of the conversion process.

Minyan   A quorum of ten men, needed for public prayer.

Mir Yeshivah   The name of the largest yeshivah in Jerusalem.

Mishna Each subsection of the tractates of the Greater Mishna are called simply a Mishna. The complete Mishna is the first written compilation of Oral Torah Law. This massive work was compiled during the Taanaitic period and eventually became the seed which developed into both the Babylonian and the Jerusalem Talmuds.

Moshe The Hebrew form of the name Moses.

Moshe Rabbeinu A term of respect for Moses. Literally, it means 'Moses our Teacher'.

N **Naaseh v'nishma** A quote from Exodus 24:7 which means that 'First we will do all of Hashem's Will, and only after we already do it will we strive to understand that Will'.

Nefesh HaChaim This is the title of a book written by Rabbi Chaim of Volozhin (1749–1821), who was one of the greatest students of the Vilna Gaon(see Glossary note). As is common practice, Rabbi Chaim of Volozhin is often referred to by the name of his most famous book.

Noach This is the way the name Noah sounds in the original Hebrew.

P **Pi HaChiros** Literally: the mouth of freedom. This is one of the first stops of the Jewish people as they were exiting from Egyptian bondage.

Pirkei Avos The Hebrew name for 'Ethics of the Fathers', a tractate of the Mishnah.

R **Rabbeinu** This translates as 'Our Rabbi'.

Rabbeinu Pinchas (of Plutsk) Student of the Vilna Gaon and author of Siddur Shaar HaRachamim.

Rabbi Yonasan ben Uziel See 'Targum Yonasan'.

Rambam An acronym for Rabbi Moshe ben Maimon. Born in 1135 in Cordova, Spain, he died in 1204, in Cairo, Egypt. He was a great Talmudic commentator, Halachic authority, codifier, and philosopher. Also known as Maimonides.

Ramban An acronym for Rabbi Moshe ben Nachman. A famous Torah commentator from Gerona, 1194–1270.

Ramchal   An acronym for Rabbi Moshe Chaim Luzatto (1707–1746), who wrote a classic work on Jewish thought called Derech Hashem (The Way of God).

Rashi   An acronym for Rabbi Shlomo Yitschaki (1040–1105), a major Medieval commentator.

Rav   Hebrew word for rabbi

Rosh HaYeshivah   Head of the Torah academy. This figure is usually much more than just a principal. He also helps guide the students in their religious growth.

Sanhedrin   High court of Torah law. This supreme court has not functioned for nearly two thousand years and will only be reinstated at the times of the Messiah.

Seder   Literally: order. It is the ceremony performed on the first night(s) of Passover. During the ceremony, we teach of the miraculous exodus from Egypt.

Seder plate   A plate with designated sections in which the items necessary for use during the Seder are placed.

Seder Olam   An authoritative book containing the timeline of Jewish history.

Sefer Yetzirah   This is an ancient, esoteric kabbalistic work. Its authorship is attributed to Avraham Avinu.

Selichos   Prayers in which we ask for atonement.

Sephardim   This refers to Jews whose ancestors stem from either Spain, Portugal, or any Middle-Eastern country, as opposed to Ashkenazim, who are Jews of European descent.

Shalom   Completion or peace

Shalom Aleichem   Peace be upon you. This is the standard way that Jews greet each other.

Shechinah   The Heavenly Presence

Shem HaNora   The Awe-inspiring Name

Shema Yisrael   This is a central Torah text (Deuteronomy 6:4) which is also a central part of the daily prayers. It proclaims the Oneness of God.

Shemoneh Esrei   Literally: eighteen. A major Jewish prayer.

Shiva   *The week of mourning following a burial. During this week, the immediate family members do not leave their home, and guests visit and comfort the mourners.*

Shleimus   *See Shalom*

Shul   *A term used by Ashkenazic Jews that means 'synagogue'.*

Shulchan Aruch   *Code of Jewish law written by Rabbi Yosef Karo; first printed in 1565.*

Sifsei Chachamim   *Rabbi Shabtai Ben Yosef Bass (Meshorer) (1641–1718). He was a commentator on Rashi (see Glossary).*

The Sulam   *An authoritative translator of the Zohar from the original Aramaic into Hebrew.*

T   **Talmud**   *The Talmud is a massive rabbinic work containing thousands of pages. It was composed during the first few hundred years of the first millennium of the Common Era. It contains all aspects of Jewish law, and encompasses nearly all facets of Jewish thought and faith.*

Tanchuma   *This is a collection of Midrashim, based upon the Midrashim of Rabbi Tanchuma bar Abba, 350–375 C.E.*

Targum Yonasan ben Uziel   *He is among the most ancient and authoritative translators and commentators of the Torah.*

Tefillin   *Literally: phylacteries. These are leather boxes that contain certain paragraphs from the Torah. They must be worn by Jewish men when they pray the daily morning prayers.*

Tikun   *Rectification, or the fixing of imperfections*

Tisha B'Av   *A fast day commemorating the destruction of the two temples.*

Torah   *The Torah is the Five Books of Moses. This term also refers to the entirety of Jewish law and other holy Jewish texts.*

Tur   *Compilation of Torah law. This was one of the precursors to the Shulchan Aruch.*

Tzitzis   *Strings that the Torah commands us to entwine on the corners of a four-cornered garment.*

U	**Unkelus**	A first-century C.E. commentator and translator of the Torah. He was the nephew of the evil Titus. Despite his Roman royalty, he risked his life to convert to Judaism.
V	**Vilna Gaon**	The Vilna Gaon (1720–1797) was a rabbi who lived in Lithuania. His first name was Eliyahu, but he was known simply as 'the Gaon' because of his great wisdom. Although this term 'Gaon' usually refers to the Torah giants of the second half of the first millennium of the Common Era, Rabbi Eliyahu's knowledge and wisdom were considered far beyond the wisdom that had been seen for many centuries. Thus he was called the 'Gaon'.
Y	**Yaah**	German term similar to the English 'yes'.
	Yarmulke	Religious skull-cap. It is actually an acronym for 'yarei mi'Kel', meaning 'fearing God'.
	Yehoshua	The original Hebrew name of Joshua.
	Yeshivah	Religious academy for studying Torah.
	Yonah	One of the prophets. In English this name is pronounced "Jonah".
Z	**Zecher La'churban**	Literally: remembering the destruction. The term encompasses all of the customs that serve to remind the Jewish People of the destruction of the Temple in their daily lives.
	Zohar	The section of the Oral Torah that contains within it many mystical teachings.
	Zt"l	Acronym for Zecher Tzaddik Livrachah—The memory of this righteous person is a blessing.